CONTENTS

PROCEEDINGS OF THE FIRST INTERNATIONAL CONFERENCE ON PRODUCT DEVELOPMENT AND MANUFACTURING TECHNOLOGY

University of Strathclyde, September 1969

PROCEEDINGS OF THE FIRST INTERNATIONAL CONFERENCE ON PRODUCT DEVELOPMENT AND MANUFACTURING TECHNOLOGY

University of Strathclyde, September 1969

Edited by Professor D. S. Ross, B.Sc., Ph.D.,
M.I.Mech.E., M.I.Prod.E.

Department of Production Engineering
University of Strathclyde

Foreword by Mr B. C. Harrison

Vice Chairman: Alfred Herbert Ltd.
Vice President: Institution of Production Engineers

MACDONALD : LONDON

SBN 356 03060 1

First published in 1970 by
Macdonald & Co. (Publishers) Ltd.
49/50 Poland Street, London W.1.

Printed in England by Balding & Mansell Ltd, London and Wisbech.

PREFACE

The need for close integration of the steps of invention, design, research, development, manufacture and marketing of new products has been clearly recognised. The introduction of new products, particularly on an international scale, may succeed or fail, depending largely on the measure of interconnection which is achieved in these stages of the innovative process. Failures in product innovation occur all too often, and in many cases could have been avoided by a proper appreciation of all the factors influencing successful industrial innovation.

Recognising this need led to the idea that a biennial conference under the general title of "Product Development and Manufacturing Technology" would provide an appropriate and recurring venue for the interchange of ideas on the important subject of production innovation and the manufacturing technologies associated with it. The purpose of the conference was to bring together representatives of the many disciplines involved in the overall innovative process, including industrialists, academics and government agencies, on an international level, in an endeavour to promote interdisciplinary discussion. The conference programme was arranged in a progressive order, as far as possible, and related subjects were suitably grouped in the various sessions, with discussion periods for each of these.

The response to the invitation issued to attend the conference was extremely encouraging and showed that considerable interest existed: 250 participants attended over the three-day period. These included representatives from Belgium, Canada, Czechoslovakia, Denmark, France, West Germany, Holland, Hungary, Israel, Italy, Japan, Portugal, Switzerland and USA. All of the meetings were held in the University of Strathclyde.

In addition to the conference sessions, an exhibition of new products and modern manufacturing equipment was arranged in the Strathclyde Centre for Industrial Innovation, a University contract research and development unit supported by the Ministry of Technology. 25 firms participated in this exhibition.

With one exception, all of the papers presented at the conference, together with additional submissions and edited discussion, are printed in this volume, grouped together in the order of delivery to the participants.

As Conference Director and Chairman of the Organising Committee, I wish to thank committee members for their valuable assistance both before and during the conference. Special thanks are due to the Organising Secretary, Mr. F. I. Simpson, to whose enthusiasm and energy the conference owes much of its success.

The registration, the day-to-day administration of the meetings, and the exhibition arrangements were carried out by the staff of the Department of Production Engineering, with co-operation from the University Administration in various ways. The Organising Committee expresses appreciation for the considerable assistance received from authors, chairmen of sessions, university staff and exhibitors in making the whole event successful.

Finally, I wish to thank Mr A. Conway of Macdonald (Publishers) Co. Ltd., who in his role of sub-editor provided valuable help in creating this conference volume.

Professor D. S. Ross

FOREWORD

Every industrial nation is deeply interested in the effective deployment of its total resources in order to maintain or to attain a leading economic position in relation to its competitors. In relation to manufactured products, many government departments, private organisations and individuals have realised the need for integration of the whole process of innovation as a key to economic success. The exponential increase in knowledge in the fields of materials science and manufacturing technology, much of which has arisen as a result of 'spin-off' from science-based industries, together with international competition, has emphasised the interdisciplinary nature of industrial innovation. In this, universities can play their part in a variety of ways. Thus, I think it was appropriate and timely that the Department of Production Engineering at the University of Strathclyde, Glasgow, organised in September 1969 its first biennial International Conference on Product Development and Manufacturing Technology.

This volume is a record of the papers and discussions given at the conference, and as a participant during the three conference days, it was clear to me that the scope of the subjects covered and the interests of the delegates were extremely wide. Clearly, this first PDMT conference opened doors to many topics which will, I hope, be dealt with in future meetings.

Professor Ross, as Conference Director and Mr. F. I. Simpson as Conference Organising Secretary, together with the staff of the Department of Production Engineering, are to be congratulated on their initiative and enthusiasm, to which much of the undoubted success of the conference was due.

B. C. Harrison

Vice Chairman: Alfred Herbert Ltd.
Vice President: Institution of Production Engineers

SESSION I

Product Design and Development

Chairman: Mr A. R. Miller
Chairman and Managing Director,
Motherwell Bridge Engineering Company

THE ROLE OF UNIVERSITIES IN INDUSTRIAL INNOVATION

D. S. Ross
University of Strathclyde, Glasgow

SUMMARY

A consideration of the traditional British preoccupation with research, to the detriment of development and commercial exploitation of its inventions, leads to an examination of the national importance of universities in producing the right kinds of graduates for industry. The attendant problem of ensuring that an adequate flow of pupils from schools into science and technology is discussed. Industry's need to define its graduate requirements, and to make proper use of its present graduate intake, is emphasised. Suggestions are made wherein industry can assist universities in fulfilling their role in industrial innovation.

1.0 INTRODUCTION

It may seem paradoxical that Britain, the source of many leading scientists, engineers and inventors of past and present generations, and one of the first industrialised nations, should now be striving to maintain its standard of living and its existence as a trading nation in this technological age. Such however is the case, despite the warnings of many of its leaders of opinion over the last three or four centuries[1]. Some countries, whose industrial resources were practically non-existent[2], in certain cases as a result of destruction by war, are now the pace-setters in particular fields, including areas of engineering manufacture. Reasons for this state of affairs are not difficult to find. One is that invention is only the first step to the market-place – and Britain has not been quick to commercially exploit its inventive talent. As a survey of major industrial innovations has shown[3], of a total of twenty-nine inventions (ten initiated by Britain, France and Germany, and nineteen by the U.S.), only seven were converted into final product innovations by the European countries compared to twenty-two by the U.S.

British inventions of tremendous potential, which should have been developed here, have been taken up elsewhere, with consequent loss of income to this country. Furthermore, one of Britain's leading industrial firms recognised only recently that it literally has given away, freely, valuable know-how which would have brought rich rewards if suitable licensing agreements had been used with its release.

In view of the evidence which exists to substantiate the statement that 'only the innovators will stay in business'[4], considerable attention has been paid over the past few years by governments, industry and universities, in Britain and elsewhere, to the whole meaning of technological innovation and its national economic importance. Concurrently, factors affecting it have been studied with a view to taking corrective measures, for national benefit. It is recognised that it is through the process of innovation that society either benefits or suffers from the application of science and technology and that it is the exploitation of the idea, and not the idea itself, which is socially important[5,6]. Consequently, each nation should have a major interest in its own capability to innovate rapidly and be able to rapidly absorb innovations from others, since being first in the field with an innovation usually brings important national gains.

In 1964 the U.S. received $550m in payments for licences and technological know-how, compared with $121.5m for the U.K. and $61.6m for Germany[7]. The lesson is surely clear. Commercial exploitation must follow invention. Britain reputedly spends £1000m per annum on research and development. What might be the *real* return on investment if the example of the U.S. were followed? To do so, every possible aid must be enlisted if success is to be achieved. Among other things, education is a key factor in the innovation process, and universities ought to be involved in fostering technological change, business innovation and *entrepreneurial* effort[8]. Universities have a major contribution to offer in improving the economy of a nation.

2.0 NATIONAL IMPORTANCE OF UNIVERSITIES

2.1 *What is a university?*

In view of the various levels of education available in Britain today, the question seems appropriate. However, a precise definition is difficult to formulate, as was noticeable during a radio discussion on the subject on the national network, between some principals of Scottish universities. Rather than seek such a definition, it might suffice here to look very briefly at universities as they once were (and as some still possibly remain!), and as many are today, noting the changes of outlook which have occurred. In other words, universities – ancient and modern – or, traditional and technological.

A curious idea exists that universities are merely a breeding ground for research workers and geniuses[9]. But this is true only to a very limited extent. Universities are in the knowledge business[10] and research is part of the process. The search for knowledge has been an ideal of British universities from their earliest history. The early traditional universities, however, were divorced entirely from things practical, and mathematics and science were completely ignored[11]. With the passage of time, the influence of more enlightened men, and the establishment of various learned societies, the situation in Britain began to change. Of special interest is the influence of John Anderson, formerly Professor of Natural Philosophy at Glasgow University, and the founder (in 1796) of the college which became the University of Strathclyde[12]. Held in extreme disfavour by some of his academic contemporaries, his lectures for artisans were exceedingly popular, so much so that Mechanics' Institutes, based on his ideas, were founded in various parts of the country. Thus some of the first attempts to provide an education in science and technology, particularly engineering, were made.

In parallel with these developments, some Continental universities willingly embraced the teaching of science. Their refusal to touch technology, however, led to the establishment of what are best described as 'technical universities', whose prime function was to provide teaching in science and technology – and to conduct research of industrial interest. As a result, those technical universities today have a major influence on the economy of their respective countries. The same is true of many of the universities in the U.S. The difficulty, therefore, of answering the question 'What is a university?' will be appreciated. In the U.K. some are 'traditional', others are 'technological'. None is devoted entirely to a single discipline, such as engineering, or even solely to science and technology, nor are they, in general, as closely involved with industry as some of their foreign counterparts. Many British universities, however, have continually under review their role in the community and their need for links with industry, and are showing a willingness to move with the times[13]. It is clear also that the influence of government and industry, as sources of finance, is being felt.

Apart from the well-known concept of a university as a 'seed-bed', a community from which one expects a flow of individuals and ideas of value to the nation, a consideration of at least one major function of a university may prove helpful. It should endeavour to teach its students how to think independently.

> What is taught should be taught in such a way as to promote the general powers of the mind. The aim should be to produce not mere specialists, but cultivated men and women.[14]

2.2 *Educational mismanagement*

> Though there are qualifications to be made about the reasons for our industrial decline at the end of the nineteenth century, it is true to say that it was characterised by our inability to mass produce, sell, innovate, and research technological advances. There can be no doubt that a prime reason for this failure was – and is – the gross inadequacy of the educational machine, the only agency which could have supplied the trained men necessary; and the complacency and ignorance of our manufacturers whose hostility to higher education, theoretical knowledge and therefore new processes was already a by-word by the turn of the century.

With such bold words do Jones and Barnes[15] condemn British management and educators alike in their examination of the history of the decline of British industry from the end of the nineteenth century until the present day. Thus, they claim, it is because of failure to utilise in an intelligent manner the brain power which is available to the country, particularly in the fields of science and technology, that Britain's international place in technological development has been lost.

It must be agreed that industrial change takes place as a result of the application of science through technology. Since scientific and technological knowledge provides the material for innovation, universities have a major part to play in the stimulation of innovation. By producing the right kind of graduates, by pursuing the right kind of research, and by establishing the right form of collaboration with industry, national needs will be greatly satisfied. From the universities, the nation expects to recruit many of its leaders, both for government and for industry. Considerable national resources are involved in the establishment, upkeep and expansion of universities – and the nation has a right to expect a return on its investment. Staff and students have a responsibility in their respective university roles to ensure that such investment is not wasted.

2.3 *Regaining lost ground*

While considerable ground has been lost as a result of former mistakes, economic recovery is possible if such mistakes are not repeated. In this, it is important that the output from universities is correct. The national return on investment in universities cannot be simply defined, but it has been suggested[16] that university output must at least include the education and training of men, the study and practical development of ideas and the investigation of specific industrial problems. Able graduates should thus be available for challenging industrial posts, and it is considered a function of universities to encourage their graduates to fill such posts[17].

Considerable concern has been expressed in the U.K. however that in recent years there has been a reduction in the proportion of graduates in science and technology entering industry[18].

For example, industrialists have found that, in many cases, graduates interviewed for marketing and production posts are not fitted by their training and outlook for such work. Preference has been expressed that the output from universities should be less specialised and that graduates should be more aware of economic realities.

In furtherance of this, the introduction of degree courses in Production Engineering, and in Production Engineering and Management, at Strathclyde and elsewhere, should go a considerable way to 'fitting the man to the job', since such courses cover a broader front than many traditional engineering courses, and endeavour to create a cost-conscious attitude of mind.

Curiosity-orientated research must be pursued, with the ultimate aim of producing and retaining scientists of international standing, but universities should also have research and development programmes which have immediate relevance to industrial needs, that is, mission-orientated[19] programmes.

3.0 EDUCATING THE EDUCATORS

There can be little doubt that Britain has failed to gear its educational machine to the optimum benefit of the nation. An ever-increasing number of publications (mainly from committees!) shows the concern which has been expressed over many years as to the provision of the most suitable education and training for this country. Unfortunately, implementation of many of the recommendations has been relatively slow – even though headmasters and careers masters could have encouraged their pupils towards careers in science and technology, as has been advocated for at least the last twenty-five years.

Referring to university intake from schools, Jones has pointed out the continuing imbalance between the number of applicants to science and technology[20], and arts, sociology and medicine. Recent statistics[21] indicate that the swing away from science in schools may be ending, since the number of science students at British universities has increased by almost 9% in the last two years. It seems a ludicrous situation, however, that university places in, for example, arts and social studies are oversubscribed, when in many universities places in science and technology cannot be filled. It is clear, from the nature of industrial vacancies today, that graduates in the latter disciplines, and particularly in engineering, are in great demand.

It is claimed that the saboteurs of the new society are the teachers who guide their pupils into the humanities, and that in this they are encouraged by their university colleagues. This may be partly true, but perhaps blame lies also with all who are engaged in science and technology (including industrialists) in their failure to adequately publicise the challenging and rewarding careers which are available in these fields. For too long it has been the pattern in British schools to encourage the brightest of pupils to go in for arts and languages, and for those considered less bright to be directed into science and technology. An appeal must therefore be made to those who are in positions of responsibility as headmasters and careers masters to consider the real need of the nation and the pupils whom they are guiding. Young people must be made to realise the challenge which exists in science and technology today, and some of the brightest pupils should be encouraged to find their careers in these areas. Two qualities which a young scientist needs in good measure are imagination and intuition[22] as a supplement to a scientific ability, and these qualities, to be expected in such pupils, can lead to the freshness of approach which is required of the *entrepreneur* in industry. Careers guidance to school leavers might be improved – and in certain respects could be continued at university level – particularly in the student's initial academic years. In both aspects, industrialists can be of great assistance. For example, next year the Scottish Council (Development and Industry) is endeavouring to attract 250 000 people to a sixteen-day exhibition to be held in Glasgow's Kelvin Hall. Manufacturing companies will put on displays, and in collaboration with universities will arrange conferences, teach-ins, and demonstrations to give young people (and schools careers masters?) a broad picture of Scottish industrial career opportunities which might be followed, the aim being to encourage potential students to graduate in appropriate disciplines.

Much remains to be done to ensure that the contribution of each individual to society is maximised[23], and in this the process of 'educating the educators' is only in its infancy – and must be linked to the changing needs of industry. This, however, is the nub of the matter.

4.0 WHAT DOES INDUSTRY NEED?

4.1 *Many pronouncements – no panacea*

From the volume of comments on the question, British industry clearly needs to find some answers. The comments made by Mr Maddock in his opening speech, together with the quotations which follow, are worthy of consideration.

> They (the winners of Council of Industrial Design awards) are the leaders, the pacesetters, and we despaerately need this sort of high performance in designers and companies.
>
> The turnover per man employed in British manufacturing is £2800 a year, compared with £8000 in the U.S. That, in my opinion, is the real measure of the technological, managerial and design gap, and this gap has got to be closed.
>
> *H.R.H. The Duke of Edinburgh*[24]

> We need top line men, and women, in engineering design, in manufacture and in sales; men and women educated and trained in the engineering profession to exploit the materials and the processes, with some of them at the consumer end to talk technology in the specialist market-place.
>
> Hence when we move to the upper strata of general management, where all the resources are present in some variety then we should expect to see an appreciable proportion of all people with engineering qualifications.
>
> If in Britain we see engineers much less in evidence in these ranks than in any other technologically advanced country, then we may wonder why we are slipping behind, not only the wealthy U.S.A. but also the war-devastated countries of Europe.
>
> *Gerald Fowler, Mintech*[25]

> One of Britain's real needs is for a large proportion of the country's best brains to be given a general training which includes science and engineering and then for them to become 'business *entrepreneurs*'.
>
> *John Duckworth, N.R.D.C.*[26]

> Other countries can sell oil – but we have no choice. We must stay successfully in the engineering business. This means innovation and the development of new products. Britain is indulging in too much research and not enough commercial application. Too many men want to stay – all their lives – in research departments remote from reality, and detached from the problems of competing in the world and making a profit. It is what they are taught. We are all taught that profits are most dangerous.
>
> *S. Z. de Ferranti*[27]

> What I would dearly like to see is British industry and commerce taking the place of the Colonial Service in the minds and the imagination of the present and future generations of good graduates.
>
> *Lord Redcliffe-Maud*[28]

> Industry's needs from the universities could best be filled by: –
>
> (a) a large number of graduates who have an appreciation of a wide range of disciplines – the generalists
> (b) a few deep specialists
> (c) vocational or specialist training and retraining through a career so that the work force of graduates can be flexibly deployed to suit current needs.
>
> *S. L. Bragg, Rolls-Royce*[29]

The evidence seems to be that in fact industry no more wants specialists in such droves than the schools want to produce them.

Willem Van Der Eyken[30]

Theoretically the problem is quite simple. Efficient performance depends on clever people who know what they are doing. Thus two things must be done. We need to find more clever people, train them in business and persuade them to work in business.

Professor Richard Lynn[31]

Industry needs men who can develop quickly and effectively to fill the enormous future need for management in the U.K. – men who could grow in stature to become complete and rounded managers so that they can stand on their own feet.

We must see that he (the potential manager) is trained, selected and served so that the way to success is open to him if he can take it.

Don Ryder[32]

Generally speaking, industry is looking more and more to universities and other establishments of further education to produce the managers of the future.

A modern business does need disciplined and intelligent minds, the right personal qualities and their practical applications.

The fact that career interests may not be known does not prevent a positive attitude and a crispness of thinking. These and the other qualities mentioned are the ones that industry wants, and those with more modest degrees who have them are unlikely to have much difficulty in finding themselves a job.

A. I. Ferguson[33]

The link between the universities and industry . . . . has to become a very much closer one than it has been in the past. Certainly . . . . experience has shown that where you have a close link between universities and industry, you get a most valuable cross-fertilisation of ideas.

It is certainly part of the philosophy of the department which I lead that . . . . technological opportunities for rapid development (exist) if only the men and the ideas are there and the Government, where appropriate, is able to make its contribution.

A. Wedgwood Benn, Minister of Technology[34]

The consensus of opinion indicates that industry must have a high-quality output from universities and like institutions, not only first-class honours graduates, but others who can fill the roles outlined – creative thinkers, clever people, profit-conscious business *entrepreneurs*, quick developers, good 'generalist' graduates, and engineers for top management.

In the field of management Britain is poorly placed in comparison with other leading industrial nations. Estimates[35] indicate that only about 10% of British industrial managers are graduates, compared to 30% for Belgium and over 50% for France. In the U.S. the figure is reputedly over 60% and in Germany it is considered that most of the managers are graduates in science, engineering or business economics. Thus Britain is well down the list in numbers of graduate managers, particularly those who are graduates in science and technology.

The need for a considerable increase in postgraduate students of management has been emphasised by Britain's National Economic Development Organisation[36]. Its report indicates that at the present time only about 10 000 graduates out of an annual total of 37 000 take up first employment in industry and commerce. In agreeing that economic growth is as dependent on technological education as it is on management education, the report shows that 75% of graduates entering industry and commerce had degrees in science and technology.

The need for management education for those already holding management positions has been recognised also – and at the same time a cautionary note has been sounded[37]:

> The introduction of glamour or snobbery into the education of managers in Britain is to be avoided at all costs – since the education system for almost everything else is bad enough in this respect already.

In the long term, however, the answer to industry's need is *people* – as has been highlighted by H.R.H. The Duke of Edinburgh[38]:

> Engineering and technology as a whole has a far more profound influence on society and the community then most of the subjects loosely described as the social sciences. We all know perfectly well that our economic situation is not as strong as it should be, and it is very easy to argue that industry as a whole must get us out of this mess. And to do this it is said that we need better engineers, better designers and better managers. Well, this may be the obvious way to look at the problem but I think that it may be the wrong way. In the end everything depends upon individuals and unless research, design, manufacturing and managing are seen as opportunities for satisfactory employment and self-fulfilment as well as a social contribution, I don't think we shall ever pull ourselves out of trouble.

Universities, together with industry, require to show individuals that personal fulfilment together with social contribution brings considerable satisfaction. In doing this, an important university role will be fulfilled.

What is needed now is not 'talking' but 'doing' – fewer questions and more answers.

If the universities are to effectively produce the right kind of people, continuous review of syllabus content must occur to meet the changing needs of industry. Educators and industrialists alike want to encourage graduates to enter industry, but critics have stated that many university courses are not ideal as a preparation for industrial careers, and indeed that they divert graduates from industry[39]. Reasons why course content is not ideal may not be hard to find. Tradition often plays a great part[40], and syllabuses have been designed and approved with no real analysis of the needs of those for whom they were intended. A more responsible and enlightened attitude must be adopted by those who undertake syllabus planning with a view to ensuring that relevant material is taught. Thought must be given to the best means of stimulating creative ability in students who are following careers in science and technology. To engender the spark of creativity that leads to invention is a very little understood phenomenon[41]. Nevertheless some attempt must be made, for otherwise the way of tradition is simply being pursued. In this, industry has opportunities to cooperate with universities in determining course content compatible with its real needs.

4.3 *What kind of engineer for industry?*

Engineers are needed in ever-increasing numbers in industry today, and in the U.K. considerable attention has been paid in recent years to analysing the requirements for engineers and for their education and training[42,43,44,45,46,47]. Strong recommendations have been made for suitably qualified engineers for the manufacturing sectors of industry.

One report[48] gives the results of an analysis of the skills and knowledge required by graduates in their first responsible appointments. Comparing these needs with what an engineering graduate actually received in education led the Bosworth working group on Engineering Training and the Requirements of Industry to make recommendations for 'matching courses', particularly suitable for science graduates, to fit them more acceptably for appointments in manufacturing industry. By suitably designed courses, a growing number of graduates in science and technology would be directed towards the art of design and production and from this group future managers would be drawn. This thinking was partly based on the findings of the first report by the Committee on Man-Power Resources for Science and Technology, which indicated that if the past pattern of higher education were continued, an increase in the proportion of students entering science and technology would be directed towards theory and research and away from design and production. Thus there was evidence, even as late as October 1965 when the Bosworth Report was issued, that the university pattern of higher education was the same as it had been for many years previously. It was implied therefore that the universities in general were still producing graduates whose subjects of study and training were really unsuitable for the needs of industry: hence the need for 'matching courses'.

The traditional courses in mechanical engineering which are given in universities are clearly an excellent preparation for the man who is going to work in, for example, industrial research. Many graduates in mechanical engineering, however, take up employment in manufacturing industries. This seems good reason for including in Mechanical Engineering syllabuses such subjects as Production (or Manufacturing) Engineering and Production Management, and possibly Industrial Design (Engineering).

In the Bosworth Report it seems strange to find that the subject of production engineering is given as a very minor heading in the appendix which lists subjects and topics for consideration in the course on manufacturing engineering. The truth of the matter is that almost all of the proposed syllabus is in fact production engineering, as defined by production engineers. It covers all the normally accepted processes of metal cutting and forming, material joining, metrology and production management subjects, to which is added a small section on heat treatment and another section on properties of materials. It is clearly a course on production engineering principles and practices, and why it is not described as such is not clear. Prejudice (academic or otherwise)? The term 'manufacturing engineering' might be more appealing to some. The real point at issue is: has there been any improvement in the provision of such bridging courses since the Report was published? The author of the present paper believes that much is still to be done in this direction.

The question is whether or not 'matching courses' are the real answer to the demand for engineers for manufacturing industry. At Strathclyde, the degree courses mentioned earlier (Production Engineering, and Production Engineering and Management) have a common first year with mechanical engineering courses, and are designed to produce engineers who are more suitably qualified for engineering development, production and management posts than their predecessors. In short, why not design undergraduate syllabuses in such a way that Bosworth 'matching courses' are not needed?

The author of the present paper is of the opinion that far too little support has been given nationally to the development of undergraduate and postgraduate education in production engineering at universities in Britain, and that positive action should be taken at the highest levels to remedy this situation as soon as possible. If industry needs graduates in development and production, universities will fulfil their role in supplying them – providing the facilities are given to do so.

4.4 *Postgraduate and short courses*

The case has been firmly established that it is now more appropriate to provide postgraduate (e.g. Master of Science) courses with a high degree of instruction, instead of with research only. Most Master's degree courses in Britain today appear to follow this pattern, in an endeavour to fit the graduate more suitably for his future industrial career. One university[49] offers a course in technological economics, designed to bring together economic and scientific considerations. While this *should* be attractive, the course has attracted relatively small numbers. Nevertheless, this is a sign of the awareness of universities of the need for innovation in course structure.

Other short courses are arranged specifically to suit industry's needs, and the subject matter and depth of treatment adjusted according to the requirements of students attending.

4.5 *What is industry doing with what it gets?*

Evidence exists that science and engineering graduates are not employed to the best advantage in industry. Too many are in research and development and not enough in design, production, marketing and management[50]. Very often the so-called 'specialist' graduate being produced by universities at the present time cannot see any outlet for his talent unless in research. Industry must therefore find outlets for graduate talents in areas other than in research and development – and should show career development plans from the start of a graduate's employment.

In Scotland, the Scottish Mechanical Engineering Training Scheme provides vacation training for undergraduates in a large number of participating firms. Thus an opportunity is afforded to both the potential employer and employee to ensure that 'fitting the man to the job' is carried out effectively to mutual advantage.

Recognising the need for engineers in industry and also the need to continually look at the training of engineers, the Council of Engineering Institutions will, on 16 September 1969, hold a one-day conference entitled 'The Engineers Industry Wants'. The Council has said that report upon report has followed on this stated need for engineers. The vital question remains unanswered, 'Just what type of engineer does industry want and what prospects can it offer?' The status and prospects of engineers in Britain do not match those of their counterparts in other industrialised countries.

5.0 THE STATUS OF ENGINEERS

> One of the concerns which was given to us when we started was to try to stimulate a proper appreciation of the role of the engineering society so that people would recognise that it is the engineer who is creating the environment in which we live.
>
> *Anthony Wedgwood Benn*[51]

The quotation emphasises that the status of engineers in the U.K. is not on a par with that of other professions, such medicine, dentistry, law, etc., whose roots lie in the 'traditional' university pattern discussed previously. Considerable attention is still being given to the problem of establishing a suitable national qualification and title for engineers in Britain. Members of fourteen chartered institutions embodied in The Council of Engineering Institutions (C.E.I.) are designated as Chartered Engineers (C.Eng.). This group includes all the major British institutions, such as those of Mechanical, Electrical, Civil and Production Engineering etc., – but excludes some thirty to forty other smaller institutions such as the Institution of Plant Engineers. Thus, in spite of attempts to present a unified image of engineering as a high-ranking profession, division still exists among engineers. Are there too many 'specialist' engineering institutions? This is an era of 'take-overs' and 'mergers'. Plant engineering is closely related to production engineering. Might this be one answer to the problem?

Universities could assist by providing graduate output qualified across a sufficiently broad spectrum, for example by the inclusion of plant and maintenance engineering subjects in production engineering courses.

Whatever the answer to the problem, a proper appreciation (and thus a definition of the status) of engineers in Britain has not yet been created, and this could very well be a major reason for many of the brightest school leavers not entering the engineering profession.

As has been well stated elsewhere[39], in society at large there is a definite status decline from University Research to Research in Industry to Development Work to Marketing and finally, to Production. Our success as a nation at research and our failure at exploitation is both a cause and an effect of these attitudes. Universities, with industry, must seek ways of presenting engineering in general and production engineering in particular as a profession of the highest order, of extreme value to the community, and worthy of standing on the same level as the 'traditional' professions. In parallel with this, industry must make clear the prospects open to engineers, and ensure that the financial attractions are commensurate with the importance of engineers' role in society.

6.0 UNIVERSITY RESEARCH AND DEVELOPMENT

6.1 *University/industry collaboration*

Few would deny the value of exposing university students to research in any discipline, primarily as a means of learning something of the manner of pursuing it. Apart from the benefit gained by the student, the university department and the company can gain considerable benefit by the interchange of ideas and experience. In the light of the readiness of Government grant-aiding bodies to assess research proposals on the basis of their eventual economic and commercial potential to the community, the importance of industrial interest need not be emphasised.

Clearly, many universities are happy to undertake research which is of specific industrial interest, and often this can be the means of attracting graduates into the sponsoring industry. Opportunity exists for joint industry/university collaboration to define fields of R. & D. which are suitable for prosecution in the university environment. For example, industrially-based R. & D. work in the production engineering field regularly provides subject matter for Final Year and M.Sc. projects at Strathclyde. The appointment, by the Confederation of British Industry, of an officer to further links between industry and universities is a welcome step.

Industry must recognise, of course, that universities with means and resources so much more limited than itself, and with academic time-tables to be met, are not geared up to produce results at *all* times. Therefore, R. & D. programmes must be carefully chosen and suitably planned. If this is done, worthwhile results can be achieved.

6.2 *University/research association collaboration*

Another aspect of research activity open to universities is in relation to the research associations of Great Britain of which there are some 45. (*Note*: one in Scotland, one in N. Ireland.) Some of the universities (including Strathclyde), have entered into forms of agreement with one or more research associations with a view to exploiting their mutual resources to their best advantage on behalf of industry. At Strathclyde, a link exists between the Centre for Industrial Innovation and the British Scientific Instrument Research Association ('Sira'), with a view to increasing the applications of instrument technology in Scotland. Cooperative research between universities and industrial research associations could and should be developed. Joint ventures between research associations as the ultimate aim of reducing costs is advocated by one research association chairman[52]. He claims that if industry and government would take a new look at this potential, results could be quite dramatic in their impact on technological innovation.

Similar effects could no doubt be achieved if universities, particularly their science and technology departments, could be brought into such cooperative arrangements. This, of course, has already been advocated for Britain by the Minister of Technology, who has encouraged closer relations between research associations, universities and technical colleges with a view to establishing collaborative research and cooperation in the fields of graduate and post-experience training[53]. Thus it is hoped that the system of research associations in collaboration with others might increase its contribution to the economy without need for any overall increase in subvention from public funds.

6.3 *University/European R. & D. collaboration*

In view of the considerable number of scientific and technological staff in universities in Britain, a further area for collaboration might lie in participation in the organisation of a proposed body to co-ordinate European research and development. International cooperation already exists to some extent as is shown by C.I.R.P. (International Institute for Production Engineering Research), but there are other areas where similar activities could be developed.

It is highly likely that many universities would be willing to consider the possibility of cooperating in such organisations.

7.0 FULFILLING THE NEED

Further consideration must be given to the expansion of collaboration between universities and industry. Many possibilities exist, including those which are now briefly considered.

7.1 *Vacation employment of undergraduates*

This is already done by many firms, but could be extended with profit. Experience has shown that vacation work often motivates many undergraduates towards an industrial career. Although the making of arrangements has a high nuisance value, many companies have been able to assess students for potential future employment. Most universities would welcome the opportunity of developing suitable arrangements if this would help to ensure that graduates in 'first employment' were in the most suitable posts.

7.2 *Short-term employment of university staff*

Under a scheme operated by the Ministry of Technology, university scientists and technologists can be attached to appropriate establishments as vacation consultants, and are paid a modest fee. Industry might be encouraged to operate similar schemes.

For example, production engineering staff from Strathclyde had short periods last year in various departments of Rolls-Royce Ltd, Hillington, and found the experience very rewarding.

7.3 *Part-time visiting lecturers from industry*

In parallel with the foregoing, suitably qualified industrialists can participate in academic work. Strathclyde already operates in this way, with specialist lecturers, and has a number of highly qualified Visiting Professors from industry, the Ministry of Technology and elsewhere. Among other things, enlargement of concepts is a benefit derived from the arrangement.

7.4 *Interdisciplinary consultancy*

Apart from the use by industry of individual staff members of Strathclyde University, group consultancy can be made available through the University's Centre for Industrial Innovation. The staff of the Centre are engaged on the task of bringing industry and university staff together for R. & D. projects.

Various people have pointed out that Britain has a weakness in its arrangements for the exploitation of minor inventions which could be developed as a contribution to the economy. Recent suggestions to overcome this problem include a proposal for an Ideas Development and Exploitation Association (I.D.E.A.), and for a Permanent Inventors' Exhibition (P.I.E.!), to assist in the technical and commercial assessment of inventions and new products. In many respects this is what Strathclyde's C.I.I. is available to do, in association with industry.

8.0 EXPANDING THE ROLE

Other activities, envisaged by the author of the present paper as an extension of the work of the Production Engineering Department, University of Strathclyde, will now be briefly considered.

8.1 *Product engineering*

Cooperation already exists between the Department of Industrial Design (Engineering) of the Glasgow School of Art, and the Department of Production Engineering at Strathclyde. Student industrial designers have a short course on production engineering, and student production engineers have a short course on Industrial Design (Engineering). Considerable scope exists for consolidating this link and for extending it to links with industrial and product design departments in industry, for commercial product development purposes. Products developed by the author in association with the University's Bio-Engineering Unit, include surgical instruments and implants, an artificial kidney, and other miscellaneous items.

8.2 *Product cost laboratory*

This Westinghouse concept[54] appears to offer scope for a university-based laboratory which would be available to industry on a consultancy basis. It could be of particular value to small firms. Activities covered could include product design and development, manufacturing methods, material selection and application, and metal finishing processes. Techniques of industrial engineering, value engineering, group technology, etc. could be used and taught to users of the laboratory.

8.3 *Product quality and reliability engineering*

Considerable interest exists in quality and reliability engineering and its industrial applications. A related field is environmental testing, including non-destructive testing methods. A Q. & R. Engineering Unit can be envisaged within the Production Engineering Department, with an associated laboratory, which would be capable of providing a real service to industry, in both teaching and practice, and at the same time provide an important contribution to the academic programme.

The Department's Metrology Laboratory already has some of the equipment necessary for the establishment of such a unit.

9.0 FINDING THE RESOURCES

Many suggestions to enable universities to fulfil their role in industrial innovation may never come to fruition. Finance is inevitably a major factor, particularly in the light of present U.K. government restriction on university finance for development. Apart from large investments in research, from both government and industry, other sources of support are trusts and foundations. Most of these, however, appear to be directed to fields not of immediate relevance to industrial innovation. It will be unfortunate if many potential university innovations are precluded from development through lack of financial support.

10.0 CONCLUSION

The role of universities (particularly the technological ones) in industrial innovation in the 20th century is to realise their importance to the community in producing the right kind of people for the future development of the nation's technological resources, and to pursue every means of collaboration with industry, and others, to achieve this end.

The author considers this P.D.M.T. conference to be something in the nature of fulfilling the universities' role in industrial innovation, in that it will provide a recurring venue for industrialists, government representatives, academics and others, from the U.K. and elsewhere, to present their latest findings and proposals on the conference theme.

REFERENCES

1 LORD BOWDEN. *Proposals for the development of Manchester College of Science and Technology.* 1956.
2 H. CUDLIPP. 'Vanquish resistance to change'. *Financial Times.* 8 November, 1968.
3 J. BEN-DAVID. *Fundamental research and the universities. Q.E.C.D. Paris, 1968.*
4 D. S. ROSS. 'Technological innovation – key to prosperity'. *Conf. Proc. – Management of Technological Innovation.* Bradford University, 1969.
5 M. LAMONTAGNE. 'The general goals of science policy'. *Senate of Canada Proceedings, Science Policy.* No 39. 1969.
6 UNATTRIBUTED. *Report: Forum on the Swann Report.* Paper 10. University of Nottingham, 1969.
7 C. TUGENDHAT. 'The technology gap'. *Financial Times* 3 February, 1969.
8 J. HUNT. 'People are the key to regional development'. *Metalworking Production.* 14 May, 1969.
9 J. P. MALDEN. *Financial Times,* 12 August, 1969.
10 S. A. GREGORY. 'Problems in university/industry collaboration', *Symposium on The Universities and Industry.* Society of Chemical Industry and the Institution of Chemical Engineers. 12 November, 1968.
11 LORD BOWDEN. *Ibid*1.
12 J. MUIR. *John Anderson, pioneer of technical education* and the college he founded. 1950.
13 S. C. CURRAN. 'Measuring a changing world – education for the eighties'. *21st W. M. Thorton Lecture, Assoc. Mining, Elect. and Mech. Engrs.* Bristol, 13 June, 1969.
14 LORD ROBBINS. *Higher education. Report of the committee appointed by the Prime Minister under the chairmanship of Lord Robbins.* H.M.S.O. 1963.
15 G. JONES and M. BARNES. *Britain on borrowed time.* 1969.
16 F. KOENIGSBERGER. 'Technological transfer – university to industry'. *ibid.*[4].
17 P. A. M. CURRY. 'How entrepreneurs exploit technology'. *ibid.*[16]
18 M. SWANN. 'The flow into employment of scientists'. *Engineers and Technologists.* Cmnd. 3760, H.M.S.O. 1968.
19 Sir H. MASSEY. *Second Report on Science Policy.* Cmnd. 3420. H.M.S.O. 1967.
20 G. JONES and M. BARNES. *Ibid.*[1], p. 206.
21 UNIVERSITY GRANTS COMMITTEE. Reported in *Metalworking Production,* 6 August, 1969.
22 J. N. BLACK. Graduation Speech. Edinburgh University. 1969.
23 S. C. CURRAN. *Ibid.*[13]
24 H.R.H. The Duke of Edinburgh. 'U.K. Productivity must be raised', *Financial Times,* 30 May, 1969.
25 G. FOWLER. 'How to produce a successful industrialist'. *Ministry of Technology Press Notice,* 1 November, 1969.
26 J. DUCKWORTH. *Financial Times,* 1969.
27 S. Z. de FERRANTI. Royal Institution discourse. March 1969.
28 LORD REDCLIFFE MAUD. *'Advice on recruitment of graduates for industry'. Financial Times,* 8 August, 1968.
29 S. L. BRAGG. 'Manpower planning: universities and the industrial society'. *Academic Consultative Conference, London,* November 1968.
30 W. VAN DER EYKEN. 'Industries' unwanted specialists'. *Financial Times,* 1969.
31 R. LYNN. *The universities and the business community.* Educational Research Foundation, 1969.
32 D. RYDER. 'Industry needs men who can develop quickly'. *Financial Times,* 1969.
33 A. I. FERGUSON. 'Universities and industry'. *Financial Times,* 30 May, 1969.
34 A. WEDGWOOD BENN. *Jnl. of Refrigeration,* 1969 February.
35 G. JONES and M. BARNES. *Ibid*20, p. 223.
36 NATIONAL ECONOMIC DEVELOPMENT ORGANISATION. Reported in *Financial Times,* 12 July, 1969.
37 EDITORIAL. 'Open Letter to Lord Franks'. *Scientific Business,* August 1963.
38 H.R.H. THE DUKE OF EDINBURGH. Open-day speech at M.T.I.R.A., 25 June, 1969.
39 UNATTRIBUTED. *Report Ibid.*6.
40 R. L. EDGERTON. 'More than repairing deficiencies'. *Scientific Business,* August 1963.
41 A. ROBERTSON. *Financial Times,* 25 March, 1969.

42 A review of the scope and problems of scientific and technological manpower policy. Cmnd. 2800, H.M.S.O. 1965.
43 F. E. JONES. 'The brain drain'. *Report of the working group on migration.* Cmnd. 3417, H.M.S.O. 1967.
44 M. SWANN. *The flow into employment of scientists, engineers and technologists. Report of the working group on manpower for scientific growth.* Cmnd. 3760, H.M.S.O. 1968.
45 F. S. DAINTON. *Enquiry into the flow of candidates in science and technology into higher education.* Cmnd. 3541. H.M.S.O. 1968.
46 H. ARTHUR. *Enquiry into longer-term postgraduate courses for engineers and technologists 1964–65.* H.M.S.O. 1965.
47 SIR S. ZUCKERMAN. *Technological innovation in Britain.* H.M.S.O. 1968.
48 G. S. BOSWORTH. *Education and training requirements for the electrical and mechanical manufacturing industries.* H.M.S.O. 1966.
49 M. DIXON. 'New kind of research scientist'. (Technological Economics Course – Stirling University). *Financial Times.*
50 *Glasgow Herald,* 11 May, 1969.
51 A. WEDGWOOD BENN. *Ibid.*[34]
52 G. LESTER. Copper Development Research Association.
53 A. WEDGWOOD BENN. *Financial Times,* 18 December, 1968.
54 T. H. BOOSINGER. 'Laboratory for Cost Improvement'. *Engineering Materials and Design.* February 1969.

4.4 *The Endomatic machine range*

4.4.1 *The original Endomatic*

The original Endomatic machine is shown in Fig. 3. Compared with that of its present-day equivalent the specification was restrictive since the work envisaged was almost entirely bar stock and forgings having to be located at one end only. For this reason only the right-hand head was provided with means for adjustment along the bed to accommodate varying lengths of

Fig. 3. Original version of Endomatic machine.

bar. A dead stop on the left-hand head located the component endwise. Self-centring vices ensured a proper relationship with the cutting heads as well as clamping the component to enable the milling and drilling operations to be progressively performed during an automatic cycle. Multi-tooth milling was selected as the most satisfactory means of machining to length.

Although spot-facing was accepted practice in many shops it was rejected because the drilling had to be carried out on unprepared surfaces. Also Trent[3] had shown that the cutting-edge breaks down owing to build-up when surface speed is too low and cratering when it is too high. With spot-facing, moreover, the cutting speed had to vary from near zero to unacceptably high levels when larger capacities of up to 6½ in diameter were being exploited. Thus tool life and finish were threatened on two counts. It was to be learned, however, that tradition dies hard. Sales of the machine were greater in Europe, where spot-facing had not become so established.

The appearance of the machine also found ready acceptance on the Continent at a time when British machine tools generally were under criticism because of allegedly outmoded designs. Professional industrial designers had not yet made their impact on the machine tool industry. In this case the services of a local artist with an interest in industrial design were employed.

It was particularly encouraging that sales to Germany and France compared favourably with those to the U.K. When sales resistance was encountered it was usually on the grounds that the machine was too productive compared with the profiling lathe and consequently could only be operated on two or three days per week. Other encouragement from Continental Europe came from an Italian manufacturer of printing machines. His applications, shown in Fig. 4, demonstrate the versatility and potential of the machine concept.

In the U.K. the greatest response came from the automotive industry. The limitations of the fixed left-hand head and end locator were soon exposed because of the need for automatic

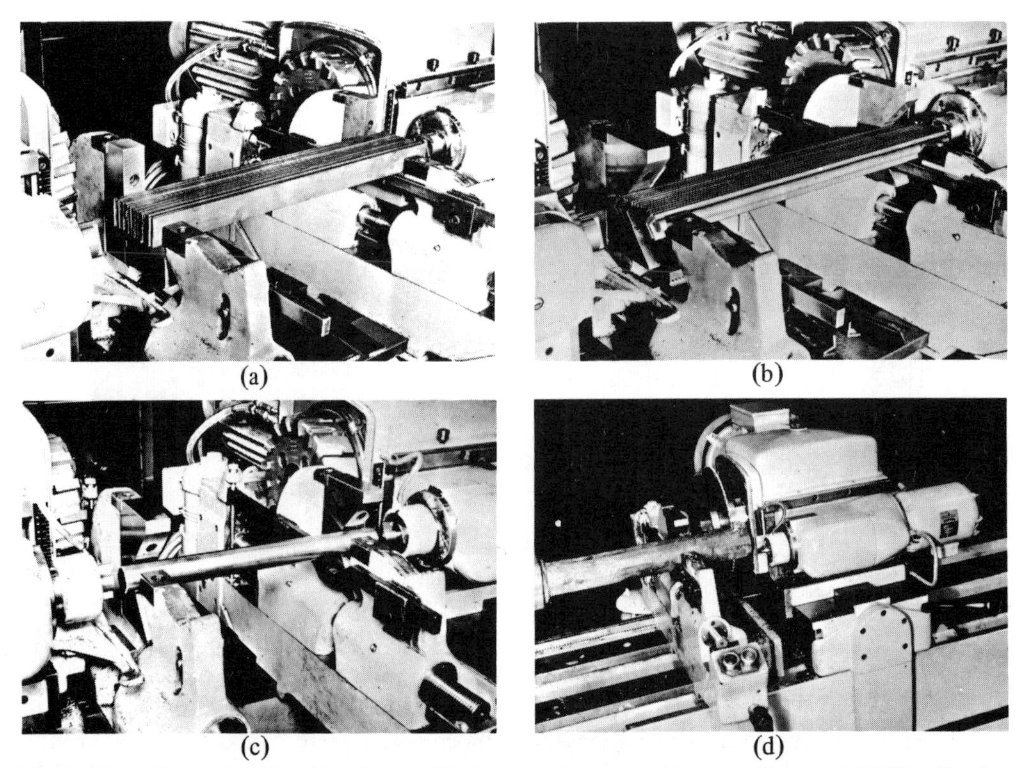

Fig. 4. Versatility demonstrated by four applications to printing machine manufacture. (a) Milling flat bars to length. (b) Milling angle sections to length. (c) Milling round bars to length and chamfering ends. (d) Sawing round bars to length and centring.

loading and unloading facilities. Also, for components such as crankshafts which had to be located between webs, both heads had to be adjustable longitudinally for speedy resetting of cutters after grinding. It also became obvious that spot-facing, within limits, could be justified in spite of the arguments which had so influenced the original design.

4.4.2 *Endomatic development*

These experiences led to progressive development from the original to the present configuration, in which both heads are mounted on cross-slides. They are adjustable along the bed as shown in Fig. 6.

Fig. 5. Modern version of Endomatic machine.

Fig. 6. Five-station Endomatic link line.

A unique feature is that the machine may be used either for milling or spot-facing as desired. Versatility is further enhanced by eight automatic cycles built into the control. In its standard form the machine can be used for duplex milling only or duplex boring only, as well as the normal cycle of milling followed by drilling. Facilities are also afforded for milling and drilling at each end alternately, thus permitting machining on one component whilst another is being loaded.

The modular construction of the machine has made possible the development of a wide range of models so that almost any length of bar and any diameter up to 12 in can be machined. The range of machines and applications is shown in Appendix 2.

Special applications have also been developed for the motor-car industry.

As the advantages of working simultaneously at both ends of components were more appreciated, the marketing disadvantages of products regarded as centring machines became apparent. Adoption of the trade name *Endomatic* did much to change the image.

4.4.3 *Endomatic link line*

The extent of application developed to a link line is shown in Fig. 6. This link line produces cluster gears at the rate of 39 per hour, the operations performed at the various stations being as shown in Fig. 7.

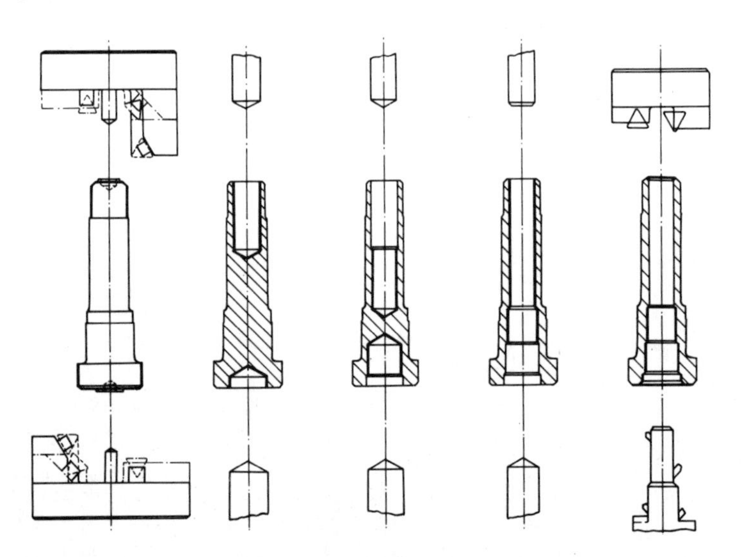

Fig. 7. Tool layout for cluster gears machined on five-station Endomatic link line.

The self-centring vices of the standard machines are used to locate the component at each station. Hydraulically operated arms transfer the component from machine to machine, thus eliminating the need for work-carrying platens. The linking conveyors provide storage between operations so that stoppages on any one machine due to tool changing (or other cause) need not affect production on the remainder of the line.

4.5 *Development for mass production industries*

4.5.1 *Design features*

Experience provided evidence of the potential for linking machines, and showed up design limitations for the work involved. The original machine had been developed from specifications drawn up with an eye to maximum versatility for small-batch production. Features not relevant to the requirements of high-volume production were therefore included. It was evident that, with the expansion of the motor-car industry, greater emphasis would be placed on reliability, productivity, retention of accuracy over long periods, safety and ease of maintenance.

These factors, and a critical analysis of the faults most commonly experienced in transfer lines and fully automatic machine tools, led to a decision to develop a completely new range of machine tools for the mass production industries.

The major causes of lost machining time in earlier models were:

- Jamming of slides by swarf
- Rapid wear of sliding surfaces
- Entry of coolant into electrical switches
- Difficulties of tool changing
- Inaccessibility of parts requiring regular maintenance

These considerations had an important influence on the choice of configuration for the new range of machines. It is shown in Fig. 8.

Efficient swarf disposal was a major design objective. Gravity and coolant flow are exploited to achieve it.

In the simplest version of the machine, quill-feed spindle-heads and vertical, self-centring vice units are mounted on adjacent upright faces of box-type columns which may be adjusted

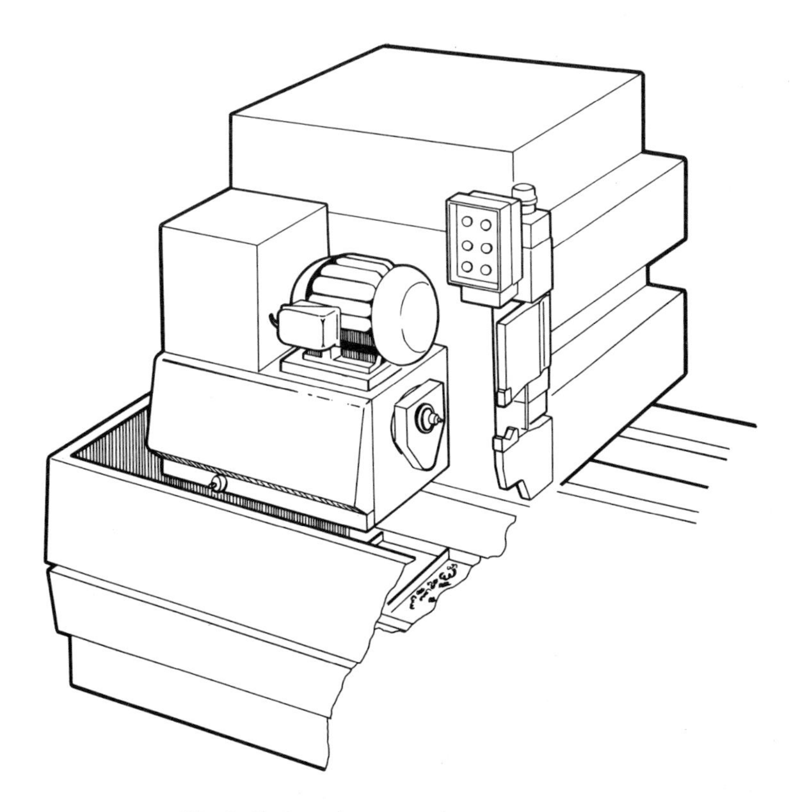

Fig. 8. Endomatic concept for high production.

longitudinally along the bed. This arrangement allows swarf to fall freely and unobstructedly on to a conveyor or tray directly below the spindles. It also provides an extremely rigid structure because the cutting loads are contained within a very short path.

The specification also called for automatic loading and unloading equipment overhead, so that conveyor operation would be, as far as possible, unaffected by swarf.

4.5.2 *Flexibility of modular construction*

The variety of modules to be used, and their most practical combinations, were established from the outset so that the maximum use of common parts and assemblies could be achieved throughout the range. Fig. 9 shows some of the various basic machine configurations envisaged. Although duplex versions only are shown, single-end versions of each type can equally well be provided.

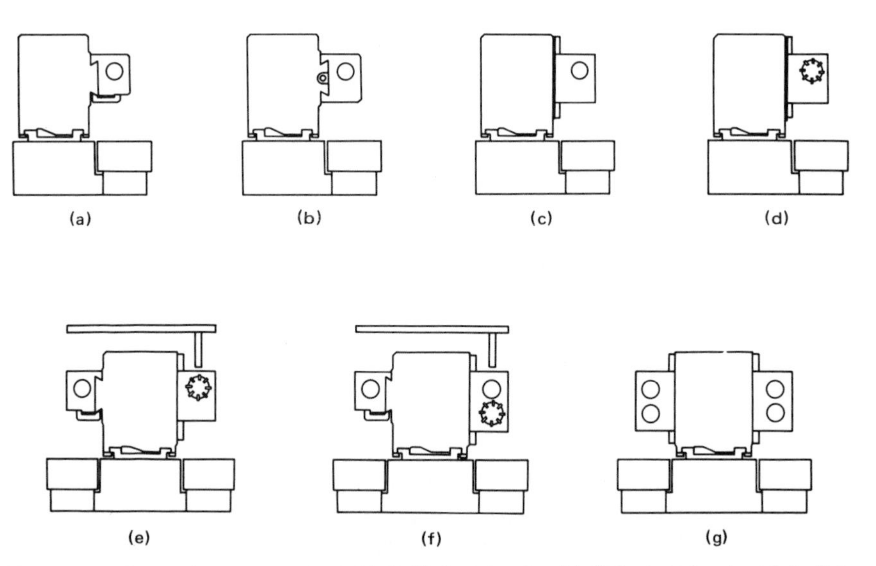

Fig. 9. Flexibility of modular construction. (a) Quill feed heads. (b) Slide feed heads. (c) Quill head with vertical feed. (d) Milling head with vertical feed. (e) Simultaneous milling and drilling machine. (f) Six-spindle machine. (g) Eight-spindle machine with quill feed spindles.

An important bonus from these designs is ability to machine box-type components on work-holding platens, as well as rotational parts (referred to previously) which require only to be located, between centres or by some similar means, when being machined. This enlarged scope is due to the much greater milling strokes available and the possibilities for co-ordinate boring inherent in the design.

Mounting of spindle heads on opposite faces of a central column makes a further important addition possible (Fig. 10). This machine permits milling and drilling, or milling and boring, on four faces simultaneously, thereby increasing machine productivity. A built-in overhead conveyor transfers the component from front to rear vices.

4.5.3 *Link line application*

Fig. 11 gives some indication of the wide application potential. This line is twice the length of that shown in Fig. 6, but the production rate (136 components per hour) is four times greater for a similar component.

Fig. 10. Endomatic for simultaneous milling and boring operations.

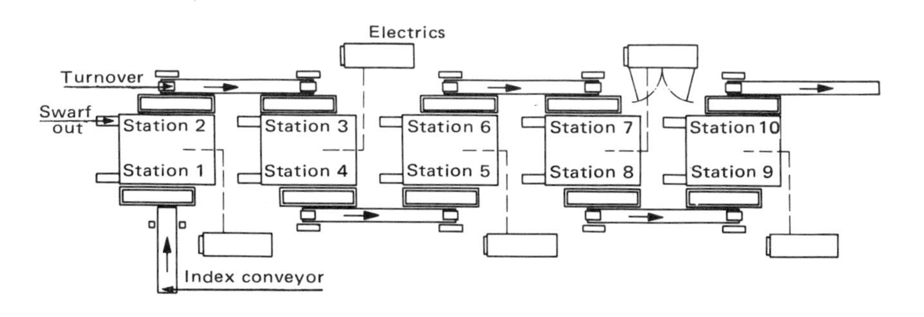

Fig. 11. Endomatic link line for mass production.

5.0 COMPANY DEVELOPMENT

All machines so far discussed were developed at Arbroath. This evidence of design resources and manufacturing skills was an important consideration when negotiations began which culminated in the formation of the present joint company of Giddings and Lewis – Fraser Ltd in August 1959. Through this merger the manufacturing programme was rapidly expanded to include high-precision horizontal boring and drilling machines. Of immediate benefit was the utilisation of capacity which had become available owing to depression in the jute industry. The know-how in all aspects of engineering associated with the manufacture and marketing of exceptionally high-quality machine tools was thought to outweigh any disadvantages of manufacturing location. The prospect of longer-term, full involvement in complex, numerically controlled, machine tools of high capital cost even suggested advantage in remoteness from industrial areas.

Giddings and Lewis planned to be foremost among machine tool manufacturers in supplying both the machine tool and its control system. Since it had been established that stiffness in structures and drives and freedom from stick-slip were essential for high performance from numerically controlled machine tools, priority was given to design of a completely new range.

The response from the U.S. and also from export markets justified this policy. The models then built at Arbroath, however, encountered increasing competition because of inability to offer some of the open-loop measuring devices which depended on centralised electrical control of operation. It was recognised that the overall corporate selling programme would be strengthened by the addition of remotely controlled, manually operated machines, and agreed to undertake the work in Arbroath.

Although this decision was in accordance with the policy, declared on the formation of the joint company, that design and development resources in Arbroath would be maintained and strengthened, it was not foreseen that the U.S. would become a principal market for the new version.

The necessity for and the economic advantages of manufacturing operations in various markets throughout the world is so well recognised that it is surprising that decentralised design and development are not always seen as an attractive investment also. Even when viewed from a narrow cost angle, the differentials in labour rates which apply to manufacture usually apply also to design and development. Again, the scarcity of creative designers is good reason for recruiting them wherever they may be found.

Potentially most rewarding, however, is opportunity for those who acquire knowledge and experience of the products to pursue their interests in creative design. Conversely, prospect of involvement in original design attracts graduate engineers, and frequently they are impressed during management development courses by the prospects of job satisfaction in other fields.

5.1 *Product development strategy*

Owing to the high standards of technical expertise required throughout the organisation to ensure success in the marketing of numerically controlled machine tools, old ideas of departmental status are disappearing. Experience of producing and servicing the horizontal boring, milling and drilling machine (Fig. 12) and the vertical machining centre (Fig. 13) has shown that qualified engineers readily accept opportunities to gain experience of manual and computer programming, quality assurance checks, contributing to customer and company training programmes and acting in an advisory capacity on sales and servicing problems. The fall-out from this has been suggestions for development of existing and new products. A forward-looking development policy exploits these enthusiasms and minimises frustrations.

Present development at Arbroath is aimed at harnessing to new projects the talents and experience acquired in the engineering and use of transfer machines, machining centres, electronic controls and computers. Palletised loading of work, group technology, numerical control and computer techniques are seen as the means by which the modularly constructed and multi-station Endomatic machine may be applied to medium-batch production as well as to the large-quantity production of specific components to which they are now restricted.

Meanwhile machine tool manufacture has become well established in the company and

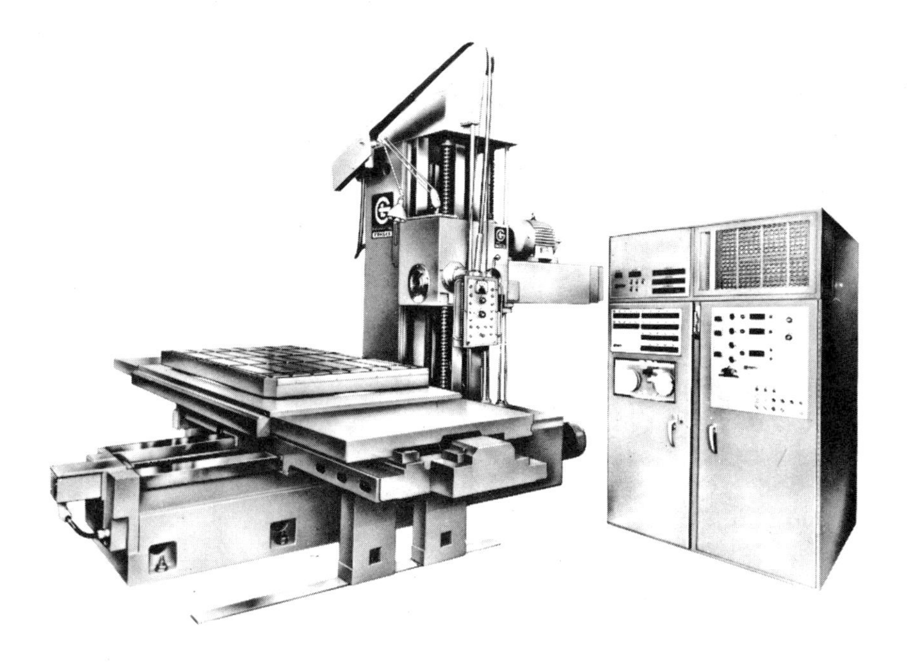

Fig. 12. Numerically controlled horizontal boring, milling and drilling machine.

Fig. 13. Numerically controlled machining centre.

represents 75% of total sales value. Arrangements are in hand to transfer textile machinery to a subsidiary company with facilities more suitable for the large batches of relatively light assemblies and components involved in the latest designs.

5.2 *Civic participation*

The company transformation envisaged and ultimately carried out could not have been accomplished without parallel development in the social sphere. Some years earlier a regional survey had reported that housing difficulties were preventing intake of skilled labour to the town[4]. In 1959 a five-year plan for the growth of the company was drawn up, based on the anticipated rate at which additional products might be introduced as well as the expansion and development of existing products. By 1965 the total labour force had increased from 720 to 1070, although a thousand had initially been forecast. The ratio of staff to hourly-paid workers increased from 13% to 28%. Since 1965 there has been a 100% increase in sales value with only a 13% increase in total labour employed, but with a further 35% increase in salaried staff.

By regular up-dating of the five-year plan it has been possible to provide the local authority with information which has enabled it to plan house-building in accordance with forecasts of numbers and grades of incoming labour. There has been similar collaboration with regard to capital expenditure, and five major extensions have been completed with minimum formalities.

Local Government participation in a new factory for the electronics division enabled the company to accelerate the programme for numerical control development. Thus a new industry was introduced to the area and the foundation laid for developing, in Arbroath, the machine tools of the future.

REFERENCES

1 E. FONTELA. Technological Forecasting and Corporate Strategy'. *European Conference on Technological Forecasting.* University of Strathclyde, Glasgow, 1968.
2 W. C. PUCKEY. *Management in Action.* Institution of Production Engineers, London, 1944.
3 E. M. TRENT. 'Some Factors affecting wear on Cemented Carbide Tools'. *Institution of Mechanical Engineers,* London, 1951.
4 R. LYLE, and G. PAYNE. *The Tay Valley Plan.* The East Central (Scotland) Regional Advisory Committee, Dundee, 1950.

APPENDIX 1 – VALUE ENGINEERING

Example 1: yarn traverse arm The requirement is maximum rigidity and minimum mass in an assembly which oscillates at up to 5 Hz. The component is a tapered tube in glass-reinforced plastic. Glass fabric is impregnated with resin and rolled onto a tapered mandrel on which curing takes place. The technique is that used for making fishing rods. The dimensions are 210 mm long tapering from 25 mm dia. to 10 mm dia., weight 9 g. The process is not a highly productive one but yields a good component in the quantities currently required. It is compatible with adhesive methods of assembly with end-pieces.

Example 2: investment castings The yarn guide bracket is glued to the small end of the traverse arm. In aluminium, it is assembled in the 'as cast' state. The knotter bill is of a kind which cannot be fully specified on paper. The form was developed empirically, and a master model (or pattern) is the specification. Investment casting reproduces it faithfully and the parts require only to be burnished at the business end. The remaining stem and pinion are ground and cut in the normal way.

Example 3: Fabrication of railway section Bright-rolled sections were first considered because they are the orthodox solution. The sections selected were not economically obtainable in the relatively small quantities needed. Iron castings were tried but involved a high scrap rate in these long, thin sections because of twist. The current design is welded from pressed sheet metal. The bogie is designed to be fairly insensitive to variations in track straightness. Welding distortion in the fabrication of the track itself is controlled. The design is giving good performance at minimum cost from easily obtainable material (length 10 ft, depth 10 in).

APPENDIX 2 – SPECIAL-PURPOSE MACHINES

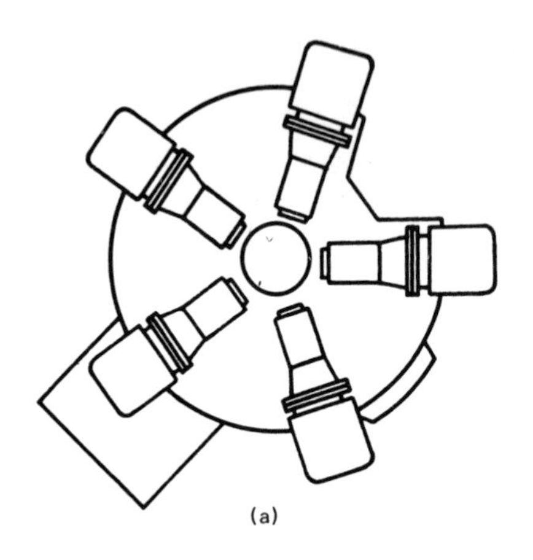

(a)

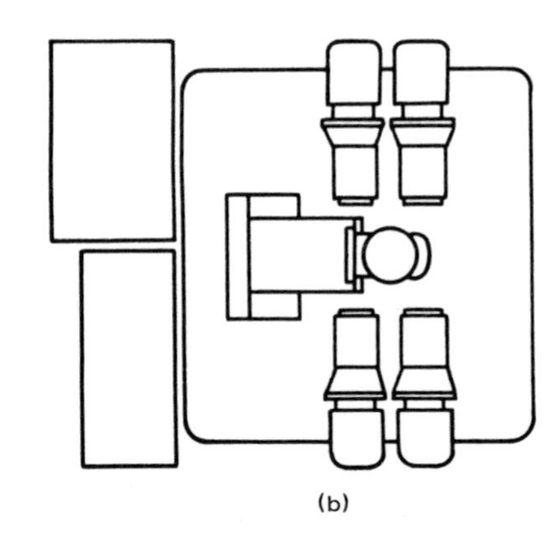

(b)

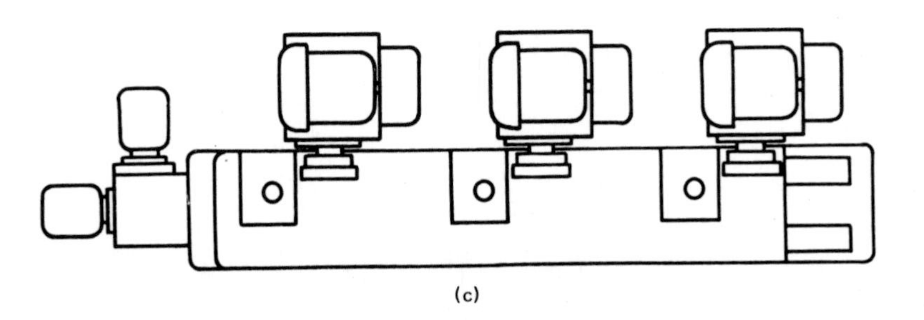

(c)

Fig. 14. (a) Five-head drilling machine. (b) Five-spindle drilling and reaming machine. (c) Auto-milling machine for hexagonal nuts.

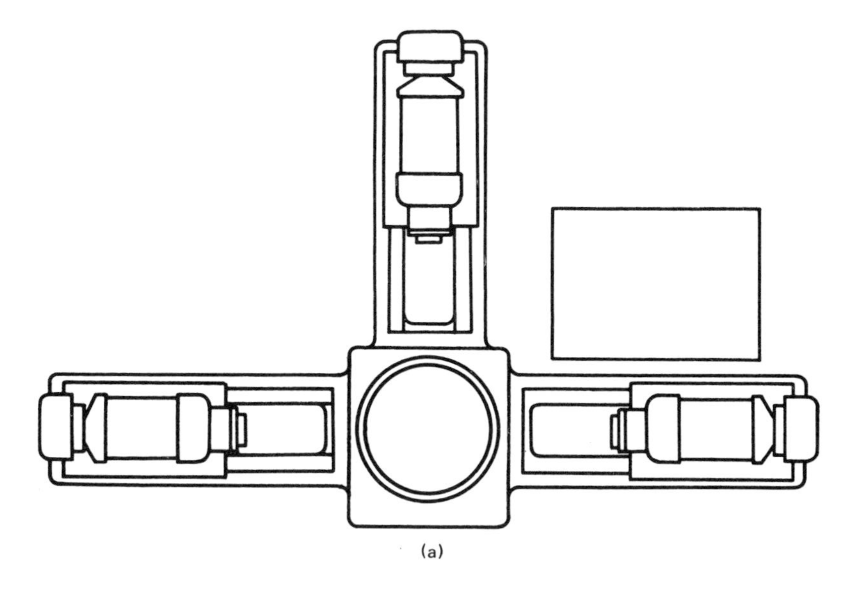

(a)

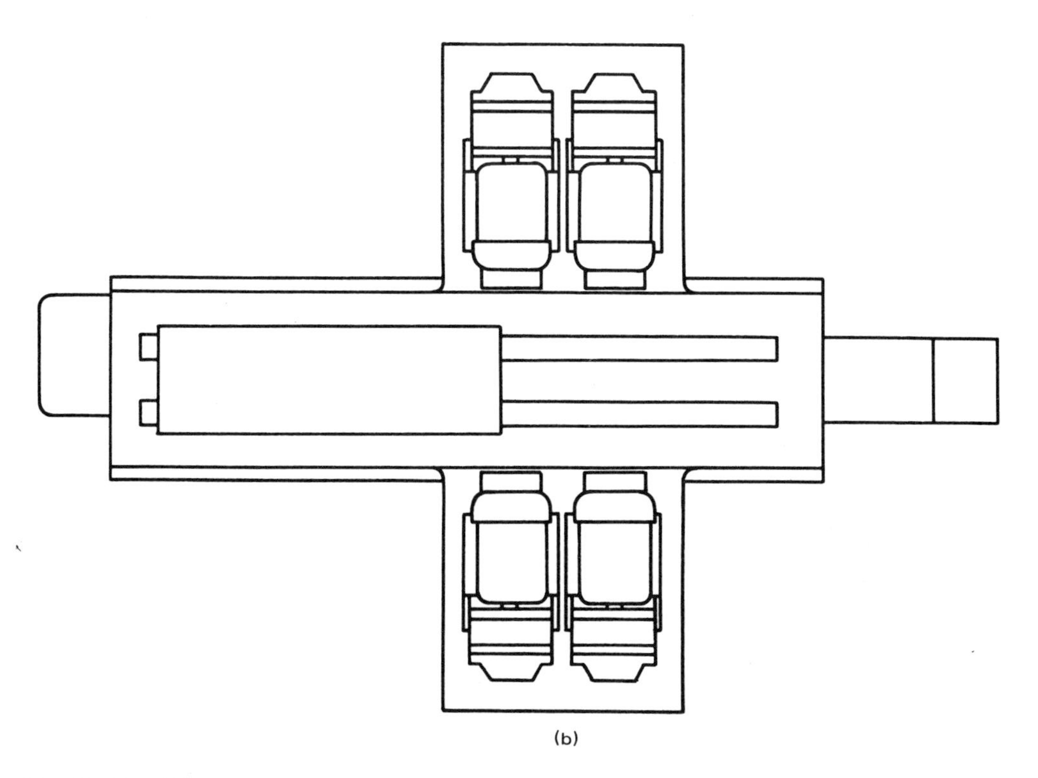

(b)

Fig. 15. (a) Drilling and boring machine with indexing table. (b) Facing, turning and chamfering machine.

ACCELERATED TESTING IN AUTOMOBILE DEVELOPMENT

F. H. Zalud
Motor Industry Research Institute, Prague

SUMMARY

Testing is one of the most time-taking stages of automobile development. Methods have been developed to shorten testing. In this paper the various stages of development are discussed mainly from the point of view of reliability assurance. Some methods of accelerated fatigue testing, and accelerated engine testing mainly for wear, are surveyed. The results of accelerated tests have to be compared with results obtained under service conditions, so the problem of revelant information systems is discussed. Some possibilities of further development in accelerated testing and other methods of shortening development are mentioned. Results quoted are based mainly on research projects undertaken by the Motor Industry Research Institute (U.V.M.V.), Prague, some of them in cooperation with other organisations.

1.0 THE DEVELOPMENT CYCLE

1.1 *Development cycle phases*

A four-year automobile development cycle is as shown in Fig. 1.

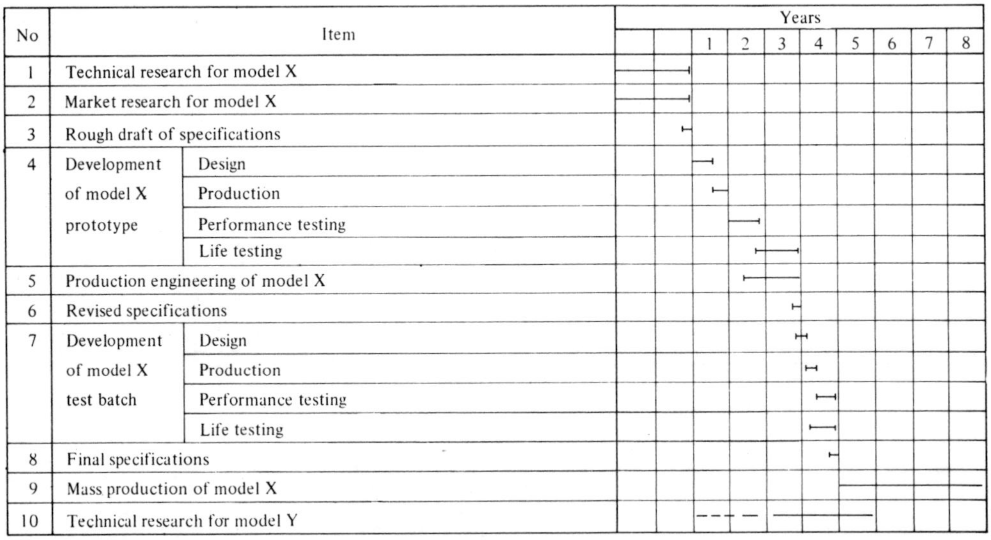

No	Item		Years									
					1	2	3	4	5	6	7	8
1	Technical research for model X											
2	Market research for model X											
3	Rough draft of specifications											
4	Development of model X prototype	Design										
		Production										
		Performance testing										
		Life testing										
5	Production engineering of model X											
6	Revised specifications											
7	Development of model X test batch	Design										
		Production										
		Performance testing										
		Life testing										
8	Final specifications											
9	Mass production of model X											
10	Technical research for model Y											

Fig. 1. Automobile development cycle.

Before a development programme is started research has to be completed to determine the technical and technological possibilities of the new model. The requirements of the market, sales possibilities and other economic problems have also to be clarified.

The main phases of the development cycle are: design, production and testing of prototypes, production engineering, design, production and testing of the test batch. The development periods vary in length with car type and manufacturer. Each main phase comprises detailed tasks relating to many parts and main assemblies. All of them must be tested to verify that they can perform their intended function over a specified period of service and to ascertain the reliability of the automobile as a whole.

1.2 *Reliability assurance*

Testing is concerned with performance parameters such as power, fuel consumption, speed, etc., and also with reliability. The former can be measured fairly quickly, but the latter, including life testing, is lengthy and costly. Reliability assurance for mass-products has to begin in the preproduction stage. The later that failures are discovered, the more costly are the corrective measures. Costs are at their highest when failures are ascertained late during the mass production process. Reliability assurance requires a special programme during the development and mass production periods. The main items of such a programme are shown in Fig. 2.

No	Item	Year									
		1	2	3	4	5	6	7	8	9	10
	Development period of model X										
	Mass production of model X										
1	Review of specifications w.r.t. service conditions										
2	Analysis of system complexity										
3	Preliminary estimate of reliability										
4	Estimate of spare-part requirements										
5	Planning of reliability information system										
6	Reliability assurance education										
7	Design review and approval										
8	Materials review and approval										
9	Production engineering review and approval										
10	Subcontractors review and approval										
11	Assessment of critical components										
12	Planning of tests										
13	Testing of components										
14	Testing of assemblies										
15	Testing of prototypes										
16	Testing of test batch										
17	Testing of mass-produced units										
18	Accelerated life tests										
19	Testing under service conditions										
20	Failure reporting										
21	Review of spare part requirements										
22	Failure analysis										
23	Recommendations for remedial action										
24	Evaluation of remedial measures										
25	Determination of actual reliability										
26	Determination of actual spare-part requirements										

Fig. 2. Reliability assurance programme.

1.3 *Final specifications and test procedures*

On completion of the preproduction phase [including development, design and production engineering for mass production (see Fig. 1) and the corresponding review activities of the group for reliability assurance (see Fig. 2)] the final specifications, incorporating reliability characteristics and their testing procedures, are established.

The testing of parts and of whole units during the development period, even if successful, is no guarantee of the reliability of the mass-produced automobile. It is necessary to test a certain number of the mass-produced vehicles under real service conditions in order to obtain correct data on performance and reliability.

It is generally impossible, because of prohibitive costs and lack of time, to test a sufficient number of cars under service conditions. Even with current practice the testing of products during the development period often takes over 50% of costs and available time.

1.4 *Accelerated testing*

Accelerated tests are useful not only because of cost savings. The shortening of the development cycle may be decisive for the sales success of a new model.

In Fig. 1 a four-year development cycle and a similar period of mass-production is shown, after which a new or modernised model goes into production. There have been cases where the actual run of a production series was much longer (e.g. the Ford model T or the first Volkswagen type were in production for over fifteen years without basic design changes).

Often the sales success of a new model depends on the timing of innovations in its design and technology. On the other hand, decreased sales of a model may be due to its ageing and low quality. Such falling sales force quick introduction of the new type. Its development costs are normally quite high.

1.5 *Minimising research and development costs*

Research and development costs, and costs of new production, planning and equipment, have to be covered when arriving at the price of a new model. If the number of new cars produced is small, these costs are high per car and may decrease the profitability of the new type. Manufacturers try to shorten the development cycle in order to increase the production period and quantities for each model.

The cycle can be shortened by concentrating and enlarging development staff, using modern computer techniques in design and testing, applying up-to-date instrumentation and planning techniques, accelerated testing, etc.

It is not usually necessary to shorten the development cycle *at any cost.* One tries to find economically optimal time limits by assessing the trend of development costs in relation to development time and the financial effect of early introduction of the new model. The mathematical problem of minimising the costs can normally be solved without basic difficulties.

2.0 ACCELERATED FATIGUE TESTS

2.1 *Stress distribution records*

Fatigue tests were among the first tests to be accelerated. They show in a simple form the fundamental principles on which other types of accelerated test are based.

If the stress on some mainly-tensioned automobile part (e.g. the front axle) is measured under normal operating conditions, then in certain road conditions stress fluctuations may be recorded[1] as shown in Fig. 3(a). The recorded amplitudes depend on road surface quality, speed, driving and other variables. Analysis of the recorded amplitudes permits construction of the stress distribution graph, in which the frequency of occurrence of stress levels is plotted against measured stress level. The distribution condenses information on stress conditions and shows the range of stress variation over a given time interval.

Determination of average stress distribution for average driving conditions would require measurements on a number of cars during their service life. This is economically not feasible. A more usual procedure is to determine the stress distribution for average service conditions by first recording stresses in intervals of 50 to 500s duration for different speeds and road surfaces, and for special driving conditions like braking, acceleration, cornering, etc. The average distribution can then be obtained from the individual distributions by weighting them according to the frequency of occurrence of the particular conditions in service. If the available instrumentation records on magnetic tape, computer processing becomes possible and it may be more appropriate to determine the stress distribution for a greater driving distance, say 5000 km, and then evaluate the stress characteristics for the whole period.

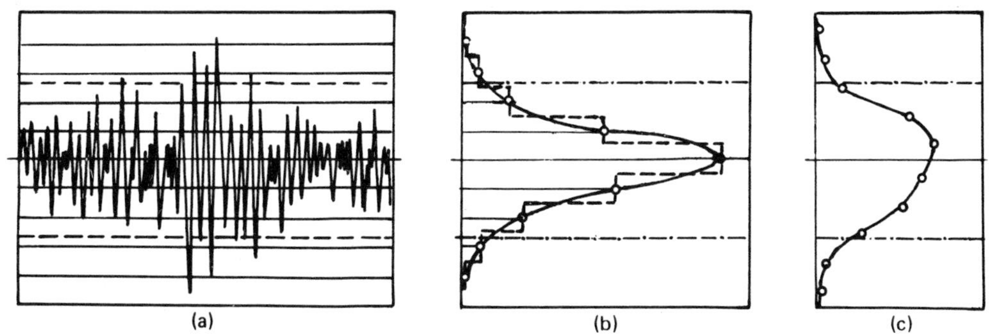

Fig. 3. (a)–Stress fluctuations under service conditions. (b)–Frequency distribution of stress levels shown full, multi-step distribution shown dotted. (c)–Frequency distribution of peak stresses.

2.2 *Frequency distribution of peak stresses*

Stress distributions are the basis for the evaluation of the fatigue life of automobile parts under normal service conditions. Fig. 3(a) shows the variation in actual stress amplitudes over a certain period. If we divide the range of stress amplitudes into intervals we can evaluate the frequency with which a certain stress level is passed, as shown in Fig. 3(b). The frequency distribution of peak stresses shown in Fig. 3(c) is obtained by evaluating the frequency of maximum and minimum stress values within selected stress intervals. These frequency distributions have theoretical models based on mathematical statistics.

2.3 *Test equipment*

Equipment for measuring dynamic stress in automobiles normally includes a tensometric outfit and moving-coil oscillograph to record stress amplitudes. A counter added to this equipment can measure the frequency with which each stress level is passed. At U.V.M.V. an electro-optical stress-level counter has been developed, but there are several other types.

Stress distribution in service is the basis for determination of the fatigue life of components, whether by further tests in the laboratory, on proving grounds with artificially worsened road surfaces, or in life tests on normal roads.

2.4 *Laboratory simulation of service stressing*

In the laboratory it is possible to use mechanical, hydraulic or other types of vibrator to induce sinusoidal stresses of constant amplitude in components under test.

The simplest comparisons between components of different design, material, etc., can be made on one stress level. More complete information can be gained from a complete set of Wöhler curves.

The random nature of actual service stressing, however, necessitates simulation in the laboratory of the observed average stress distribution. This is done in practice by approximating the distribution with a multi-step function (histogram) having five to eight stress levels [see Fig. 3(b)], and by repeating a test programme till failure occurs. The test programme consists in stressing the component at the stepped stress levels for a number of cycles corresponding to the histogram frequencies, the total number of cycles for one run of the programme being between 5×10^5 and 5×10^6.

The number of completed cycles is a measure of the expected service life of the component. Since the actual time over which the average distribution was measured is known, the actual life corresponding to the laboratory test can be expressed in service hours or kilometres.

A variety of test equipment capable of automatic programming of stress cycles has been developed. At U.V.M.V. the automobile is positioned on rotating drums with protrusions sliding in slots to form obstacles of varying height on each drum surface. Thus stress levels can be changed.

2.5 *Accelerated fatigue tests in laboratory*

Fatigue tests in the laboratory can be accelerated in three ways. The first is to increase the maximum stress level up to 10–20% above the maximum encountered in normal road tests. The second is to raise the frequency of high stresses and lower that of low stresses compared with the average stress distribution. The third is a combination of the other two procedures.

Fatigue life acceleration factors ('severity' factors) relating road tests and accelerated tests have to be determined by comparison of results.

2.6 *Proving-ground accelerated testing*

Testing is also accelerated on proving grounds by using worsened road surfaces of definite characteristics.

It is usual to test cars on a rough road route for about 2000 to 8000 km at an average speed of about 35 to 50 km/h. From our own test results and the results of other car manufacturers[2] it appears that about 120 000 km of normal European roads are equivalent in fatigue tests to about 20 000 km on cross-country roads. On a proving ground 2000 km of rough-surface route covered at an average speed of 36 km/h will produce similar results. Theoretically, 120 000 km correspond to about 2000 h of uninterrupted driving on normal roads. Practically this represents about one year's test driving if servicing periods are included. At the quoted average speed 2000 km represent about 57 h of driving time.

Because of the heating of shock absorbers spells of cooling on smooth-surface roads are necessary. With these the test should theoretically require 125 h, but with unavoidable stops takes about 200 h.

A laboratory vibration test on a car body, taking about 50 h, is equivalent to 2000 km of rough-surface routes. Including time for fitting the laboratory equipment, such a test can be completed within approximately 75 h. A test-acceleration ratio of about 2·5 can be achieved between laboratory and proving-ground test times, and a ratio of approximately 10 between proving-ground and normal road-test times.

More data on accelerated fatigue tests have become available since about 1955.[3] Little has so far been published on accelerated engine tests, which are discussed in the following section.

3.0 ACCELERATED ENGINE TESTS

3.1 *Test variables*

In accelerated fatigue tests the variable stress is normally one-dimensional. In accelerated engine tests the variables are more complicated because failures may be caused by thermal or mechanical stresses, abrasive or corrosive wear, etc.

When considering the reliability of an engine, it is necessary to define the permissible or limiting values of such variables as power, speed, fuel consumption, smoke, temperature, etc. Failure is said to occur when these limits are exceeded. This definition makes it possible to state permissible limits of wear for the individual engine parts which may cause 'failure' in engine performance, e.g. it is possible to determine the permissible dimensional changes due to wear on piston rings, liners, bearings, valves etc.

Failures due to such other causes as thermal or mechanical stress result in direct fracture of the overstressed component, e.g. a crankshaft or an exhaust valve.

3.2 *Engine data recording*

In order to evaluate the suitability of accelerated engine tests it is necessary to characterise engine service conditions and get actual reliability data for these conditions.

Engine service conditions can be characterised by measuring main variables such as torque, speed, temperature, etc. over a certain period and drawing their frequency distribution. Such evaluations can be made using a variety of equipment for counting the frequency with which given levels are passed by the variable under consideration. For simpler measurements a counter is used at U.V.M.V. to evaluate two-dimensional frequency distributions (Fig. 4).

Fig. 4. Stress-level counter or selective threshold analyser.

For more complicated investigations the measurements can be recorded on punched tape, from which further calculations can be made. For even more detailed analysis the measured variables are recorded by oscillographs, or on magnetic tape from which direct transfer to a computer is possible. This method is particularly useful when special non-stationary service conditions are being investigated, for instance strains in the engine mechanism at overrun speeds due to use of the engine as a brake. Moving-coil oscillographs have been used by U.V.M.V. to record non-stationary engine conditions during service. An example is shown in Fig. 5, recorded during uphill gear-changing conditions.

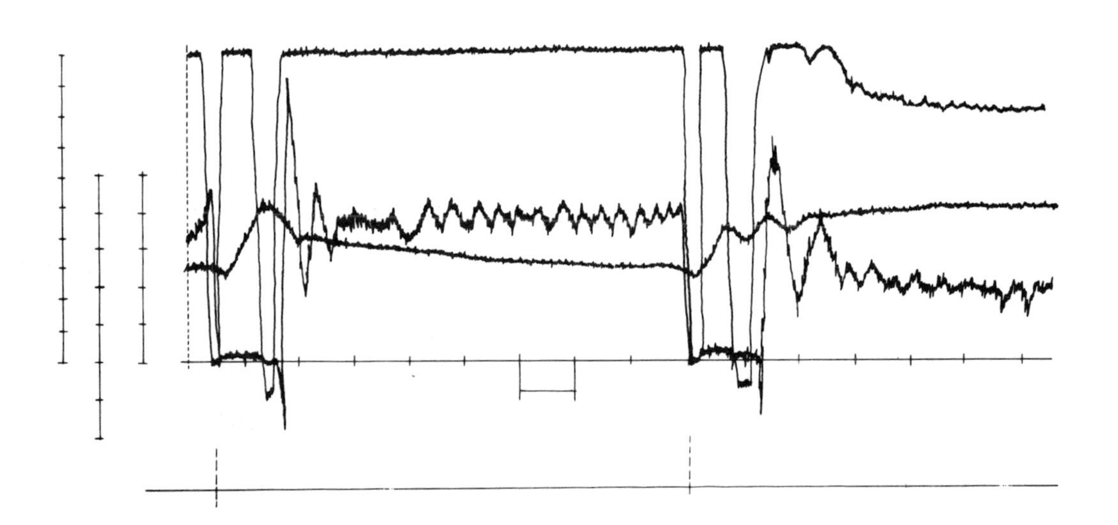

Fig. 5. Oscillogram of engine parameters.

3.3 *Wear and corrosion*

Engine component wear is normally assessed by weighing or measuring dimensional changes, which requires dismantling. Small changes caused by refitting can affect wear. Experience shows that dismantling often causes difficulties in wear tests.

Isotope tracer methods have been found useful, especially for short wear tests on components lubricated by a circulating oil system. They make it possible to determine engine wear under running conditions. Their great sensitivity also permits indications of minute wear.

At U.V.M.V. isotope tracer methods have been used to measure engine wear in the laboratory and in road tests since 1960. It is usual to irradiate piston rings, bearing shells or other suitable components in a reactor, fit the parts into the engine, and measure the radiation of the wear debris circulating in the lubricating oil or collected in the oil filter. Interest so far has been mainly in the effects on wear of engine speed and torque, various oils and oil changes, and different types of filtration. Lately the scope of tracer methods has been extended to the study of cam and tappet wear and wear of fuel injection equipment.

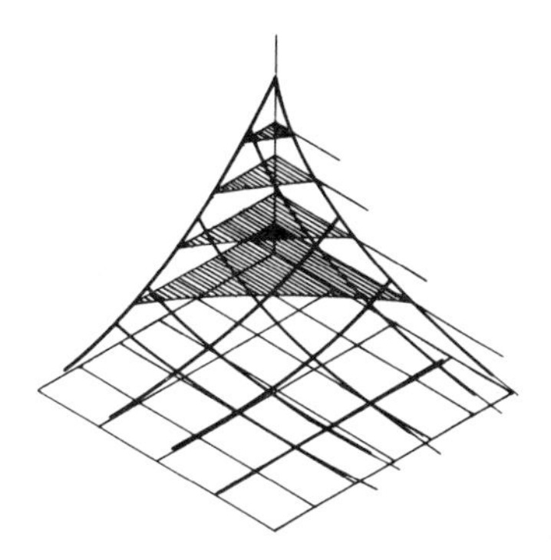

Fig. 6. Three-dimensional diagram of piston-ring wear.

As an example of the results of measuring wear Fig. 6 shows the effect of engine load and speed on piston-ring wear[4]. A typical result of the effect of lubricating oil filtration on bearing wear is shown in Fig. 7.

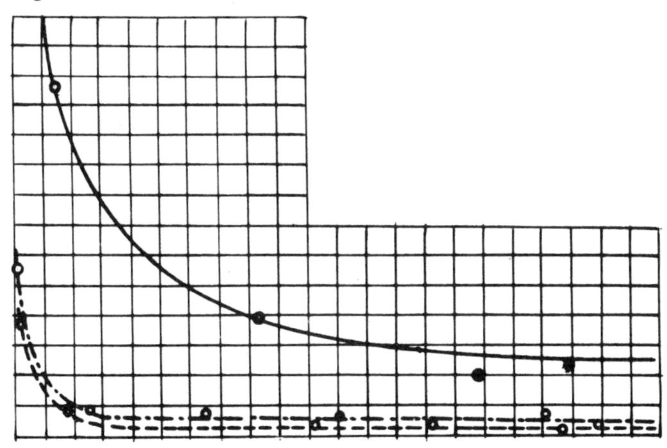

Fig. 7. Influence of oil filtration on bearing wear rate.

At different engine speeds the piston rings do different amounts of work. The radiation figures have therefore to be calibrated in mg per total number of strokes during a given test period.

The radioactive technique makes it possible to study wear effects under non-stationary conditions which could not otherwise be investigated in such detail. Thus it has been proved that the wear on piston rings and bearings is proportional to the number of changes of load and speed. Also oil changes lead to an increased wear rate during running-in. The causes of these effects are not yet fully understood.

As in other types of accelerated test, it is necessary to find acceleration (severity) factors relating short-time radioactive-tracer wear tests and wear tests under normal working conditions. It is not possible simply to extrapolate short wear tests to normal wear conditions. One can, however, compare the wear qualities of oil, materials, filter types, etc., within two to three hours, whereas with normal working conditions and measuring techniques such comparisons would require about a hundred times longer.

By feeding small amounts of abrasive dust continuously into intake air, fuel and lubricating oil, it is also possible considerably to accelerate wear tests and to achieve wear patterns similar to the normal, provided that correct relations are maintained between the quantities of dust fed into air, fuel and oils. Corrosion tests have been accelerated by adding small quantities of sulphuric acid to the lubricating oil or by running undercooled engines, so increasing the corrosive effects of exhaust products.

U.V.M.V. has been cooperating for some time in an international research project to improve automobile reliability. Accelerated test methods are being used by different laboratories and recently some instructive comparative test figures were made available,[5] as shown in the table on the next page. Methods used included frequent starting and stopping of the engine, running with undercooled engines, feeding dust etc. This latter method gave quick and quite comparable results for wear under normal service conditions, though acceleration factors for various engine components were somewhat different.

By changing the relative amount of dust fed into the intake air, fuel or oil the acceleration factors for various components can be changed. This is reminiscent of accelerated fatigue tests on rough-surface routes, which also give different acceleration factors for the failure rate of different components for rough-road and normal-road conditions.

3.4 *Systematic and random failures*

Failure in automobile engines is not due only to wear. It may be caused by bad fitting, high mechanical or thermal stresses or other unexpected conditions. Hence one differentiates between systematic and random failures.

The accelerated test methods described relate mainly to systematic failures due to wear. It is fairly easy to get comparative wear figures from normal service conditions, thus permitting comparison of accelerated and normal wear. This is so because, when an engine is dismantled for repair, its length of service is normally known and worn parts can be measured. Such comparison is more difficult with random failures under normal service conditions because reliable information is rarely given. Indeed, the service conditions which led to failure are seldom known. Such information can only be obtained by systematic efforts.

To accelerate random failures caused mainly by mechanical and thermal stresses a test programme has been tried out with engine running at full load and full speed, and vibrating severely as under rough road conditions. In some cases slight overloading and overspeeding has been added to such tests. There are as yet not sufficient data to give acceleration factors relating random failure at such high loading with normal service conditions.

Random failures occur frequently under unusual operating conditions which cause overloading of the engine. For instance, when a vehicle is decelerating with a Diesel engine acting as a brake on a steep downhill drive, the engine revolutions are forced above those permitted by the fuel injection pump governor. Rapid thermal changes in repeated uphill and downhill driving can cause excessive thermal stresses. Lately, also, the effect of engine vibrations during severe operating conditions such as earth-moving etc. have been studied, and it has been found that they do increase the failure rate.

In general, enough experience has now been accumulated to show that, to accelerate engine tests, intensified service conditions can be simulated, such as increased mechanical and thermal loading in mechanical equipment, increased electrical loading for electrical equipment, etc. Whatever means are used to accelerate tests it is also necessary to study actual service conditions and to accumulate information on the failure rate when they prevail. This survey would therefore be incomplete without some comment on reliability information systems.

ENGINE WEAR UNDER VARIOUS TEST CONDITIONS

	Engine test conditions		Wear rate of components [0·001 mm/1000 km]				
		Cylinder	First piston ring (width)	First piston ring (height)	First piston groove (height)	Crankshaft journal diameter	Crankshaft pin diameter
1	Normal service conditions on good and rough roads 60 000 – 80 000 km	2 – 4	3 – 7	0·2 – 0·5	0·5 – 1·0	0·7 – 2·5	[illegible]·8 – 3·0
2	Homologation test on engine brake (400 h)	0·8 – 1·2	0·8 – 1·5	0·2 – 0·4	0·2 – 0·4	0·2 – 0·4	0·2 – 0·4
3	Varying load test *20 cycles* Idling n_m 30 min Load 100% at n_N 30 min Load 100% at n_M 120 min Load 100% at 2700 rev/min 120 min T_o 75 – 85°C. T_v 70 – 80°C *Total 100 h*	0·5 – 0·8	2·3 – 3·0	0·3 – 0·8	–	0·8 – 1·0	0·3 – 0·8
4	Light load test *33 cycles* Idling n_m 30 min Load 15% at 1100 rev/min 120 min Stop 30 min Repeated stops and starts every 15 min T_o 50 – 75°C. T_v 70 – 75°C *Total 100 h*	1·3 – 2·3	5·0 – 6·5	0·7 – 1·7	2 – 4	0·7 – 1·7	0·7 – 1·7
5	High load test *20 cycles* Load 100% at n_M 120 min Load 100% at n_N 120 min Idling n_m every hour 15 min T_o 80 – 90°C. T_v 75 – 80°C *Total 100 h*	1·0 – 1·5	2·3 – 3·9	0·3 – 0·4	0·8 – 1·2	0·3 – 0·8	0·5 – 0·8
6	Low cooling water temperature test – 400 starts *33 cycles* Idling n_m 30 min Load 15% at 1100 rev/min 120 min Stop 30 min Repeated stops and starts every 15 min *Total 100 h*	6·5 – 8·0	6·5 – 10·0	3 – 5	2 – 4	1·3 – 2·3	1·3 – 2·0
7	Accelerated wear test with 4 mg/m³ abrasive dust 50% fed to air 50% to lub. oil *20 cycles* Load 100% n_M 120 min Load 100% n_N 120 min Idling n_m every hour 15 min T_o 80 – 90°C. T_v 75 – 80°C *Total 100 h*	28 – 32	118 – 122	23 – 25	65 – 70	6 – 8	9 – 11
8	Accelerated wear tests with 2 mg/m³ abrasive dust 50% fed to air 50% to lub. oil *20 cycles* Load and temperatures as per 7 *Total 100 h*	14·0 – 15·5	52 – 55	13 – 15	15 – 20	4·0 – 5·5	10·0 – 11·5
9	Accelerated wear tests as per 8 with cold cooling water *20 cycles* Idling n_m 30 min Load 15% at 1100 rev/min 120 min Stop 30 min Warming 15 min Load 100% n_M 60 min Idling n_m 15 min Load 100% n_N 60 min *Total 100 h*	16·0 – 18·0	23 – 25	13 – 15	24 – 28	4·0 – 5·0	7·0 – 9·0

Comments: Tests 2 3 4 5 6 with the exchange of oil after 50 h

n_m idling speed

n_N speed at N_{max}

n_M speed at T_{max}

T_o lub. oil temperature

T_v water temperature

N_{max} maximum output

T_{max} maximum torque

Corresponding average speeds of car are in engine test

Tests	Speed
3 5 7 8	65 km/h
4 6	30 km/h
9	50 km/h

4.0 RELIABILITY INFORMATION SYSTEMS

4.1 *Reliability data*

Low-reliability parts of an automobile can be traced by relatively simple tests in the laboratory. But only longer experience with a number of mass-produced cars in normal operating conditions can give real reliability data. Various methods have been used to obtain field reliability figures.

Several years ago reliability data were collected for certain subassemblies that were particularly troublesome, e.g. radiators, brake drums, etc. An extensive investigation was made of over 100 Skoda 1200 cm^3 engines in taxicabs[6,8]. It was found that the average engine life up to the first general overhaul was 143 571 km. Between the first and second overhaul the average life decreased to 84 302 km, and between the second and third to 42 326 km. For each complete taxicab 2·6 engines were used on the average, while the other main parts required no basic renewal.

Requirements for spares were obviously too high and overhauls not economical. A more detailed investigation showed that engine life was shortened by fitting procedures in the local repair shop, where partly worn parts were fitted into the repaired engine. This practice was naturally stopped.

4.2 *Failure reporting*

The first complete information system in Czechoslavakia on automobile reliability under service conditions was introduced by the makers of Tatra lorries several years ago. It uses a failure reporting system with suitable classifications of failures. The data are recorded on punched cards and regularly processed on a computer[7]. The results gained from this survey are instructive. They show for instance that 62% of warranty expenses for the Tatra 12t lorry in 1966 were caused by engine failure. Similar figures from other firms also showed that engine failure causes about 50% of warranty expenses.

Some time ago an attempt was made to induce various transport companies to place log books into every lorry. The intention was that drivers and other service personnel should enter details of failures, repairs and spare parts. This method of obtaining information was unsuccessful at first. Entries in the log books were often incomplete and misleading owing to the financial interests of the transport company or driver concerned. It has been found that reliable information on failures in service conditions can be obtained only by cooperative effort between the car manufacturer and the customer.

Detailed investigations are now being made by special groups of field engineers attached to the manufacturer. They follow in detail a small but statistically significant number of vehicles in actual service and themselves record the failures. Evaluation of the information and recommendation of measures to improve reliability requires further specialists and a reliability-assurance organisation whose responsibility is detailed feedback to design and production. This ensures that necessary remedies are taken when excessive failure rates are reported.

5.0 CONCLUSIONS

Accelerated tests can shorten the testing period in the development cycle and improve the reliability of automobiles. The experience gained in testing procedures, development planning and reliability information systems can also be useful in product development in other industries.

Further improvements in accelerated testing techniques can be expected in a number of directions. New test methods can be used. Valuable results have already been achieved by spectrometric and polarographic determination of various wear debris in lubricating oil. These methods are very sensitive and show minute wear or ageing affects and they do not have the disadvantage of radioactivity health risks, which are a handicap for the wider use of radioisotope tracer techniques. Of considerable importance are new non-destructive flaw-detecting methods such as the ultrasonic detection of fatigue damage.

Much progress in shortening development time has already been made and more can be expected from new planning techniques such as C.P.M., P.E.R.T. and similar methods. Operational research methods and various applications of mathematical statistics will undoubtedly play a major role in the future. Computers are already being widely applied to shorten and improve design methods, and in many cases they can be combined with automated test equipment to evaluate test results. There is little doubt that by using such new procedures it will be possible to achieve economically optimal development periods.

REFERENCES

1 M. HANKE 'Fatigue life of automobiles'. *Symposium on fatigue life in transport machinery.* CsVTS, Prague, 1966.

2 E. FIALA 'Das dynamische Verhalten von Pkw Aufbauten'. *Automobil Industrie,* No 2. Wurzburg, 1963.

3 W. McCONNELL *How good is testing?* SAE Preprint No S 210. New York, 1959.

4 M. BURIANOVA 'Combustion engine wear studies by a radioactive tracer technique.' *Symposium on Radioisotope tracers in industry and geophysics.* International Atomic Energy Agency. Vienna, 1967.

5 L. B. GURVIC *Dolgovecnost avtomobilnych dvigatelej.* Masinostrojenie Moskva, 1967.

6 P. LUKECA *The use of reliability information for planning spare part requirements.* U.V.M.V. report No 17. Prague, 1965.

7 J. ZASTRESEK 'Benefiting by user experience from the point of view of the state user.' *Symposium of the European Organisation for Quality Control.* London, 1967.

8 A. H. ZALUDOVA 'Problemes de duree de vie. Applications à l'industrie automobile.' *Revue de statistique appliquée.* No 4. Paris, 1965.

PRODUCT DEVELOPMENT AND THE INDUSTRIAL DESIGNER

L. Bruce Archer
Royal College of Art

SUMMARY

This paper attempts to answer the following questions. What is an industrial designer? What can an industrial designer do that a good design engineer cannot? What is the role of the industrial designer in well-managed product development? And, in view of the changes in attitude to industrial innovation which we are now witnessing, what changes in the role of the industrial designer, and in the relationships between industrial designers, design engineers and industrial managers, are likely to occur?

1.0 DEFINITION AND ROLE OF THE INDUSTRIAL DESIGNER

To begin, what is an industrial designer? The definition produced by the International Congress of Societies of Industrial Design is as ponderous as that produced by the Feilden Report for the design engineer.

The Feilden Report[1] on engineering design defines mechanical engineering design as: *the use of scientific principles, technical information and imagination in the definition of a mechanical structure, machine or system to perform pre-specified functions with the maximum economy and efficiency.* The Feilden Report also defines the mechanical engineering designer's responsibility: *The designer's responsibility covers the whole process from conception to the issue of detailed instructions for production and his interest continues throughout the designed life of the product.*

The International Congress of Societies of Industrial Design[2] has defined the industrial designer as: *One who is qualified by training, technical knowledge, experience and visual sensibility to determine the materials, construction, mechanisms, shape, colour, surface finishes and decoration of objects which are reproduced in quantity by industrial processes. The industrial designer may, at different times, be concerned with all or only some of these aspects of an industrially processed object. The industrial designer may also be concerned with the problems of packaging, advertising, exhibiting and marketing when the solution of such problems requires visual appreciation in addition to technical knowledge and experience.*

1.1 *Education and training for the industrial designer*

Neither of the above definitions reflects the common-sense distinctions which one would make between industrial designers and design engineers. The most obvious is the *ambience* of the industrial designer, which is that of art, architecture and the quality of life in the home and public place, whereas the *ambience* of the design engineer is that of science, the factory and the art of the practicable.

The typical industrial designer goes to a School of Art at the age of eighteen and takes a four-year course leading him to a diploma in some specialisation such as typography, graphic design, textile design, furniture design, product design and so on. Such courses may have a considerable technological content, and increasingly the entrant is expected to have a minimum of five 'O' level subjects, some of them on the science side. Alternatively, he may enter a more general first-degree course (or degree equivalent course, such as the Diploma in Art and Design) at a school of art, technical college or university, in which case he would require at least two 'A' levels including at least one on the science side, and then go on at the age of 22 to a post-graduate diploma or second degree calculated to add a professional training to a broad, art-biased but general education.

So far as industrial design students aspiring to work in engineering product design are concerned, their training will largely parallel, and in certain respects exactly duplicate, that which their contemporaries in design engineering courses at technical colleges and universities undergo.

1.2 *The industrial designer and the design engineer*

What, then, can a good industrial designer do that a good design engineer cannot? The honest answer has to be 'not very much' if a good industrial designer is pitted against a good design engineer, each in a field in which he is trained and experienced.

Both will provide complete solutions to a product design problem. Ideally there would be little to choose between them. But the industrial designer bases his strength on sensitivity, imagination and training in handling the human factors – aesthetics, ergonomics and market presentation and perhaps in conceiving radically new product concepts; whilst the design engineer builds upon competence, knowledge and skill in handling the technological factors – mechanisms, structure and production engineering – perhaps with an emphasis upon reliability and durability.

The character of their respective solutions to an identical problem would probably reflect these differences. Ten years ago, when industrial designers were more arty and design engineers were more earthy than they tend to be today, the differences would have been more marked. That is not to say, of course, that there are not a lot of arty and impractical industrial designers about still, or that the dull and hidebound design engineer has completely disappeared. It is certain, nevertheless, that there has been a remarkable convergence of standards and attitudes in recent years.

However, it is hypothesised in this paper that this tendency will not necessarily continue, and in the light of new attitudes to industrial innovation, may indeed be reversed.

1.3 *Industrial design and product development*

Before dealing with this hypothesis it might be useful to comment on the role which the industrial designer can play in well-managed product development. In order to do so one must say something about the nature of product development.

Product development can be thought of in two conceptual dimensions: first, the range of disciplines involved in identifying and providing the properties required in the product, and second, the sequence of activities necessary to bring it into being. Both the disciplines and the phases vary in detail from one class of product to another, of course, but they follow a fairly consistent pattern. The disciplines can usually be described under such headings, for example, as:

CHARACTERISTIC FACETS OF PRODUCT DESIGN

function	servicing	brand presentation
mechanism	production	motivation
structure	economics	aesthetics
reliability	distribution	ergonomics

It is interesting that, although this list has been constructed to form a logical continuum (each item linking and merging with its two neighbours, and the last, *ergonomics*, leading back to the beginning, *function*), traditionally the design engineer has been regarded as excelling in the items in the first half of the list and the industrial designer in those in the second half.

Design is necessarily cross-disciplinary, and a product designer is therefore usually concerned with reconciling in his design the advice and demands of all those who have some concern in the product's construction, marketing and use. Perhaps the best kind of designer is the Jack-of-all-trades who is also a master of one, and perhaps it does not matter a great deal whether his own speciality and background is in mechanisms, in production or in aesthetics, so long as he is capable of understanding and commanding the respect of his advisers and team mates. The good industrial designer, therefore, like the good mechanical engineer and the good production engineer, should be capable of either leading the team or serving as a specialist in the team, as occasion arises.

We should not assume without argument, however, that the disciplines of aesthetics, ergonomics, brand presentation, styling and so on, which are the industrial designer's special field, have any real value outside fashion goods and consumer durables. To question this assumption we must go back to the problem of what industrial production is all about.

2.0 NATURE OF INDUSTRIAL PRODUCTION

A manufacturer is not in business just to toil at manufacture. He is in business to make money. He makes money by creating wealth, putting some of it into his own pocket and letting his workers, his customers and the community at large take a share in the rest. And he creates wealth by converting raw materials into products which have a value-in-exchange which is greater than their cost. In fact, one can argue that manufacture cannot long continue unless every party to the game – capital, labour, consumer and society-at-large – has something to gain by it, and that the one absolutely indispensable property of a product, whether it is cheap or dear, efficient or inefficient, beautiful or ugly, is that its value-in-exchange be greater than its cost.

The price at which exchange actually takes place will be pitched somewhere between value and cost. The price will be close to value in a seller's market and close to cost in a buyer's market. The preoccupation of the product design and development team must therefore be to provide in the product those properties or attributes which will maximise value and minimise cost. One need not consider at length the important and difficult – but circumnavigable – problem of the relationships between absolute values, relative values and cash values. Numberless volumes have been written on the subject[3]. The question now raised is how the product designer causes to be provided by his design those properties or attributes which will give it, first, a higher value-in-exchange than its cost of manufacture, and second, more attractions in the eyes of prospective purchasers than competitive designs.

One can generalise a little on what these attributes are likely to be.

The evidence of the market place suggests that – in general, within limits, and other things being equal – the greater the utility of the product the more the purchaser will be willing to pay. The economist, of course, will say that anything which adds value is utility, but we are here using the term 'greater utility' to mean more efficiency, more capacity, more durability, and so on.

Similarly – in general, within limits, and other things being equal – the greater the scarcity or rarity of a product, the more the purchaser will be willing to pay. The uniqueness of a curio, the exclusiveness of a fashion garment and the originality of a piece of furniture are all examples of a kind of rarity and add value in the same way.

Both technological invention and aesthetic invention can contribute to originality. But they can have other effects, too. A purely sensual response to the sight, sound, feel, smell or taste of an artifact can make it desirable or repulsive, quite apart from its usefulness. Aesthetic responses are usually more subtle than this, however, and contain habitual, social and intellectual elements. The possession of some artifact with certain technological or aesthetic features can give the possessor some sense of security, status or belonging, which is quite independent of its actual utility or rarity. In general, within limits, and other things being equal, the presence of positive emotional attributes in a design will tend to add value.

And it is paradoxical that, since it has been said already that rarity adds value, the evidence is that people will tend to be willing to pay more for a product that they can have on demand (the 'impulse-buy' or the 'carry-home' offer) than for something they have to wait for. So in general, within limits, and other things being equal, the attribute of availability adds to value-in-exchange.

These four classes of attribute – utility, rarity, emotivity and availability – give a product its value[4].

Returning to the question as to what industrial production is all about, one can say that the purpose of industry is to create wealth by converting materials into more valuable forms, and to profit from so doing by encashing that value at the best price that can be obtained in the market place. The purpose of product design is to identify and provide in the product those properties or attributes which will maximise the differential between value-in-exchange and cost, and which will offer the optimum scope for marketing.

Going back one question further, one must ask again whether or not the industrial designer has any significant contribution to make to products other than fashion products and household goods. If the list of value-inducing attributes of a product is associated with the list of aspects of design which normally have to be considered, certain conclusions can be drawn.

3.0 FACETS OF PRODUCT DESIGN AND THEIR VALUE-INDUCING ROLE

Consider again the list of design facets in Section 1.3. The four classes of attribute relate to it as follows:

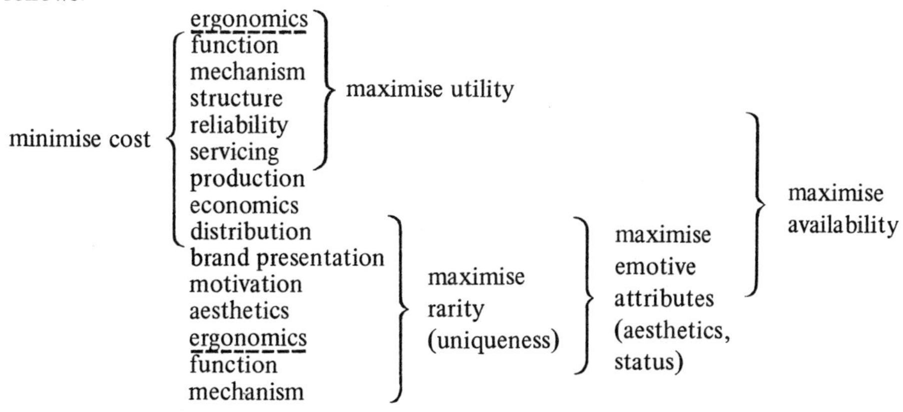

This would suggest that when the designer is handling, say, the problem of the mechanism of the product, he is striving to maximise utility (efficiency?), maximise rarity (patents?) and minimise costs. Sometimes he will be trying to add as much value as he can, compared with previous designs, with as little added cost as possible. Sometimes he will be trying to cut out as much cost as he can, with the minimum loss of value. Similarly, when the designer is handling the problem of aesthetics in his design, he is concerned with maximising rarity, maximising its emotive and intellectual appeal and minimising cost. For some circumstances and classes of product it is far more likely that a significant advance in value can be made at a low penalty in cost in respect of improved mechanisms than in respect of aesthetics, and for other circumstances and classes of product a striking advance in value at low cost is more likely to be obtained in respect of aesthetics than in respect of mechanisms.

If one can generalise at all on the question as to whether or not the industrial designer has a contribution to make to products other than fashion products and household goods, it would perhaps be to say that, when a product has reached a high state of technological development and is thus less susceptible to striking advances in value through attention to the disciplines in the first half of the list of design factors (Section 1.3), at which the design engineer tends to excel, then some advances in value might be achievable through attention to the factors in the second half of the list, which are the industrial designer's speciality. Advances through technology are usually more durable, once achieved, but can be slow and very costly. Advances through human factors or industrial design are often more transitory, but usually quicker and cheaper.

4.0 PRODUCT DEVELOPMENT PROGRAMMES

Turning now to the other dimension of product development – the time sequence of activities necessary to bring a product idea and a product into being – one sees a different kind of picture. Many model product development programmes have been published[5], and such programmes must necessarily vary from circumstance to circumstance and from product class to product class. However, the following seems to be a fairly characteristic pattern.

	Phase 1 – Policy formulation
	1 establish objectives 2 lay down outline time-table and budget
RESEARCH	Phase 2 – Preliminary research
5–10%	1 identify problem boundaries 2 establish the existing state of the art (library research) 3 prepare outline performance specification (a verbal prescription for a proposed product – specification 1) 4 identify probable critical problem areas
	Phase 3 – Feasibility study
	1 establish technical and financial feasibility 2 resolve critical problems (inventions?)
DESIGN 10–20%	3 propose outline overall solution(s) (sketch designs 1 – product ideas) 4 estimate work content of phase 4 and 5 and probability of a successful outcome

Phase 4 – Design development
1 expand performance specification (specification 2)
2 develop detailed design (design 2)
3 prepare design documentation

Phase 5 – Prototype development
1 construct prototype (prototype 1)
2 evaluate technical performance of prototypes
3 conduct user trials

Phase 6 – Trading study
1 reappraise market potential*
2 appraise marketing/production problem
3 revise objectives and budget
4 finalise performance specification (specification 3)

DEVELOPMENT 40–60%

Phase 7 – Production development
1 develop a production design (design 3)
2 execute production design documentation
3 construct pre-production prototypes (prototype 2)
4 conduct technical, user and market field tests

Phase 8 – Production planning
1 prepare marketing plans
2 prepare production plans
3 design jigs and tools

MANUFACTURING START-UP 5–15%

Phase 9 – Tooling
1 construct jigs and tools
2 construct trial batch of products off tools (prototype 3)

MARKETING START-UP 10–15%

3 test trial batch
4 install marketing machinery and production control

* Marketing considerations will also have figured prominently in Phases 1 and 2, of course.

PRODUCTION

Phase 10 – Production and Sale
1 initiate marketing effort
2 commence production and sale
3 feedback market and user information

5.0 PRODUCT DEVELOPMENT COSTS

Several recently published reports, including the Blue Paper *Technological Innovation in Britain*[6], have argued that British industry, although it spends quite enough money and effort on research, consistently fails to spend enough money, effort and skill on post-prototype development. The Holloman report[7] estimates that 5 to 10% of the cost of new-product development goes on research leading to the invention or product idea, 10 to 20% goes on design leading to a working model or prototype, 40 to 60% on development leading to a producible product, 5 to 15% on tooling and manufacturing start-up expenses and 10 to 15% on marketing and distribution start-up expenses. Thus, much more than half the cost of product development comes *after* success with a working prototype. Much of the development work can be classes as debugging, productionising and reliability engineering. Development engineers and production engineers are quite familiar with these disciplines.

A significant sector of the problems involved, however, might be described as 'small-print engineering'. For example, the questions: whether a proposed product does or does not attract a certain rate of tax; whether or not it implies the realignment of professional or trade skills and responsibilities; whether certain standard specifications, codes of practice and safety regulations apply, do not apply or can be modified; whether existing practices and machinery for approvals, specification, procurement and supply would admit the product or impose certain limitations on it; whether patents, copyrights, registrations, licences, trade agreements and the like affect the design – these are all 'small-print engineering' problems.

Sometimes the difficulties of mechanical engineering, production engineering, and reliability engineering pale into insignificance beside the intractability of the small-print engineering problems. The most marvellously devised mechanism in the world is absolutely useless unless the red tape and the small print have been equally flawlessly manipulated.

6.0 IMPORTANCE OF *ENTREPRENEURSHIP*

Most of the recent exhortations for better industrial performance in Britain have hinged on 'technological innovation' and 'vertical integration'. The potentiality of the pay-off from technological innovation has already been discussed. By vertical integration is meant taking into account at the beginning of new-product development, and all the way through, the balance of needs of function, production, marketing and small-print engineering as a single optimisation problem.

The real weakness in the British industrial character is not lack of inventiveness but lack of *entrepreneurship.* It is no myth that a great many things are invented and developed in Britain, and then left to lie idle until they are taken up and exploited in North America. *Entrepreneurship* is of two kinds: *technical entrepreneurship* which notices what science is doing and finds some way of putting it to good use, and *marketing entrepreneurship* which notices people's needs and finds some way of meeting them.

Even if a complete standstill in every kind of basic research and discovery were to be called today, at least ten years of unabated progress could be sustained by exploiting the knowledge we already have. Britain, particularly, needs to devote more money, more intellectual endeavour, more creative imagination and, above all, *more prestige,* to the *entrepreneurial* role, which is primarily concerned with small-print engineering, than she has been in the habit of doing until now. The new generation of professional managers who are now taking up the reins in British business seem ready to recognise this. Trained in the logic and techniques of operational research, they are likely to be able to communicate more effectively with engineers, marketing men, statisticians and the rest than their predecessors were. And they are likely to demand more strongly the predictability as well as the inventiveness of their designers' proposals.

This probability brings us back to the main question which this paper is intended to discuss: what changes are likely in the roles of the industrial designer and the design engineer? And it brings us back also to the hypothesis that the paper proposes, namely, that the convergence which has characterised their respective developments over the past 25 years may not now continue and may indeed be reversed.

7.0 THE SMALL-PRINT ENGINEER – A NEW BREED OF INNOVATOR

The design role is necessarily a co-ordinating or cross-disciplinary one. The increasing breadth and subtlety of the facets of product design problems has led the design professions to liberalise their skills. The more each kind of designer has widened his scope, the more like he has become to the other kinds of designer, also broadening their scope. Hence, the convergence of industrial designer and design engineer in the field of product design.

The new attitudes being taken by industrial managements, however, emphasise that co-operation or co-ordination has to occur not only breadth-wise, in the comprehensiveness of the treatment of the design, but also length-wise, in the comprehensiveness of the treatment of implementation. Teamwork in industrial innovation has to be seen NOT as the teamwork of the relay race – research workers passing the baton to designers, designers to draughtsmen, draughsmen to production planners, production planners to tool designers, tool designers to production, production to sales – but the teamwork of the schooner race, each specialist playing a different but entirely complementary role *throughout* the race.

Perhaps the industrial designer, who is a sort of cross-bred artist/technologist, need never have been invented if a whole generation of design engineers had not proved to be hidebound and unskilled in certain important aspects of design at a critical time. Perhaps the small-print engineer, a new sort of cross-bred business man/technologist, will need to be introduced in order to achieve the 'vertical integration of the process of industrial innovation' which is being called for in all the most authoritative pronouncements at the moment. Perhaps either the industrial designer or the design engineer will make a take-over bid for the new role. In either event, we are likely to see major changes in the composition and structure of product development teams. Small-print engineering, as much as manufacturing technology, is going to dominate product development in the next decade.

REFERENCES

1 Council for Scientific and Industrial Research, *Engineering Design*, Her Majesty's Stationery Office London 1963.

2 International Congress of Societies of Industrial Design, *Constitution*, Unesco, Paris 1959.

3 GORDON W. ALLPORT, PHILIP E. VERNON, and GARDINER LINDZEY. *The Study of Values*, Houghton Mittlin, New York 1960.

4 L. BRUCE ARCHER, *The Structure of Design Processes*, PB 179321 Clearinghouse for Scientific and Technological Information, Springfield, Virginia, U.S.A., 1969.

5 J. CHRISTOPHER JONES (editor), *Conference on design methods, Pergamon, London 1963.*

6 Central Advisory Council on Science and Technology, *Technological Innovation in Britain*, Her Majesty's Stationery Office, London 1968.

7 U.S. Department of Commerce, *Technological Innovation: Its Environment and Management*, Clearinghouse for Scientific and Technological Information, Springfield, Virginia, U.S.A., 1967.

SESSION 1. DISCUSSION ON THE PAPERS BY D. S. ROSS, A. F. DE VITRY, F. H. ZALUD AND L. BRUCE ARCHER

P. P. LOVE (*Glacier Metal Co.*): This is a conference about innovation, and part of the process of innovation is finding out what the customer wants. Why should the university expect industry to tell it what it wants? The universities don't appear to pay very much attention to the papers written about what industry wants.

The answer to the question 'Why do good graduates move around so much?' may be that good graduates want to get a lot of experience. I think that graduates stay with the company they joined in the first instance.

Professor D. S. ROSS: Because many papers have been written doesn't necessarily mean that the message is getting across either way. I agree that universities in general need to go out more into industry. However, I am quite convinced that industry in general doesn't know what it wants as far as graduates are concerned. If it did there would be fewer papers written on this subject.

L. A. WOOLFSON (*Wales Low-cost Automation Centre*): It seems to me that if you approach industry on their immediate problems you gain their confidence. This will enable the universities to get, not only the knowledge of what people want, but also the funds which are so necessary to carry the work out.

F. W. COOPER (*Institution of Production Engineers*): I would like to support Professor Ross, who has laid some little blame on industry. He won't be thanked for it; I have never been thanked for it in twelve years.

One of the things he has said is that we read so much about industry wanting more generalised degrees. He has, I think, made a wonderful and valuable suggestion: that a first degree in production engineering, with a very broad front, does give it. It offers to the young man, the schoolboy perhaps, a rewarding and challenging career.

I would like everyone here to see what a young engineer, trained in aircraft and then in consultancy, is doing to reorganise the whole of his flower-growing industry in Essex. He is now in demand from Italy and Holland on how to grow flowers more efficiently. Professor Ross quotes the United States' output per man. This young man has beaten it completely.

H. ODGEN (*Ferranti*): M. de Vitry emphasised that the very high risk of engineering innovation is not in the research and development side, but rather in getting into manufacture. Many such high-risk ventures fail. Those that succeed, like Xerox, show tremendous profitability. Perhaps Europe must change its attitude to risk in order to gain high profitability. Britain tends to be conservative while American industry makes bigger strides because it gambles, with an end-result in view.

C. W. DEE (*Aerostatic*): Americans grasp a new idea first, investigate it, and then make their decisions. In Britain our reaction seems to be to cursorily look at the thing, make a decision, and that is it. There is no reconsideration whatsoever. Can we make a plea to industry in this country to somewhat change its line of thought? Technology is advancing rapidly. Reconsideration should be given in many cases to new ideas which are just being tossed aside by British industry.

W. A. A. WITHAM (*MacLaren Controls*): Dr Archer, in distinguishing between the industrial designer and the engineering designer, notes the remarkable convergence of their attitudes in recent years, but suggests that the tendency will not necessarily continue. It does not make sense to separate the disciplines of functional and aesthetic design. Both are essential in the well balanced design team. In education for design it is essential that courses provide for the whole task of design, not just a part of it. We need a new teaching method which combines both the art and the science of design. Perhaps teaching institutions of the future will devise courses which will produce men and women with the right balance of scientific and artistic knowledge and ability to improve the quality of design and innovation in industry. Will these graduates of the future be known as engineering designers or will a new class emerge? Perhaps titles do not matter if we reinforce industry with a new breed of *design executives* competent in ALL aspects of design.

Dr BRUCE ARCHER: I agree that there should be the minimum difference between the abilities of the industrial designer working in the engineering field and the engineer working in product design. The word *designer*, as I like to use it, covers anybody who creates anything new. The point is that engineers have tended to rather look down on sales problems, look down on Trades-Union-practices problems, etc. as being a nuisance and nothing to do with him. What I am saying is, they *are* to do with us.

G. PRICE (*Council of Industrial Design*): I agree with Dr Archer that industrial design and engineering design will continue to gradually merge over the years. It has been my experience in advising industry on the use of industrial designers that much of the benefit of it comes because their background and discipline differ from those of the design engineers normally working in a team. Industrial designers tend to see the problem from a completely different viewpoint. Obviously this is more pronounced when the industrial designer comes into a firm as a consultant rather than when he is a member of staff. But the same thing does occur even in the case of a staff designer, and I would like to ask Dr Archer whether he considers that when the two professions do eventually merge – if this does happen – some of this sort of benefit might be lost.

Dr BRUCE ARCHER: I had one of our own staff psychologists carry out an attitude study of all members of staff, to see what were their attitudes to moving to another location, to what extent they were wedded to the place, to the institution, to the work, to their colleagues, to me perhaps, to what extent their attitudes were coloured by the conditions under which they were then working. The most interesting result was that by far the most enjoyable and attractive thing about their work was the opportunity to work in multi-disciplinary teams.

The multi-discipline team is very rarely complete unless you have an outsider, a real outsider from another firm, to bring another viewpoint. If design engineers and industrial designers were to become exactly the same animal, the team would be weakened. I would deplore their total merging.

C. W. DEE (*Aerostatic*): I wonder, Dr Archer, how far you felt that the n.i.h. parameter – 'not invented here' applied to the rejection of ideas, and when you referred to your battlefields within the field of endeavour, whether you indicated this as an international one or purely a national one.

Dr BRUCE ARCHER: I would prefer to regard it almost as a battle against nature. One is trying to wrest wealth from *nature*, competitively, which is very important to a trading nation. Should we get as big a ratio of first cost to ultimate value as is possible? If we do it badly, as we have seen from Mr Maddock's graphs, the flow of money through the exchequers of various countries is badly affected. On a company level we have the same sort of thing. It is a competitive battle, not against one another, but against nature.

On the first part of the question (the n.i.h. factor), my feeling is that it is diminishing rapidly. I think the new managers coming from business schools or from the universities – not from the conventional arts background but some special background – are putting a drive on to their own staffs which is causing the not-invented-here factor to be operating at a low or intermediate level rather than at top level. I think the n.i.h. factor will continue to diminish as mobility of technologists becomes more pronounced.

Dr M. FIELD (*Metcut Research*): What are the most common mechanical fatigue failures that you have to face, Dr Zalud? What are the causes of these failures? Are they associated with materials selection, with the surface produced or with the manufacturing process?

Dr ZALUD: I cannot give you a definite answer to this. In a well-designed product the failures are random. It is the task of the development and reliability engineers to find the various causes. We have gone into measuring the details of actual working conditions because we have found that it is not normal loading that causes difficulty, but unexpected conditions.

G. R. FRANKLIN (*W. E. & F. Dobson*): This question is directed towards either Dr Zalud, Dr Archer or both. In balancing economic feasibility against good customer relations, what are the speakers' views on designing products for abuse as well as use?

Dr ZALUD: We have to design our products. We should do our best for them to be foolproof and we have to add a certain amount of finance on this, to prevent failures owing to unexpected use. There is a limit to what can be done in this line, and it depends to a large extent on the market to which we direct our products. This is a game where one has to count on fair play, and the intelligence and decency of the user.

Dr BRUCE ARCHER: It is very difficult to generalise. I would say that one must look at the total system and the inputs one is prepared to put in and outputs one wishes to get out. In some circumstances the answer will be small print in the contract. In other circumstances it will be high safety factors.

SESSION II

Manufacturing Technology I

Chairman: Mr F. O. Thornton
Director and General Manager
Aero-Engine Division
Rolls-Royce Ltd.
Hillington

MICROELECTRONICS – A NEW TECHNOLOGY

I. M. Mackintosh
Mackintosh Component Consultants Ltd, Fife

SUMMARY

The glamour of microelectronics comes from its remarkable effect in reducing the *size* of electronic systems. Its real value in industrial electronics, however, lies in the equally remarkable effect it is having in reducing the *cost* of electronics. For example, representative integrated circuits which were priced at £2 to £10 three years ago now cost 8s. to 20s., and will probably be as cheap as a few pence in five to ten years. This is a real price revolution, which no electronics engineer can afford to ignore. In this paper the present state of microelectronics is reviewed, with particular emphasis on the various techniques involved in the all-important planar process for making monolithic silicon integrated circuits. Comparisons of integrated circuits with deposited film (i.e. thin-film and thick-film) microcircuits are also made. The reasons for the relative advantages of integrated circuits in respect of cost, reliability and electrical performance are discussed, and the paper concludes with a brief survey of some technological and economic trends in microelectronics.

1.0 HISTORICAL BACKGROUND

The history of the electronics industry has been punctuated by the arrival of important new technologies which have changed its entire pattern. A recent and well-known example is the transistor, which since the early 1950s has revolutionised almost all branches of the electronics industry. The newest technology, and perhaps the most important yet, is micro-electronics[1,2]. Microelectronic circuits are invariably smaller, and generally more reliable, and they consume less power than their more conventional counterparts. Also, in most cases, system costs can be lowered significantly by using microcircuits rather than conventional discrete components. These advantages, particularly the last, ensure that microelectronics will be widely used in most new electronic systems.

The three generic techniques of microelectronics were first developed to a state of practicality in the United States. The 'micro-module' approach, sponsored primarily by the U.S. Army, was aimed at obtaining maximum packing densities by ingenious layout of conventional (discrete) electronic components.

The U.S. Air Force continued to sponsor research on transistor technology, although the development of the all-important planar process was primarily a company-sponsored programme by the Fairchild Semiconductor Division. The U.S. Navy put its effort into thin-film technology, with the long-term aim of obtaining all-evaporated electronic circuits. This entails the successful development not only of passive devices but also of a practical and reliable thin-film active device (transistor). As yet there has been only limited progress towards the latter goal.

All three technologies have now become well established. A dramatic increase in their application to industrial systems is in progress as the cost-reduction benefits of microelectronics become more widely recognised.

Although smallness is no longer the most important advantage of microcircuits, the achievable size reductions are quite impressive. This is illustrated in Fig. 1, which shows the development of a typical computer logic circuit over a number of years. The thermionic valve circuit shown on the right was in use around 1956 and was replaced by the transistor circuit shown on the left (vintage *circa* 1961). A modern integrated circuit form of equivalent complexity is shown in the centre.

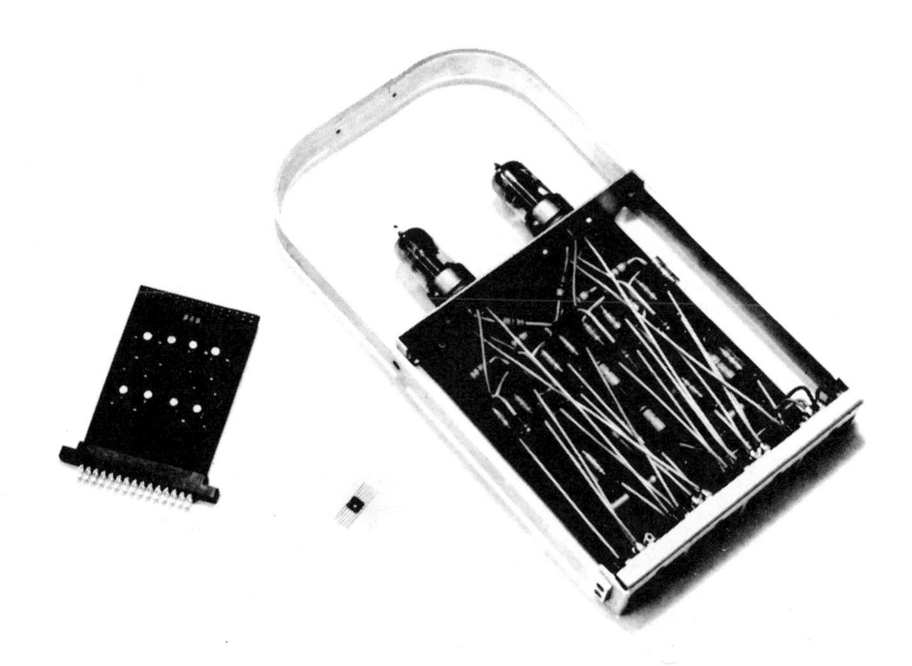

Fig. 1. Progressive miniaturisation of a typical digital electronic circuit.

2.0 THE BASIC TECHNOLOGIES

2.1 *Modular circuits*

The micro-module or cord-wood technique is intended simply to achieve maximum packing density with discrete components by physically laying out the circuit so that as small a volume as possible is occupied consistent with thermal and mechanical requirements. The only processes involved are soldering or welding and – usually – some kind of potting.

There has developed from this basic micro-module technique a 'user' acceptance of small electronic 'building blocks' that provide a total electronic function at the external leads which is much more complex than a single component could provide. The Elliott Minilog series is a good example. Fig. 2 is a photograph of a typical element, showing internal details.

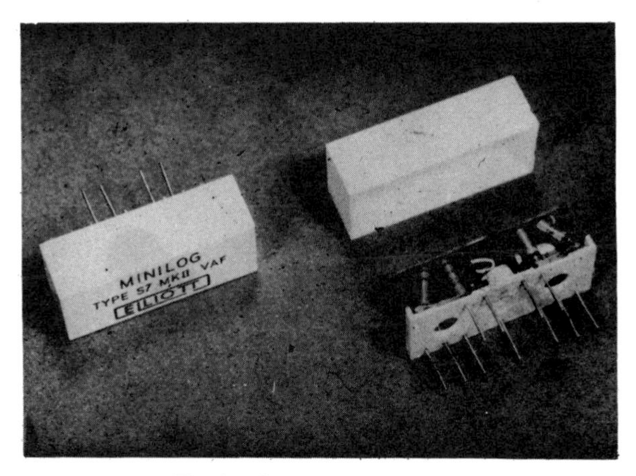

Fig. 2. Micro-modular circuit.

2.2 *Deposited-film circuits*

Thin-film circuits are circuits with passive components of which the conducting and dielectric layers are of the order of 15 000 Å thick or less. In their manufacture films are deposited on an insulating substrate by vapour deposition, sputtering or chemical deposition. Resistors, capacitors, and low-Q inductors can be made in this way, but reliable active devices have still to be developed. Thus it is necessary to attach external active devices to the thin-film circuit, and, as will be seen, this results in an inherent cost disadvantage relative to integrated circuits. Fig. 3 shows a typical thin-film passive circuit to which external transistors have been attached.

Fig. 3. Typical thin-film circuit.

Fabrication of a thin-film circuit begins with a drawing of the circuit scaled up approximately fifty times. Photographic copies are made of this layout, one for each thin layer of material, and photographic masks are then produced in the actual sizes required, commonly of the order of 1 inch dimensions.

The design of a thin-film circuit is relatively straightforward, since the designer can go directly from a conventional 'bread-board' circuit into thin-film form. This comes about because no significant new or extra parasitic capacitive or inductive effects are present with thin-film components, and their electrical characteristics are substantially the same as those of conventional circuits.

The most probable application of thin-film circuits will be where the attachment of active devices is not required, e.g. in filter networks, or in precision resistive networks. The use of such networks, in conjunction with other forms of microcircuit in which gain can be supplied readily (i.e. monolithic integrated circuits), appears to be promising.

Thick-film circuits are generally manufactured by the silk-screen process. Here patterns of conductive and resistive materials are 'screened' on to a substrate, to which they are subsequently bonded by firing in a high-temperature kiln.

A wide range of resistor values can be obtained by this technique, although the temperature coefficients are relatively poor. The tolerances on the final resistor values are also wider than with thin films and individual adjustment is frequently necessary. Capacitors can also be manufactured over a wide range of values, but again the tolerance is relatively poor.

As with thin-film techniques, the thick-film process does not permit simultaneous production of active devices, and again transistors and diodes have to be attached separately.

2.3 *Planar integrated circuits*

The outstanding feature of the planar technique in comparison with the other microelectronic technologies is that it allows both active and passive components to be manufactured simultaneously. Another very important advantage is the ability to produce large numbers of complex circuits simultaneously. Thus, a typical slice of silicon (1 to 2 in diameter) can contain 500 to 1000 circuits after processing, which results in great economic advantages.

The process schedule for the manufacture of an integrated circuit consists of a large number of steps, based on a central repetitive cycle involving the use of 'photo-resist' and diffusion. The description of the process can be simplified by reference to Fig. 4, which shows a schematic representation of the sequence.

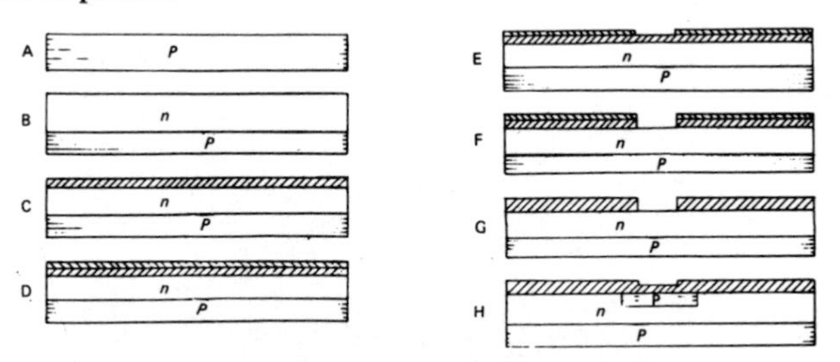

Fig. 4. Schematic of planar process.

The cycle begins with a slice of single-crystal high-purity *p*-type silicon as at A. On this is grown a thin epitaxial layer of *n*-type silicon, the *n*-type crystal structure being a continuation of the same crystal lattice as the *p*-type substrate below, as at B. On the surface of the *n*-type silicon a layer of silicon dioxide is grown thermally. The layer is shown shaded at C. A photo-engraving process follows in which a thin layer of a light-sensitive lacquer ('photo-resist') is spread over the oxide (D) and is exposed to ultra-violet light through an appropriate photographic mask. Exposure to light hardens the lacquer so that in the subsequent development stage it is removed only in the soft, unexposed regions (centre of E). The remaining lacquer acts as a mask against the etchant used to remove oxide from the unexposed areas, as at F. The hardened layer of lacquer is now removed, leaving the original oxidised silicon slice with a pattern of holes etched in the oxide (G). Finally, the whole slice is placed in a high-temperature (e.g. 1200°C) furnace through which flows a gaseous chemical compound containing a *p*-type impurity such as boron. Atomic boron is chemically released at the unoxidised 'windows' and diffuses into the silicon to form *p*-type 'islands' in the *n*-type layer (H).

The final result of this sequence of crystal-growing, oxidation, photo-engraving, diffusion and evaporation processes is illustrated schematically in Fig. 5. This shows: (a) the plan view of a basic integrated circuit consisting of three separate elements (one diode, one transistor and one resistor), (b) the component's electrical symbols, and (c) a cross-section through part of the integrated circuit. Separating (i.e. isolating) these devices are *p*-type walls (shaded) extending from the *p*-type substrate, through the epitaxial *n*-type layer and reaching to the surface.

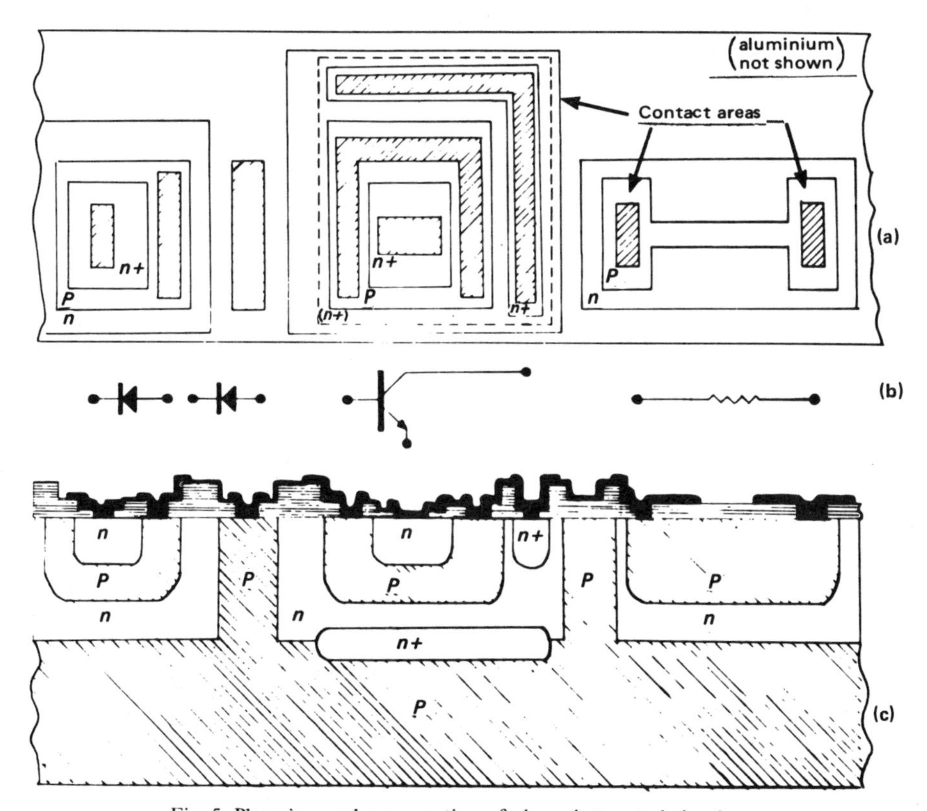

Fig. 5. Plan view and cross-section of planar integrated circuit.

The *p–n* diode consists of a small *n*-type region inside a *p*-type area which itself is totally enclosed in an *n*-type 'island'. Contact is made to the *n*-type and *p*-type regions by means of the evaporated aluminium leads shown in black. The isolation areas are always connected to the least positive voltage in the circuit to keep the *n*-type islands reverse-biased and thus electrically independent of each other. This voltage is applied to the single contact shown to the *p*-type substrate.

The transistor consists of the *n–p–n* structure in the centre. Contact to the deep *n*-type (epitaxial layer) collector region is made *via* the low-resistivity n^+ region on the right. The other 'buried' n^+ region shown deep inside the transistor structure is merely to reduce collector resistance problems and is not of particular importance in this discussion.

The resistor consists of a *p*-type 'track' inside the *n*-type island on the right. As all the resistors in an integrated circuit are produced simultaneously, and are of the same predetermined value of resistivity as the *p*-type base regions, the resistor values are determined mainly by the length and width of the track.

The oxide remaining on the surface serves to 'protect' the *p–n* junctions and to insulate the silicon from the deposited metallic interconnections running across the oxide surface. The different heights of oxide arise from the multiple heat treatments to which the silicon slice has been subjected, and have been exaggerated in the figure for clarity. The whole wafer, from top surface to the lower face of the substrate, is approximately 150–200 microns (or micrometres) thick. The total oxide thickness is generally of the order of ½ to 1 μm while the n^+ diffusion depth (emitters of transistors) is approximately 1·5 μm and the *p*-type diffusion (resistors and bases of transistors) is about 2 μm deep. The width of a resistor is typically 60 μm.

Most important in the above sequence of operations is the inherent quality of the optical masks and the accuracy of their registration with each other. The mask-making process usually begins with a set of patterns, 500 times final required size, each representing one masking operation for a given integrated circuit. These are reduced photographically by a factor of between five and ten. The final reduction to working size takes place in a step-and-repeat camera which both reduces the image and steps it automatically to produce a final photographic plate containing hundreds of identical patterns of the actual final size. These final patterns are those actually used to photo-engrave the hundreds of integrated circuits on a slice.

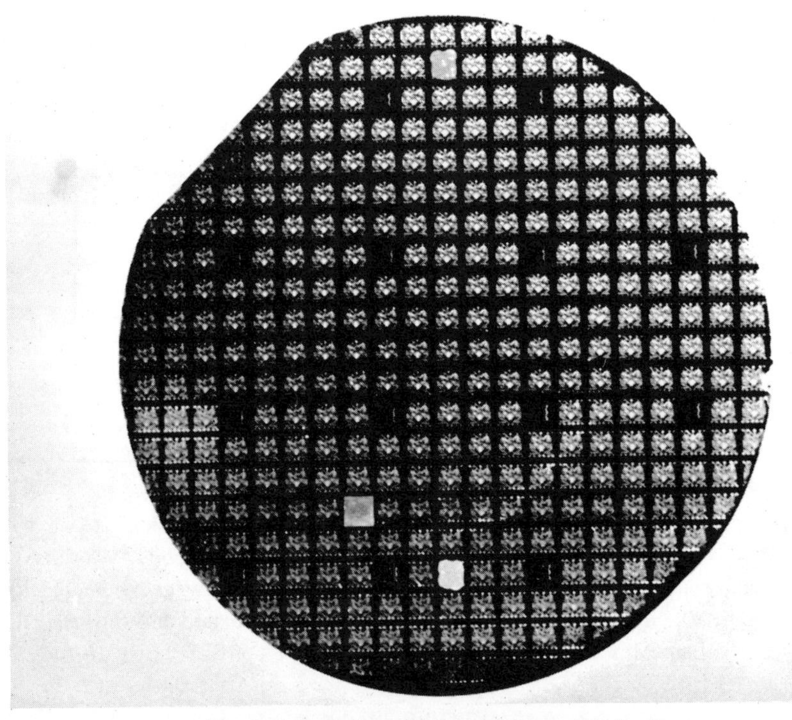

Fig. 6. Typical slice of processed integrated circuits.

A typical processed slice is shown in Fig. 6. It contains more than 300 individual integrated circuits of a complex type. After completion of the fabrication processes the slice is subjected to full electrical test with the aid of an automatically-stepped, multi-contact probe in combination with a programmed electrical tester (Fig. 7). This operation results in automatic ink-marking of reject circuits, which are subsequently discarded after the slice has been diced up into individual integrated circuit 'chips'. Only circuits which have passed this initial test are allowed into the subsequent assembly phase, which is where both labour and material costs on individual circuits become significant.

Fig. 7. Multi-probe slice-tester.

Fig. 8. Bonded integrated circuit before final encapsulation.

In the assembly phase the integrated-circuit chips are first mounted on the base of the package being used. Very thin wires are used to connect the aluminium contact pads on the chip to the package leads. For greatest reliability of these bonds it is usual to employ aluminium wire and an ultrasonic bonding technique. Fig. 8 shows an integrated-circuit chip after wire bonding. The silicon chip in this photograph is only 0·040 in square. The final stage of assembly is to seal the package lids hermetically, after which the completed integrated circuit is ready for hermetic, environmental and additional electrical testing.

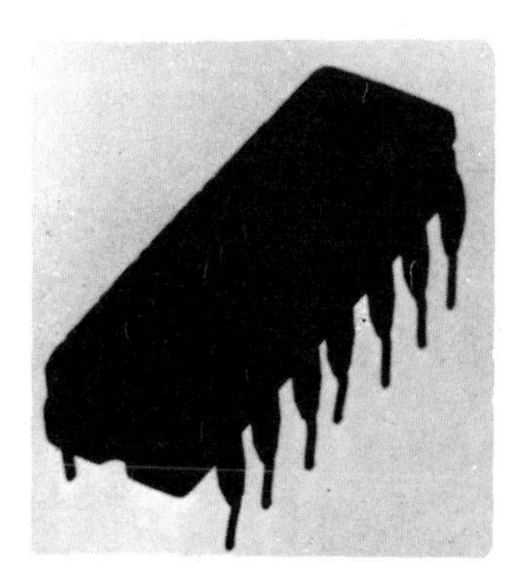

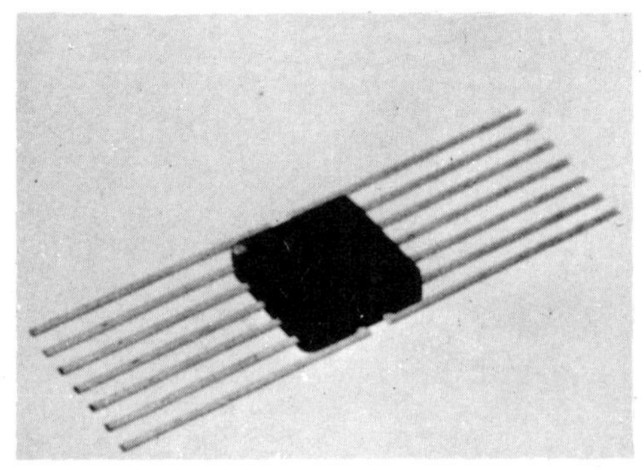

Fig. 9. Types of integrated-circuit package.

Fig. 9 shows some examples of integrated circuit packages in common use. An early type of encapsulation was the conventional TO-5 transistor can, modified by the inclusion of additional leads, as shown on the right-hand side of Fig. 9. The first package specially designed for integrated circuits was the 'flat pack' (centre of Fig. 9) and is particularly useful where space and weight are important. The most common type today, however, is the D.I.P., or dual in-line package, shown on the left-hand side of Fig. 9. This can be inserted directly into a printed circuit board and is particularly suitable for industrial electronic systems.

3.0 THE SPECIAL CASE OF INTEGRATED CIRCUITS

It is now quite clear that monolithic, silicon, integrated circuits will dominate microelectronics even more in the future than they have in the past. This superiority of integrated circuits is founded on the planar technique, and it is useful to consider what particular features suit it so overwhelmingly to most electronic system needs.

Technologically the planar process has two outstanding advantages. First, planar devices are protected at each stage during fabrication by an oxide layer, and the risk of outside contamination is thereby much reduced. Secondly, the process results in a final surface which is essentially flat (i.e. planar). It is this feature which enables metallic interconnection to be made between devices by evaporation techniques, thus avoiding many of the complex, costly and relatively unreliable wired connections.

Because the processes used to produce the well-tried planar transistors and the newer integrated circuits are almost identical, many characteristics are common to both. In particular, it is to be expected that the excellent *reliability* record of planar transistors will be emulated by integrated circuits[3,4]. Indeed, there is already good reason to believe that overall system reliability is improved considerably with integrated circuits. Because of the high degree of surface protection given by the oxide layer in the planar process, the relatively few failures which have occurred with transistors have been mainly due to the failure of wire bonds. The number of bonds in an integrated circuit system, however, is very much smaller than in a system using conventional transistors. This becomes obvious when one considers that four bonds are needed for a conventional planar transistor, whereas the 28 bonds of a fourteen-lead integrated circuit could typically enclose a total of fifty active and passive components, i.e. the risk of bond failures has dropped by at least 4:1.

For most circuit requirements the *electrical performance* obtainable from components within a monolithic integrated circuit is perfectly satisfactory. Passive components can be made in integrated circuits with acceptable frequency capabilities as high as many hundreds of MHz. For most circuit work now and in the foreseeable future this is an adequate frequency range. Much of the design experience gained in making conventional planar transistors is relevant to integrated circuit design, and very-high-performance transistors and diodes can be made in monolithic form. Indeed, for some high-frequency applications, higher performance can be obtained from integrated circuits than from the equivalent discrete form. High-frequency performance is improved because of the absence of the stray lead capacitance and inductance normally associated with a conventionally encapsulated transistor. The table gives some typical integrated component characteristics.

CHARACTERISTICS OF TYPICAL
PLANAR COMPONENTS

Parameter	Value	Precision	Matching	Thermal coefficient (p.p.m.)	Upper useful frequency (MHz)
Resistance	10 Ω 20 000 Ω	±10%	±3%	1000	> 100
Capacitance	100 pF	±10%	±3%	1000	> 100
Transistor cut-off frequency	1000 MHz	±30%	±10%	–	–

In addition to their satisfactory high-frequency performance, integrated circuits possess performance advantages which are not obtained with other microelectronic techniques. These qualities are associated with the processing of all the circuit components both simultaneously and on a very small area of material.

This results in the characteristics of all components on a chip being exceptionally well matched. In particular, transistors have extremely close thermal matching and tracking characteristics in parameters which are very important in the design of low-drift d.c. amplifiers and in memory-core read-out amplifiers. Many present-day linear integrated circuits take advantage of these special characteristics.

Finally, the *cost advantage* of planar integrated circuits is mainly due to the processing of a large number of circuits at a time. During the actual diffusion operation, for example, not only are several hundred devices (e.g. up to a thousand circuits) being processed on each slice, but up to fifty slices are in the furnace at any one time. Thus, during diffusion, there can be approximately 50 000 circuits being processed simultaneously, i.e. about two million electronic components! Despite the complexity of the processes used, it is clear that the cost of each circuit at this stage must be extremely low and this relative cost advantage is not seriously eroded in assembly and testing stages since all forms of circuit must also go through them.

4.0 FUTURE TRENDS IN MICROELECTRONICS

New techniques are being put into use continuously as a result of the 'leap frog' situation in which 'user' demand is met by technical progress and is then left behind by further innovations.

One way in which the planar process is being improved, for example, is by continual reduction in the size of the integrated-circuit chips themselves. This gives two benefits: first, it permits more circuits to be built into a given area of silicon, and thus the handling of more devices at any one time; and, second, higher yields can be obtained as the size of each individual circuit goes down. This latter advantage arises because of the finite number of very small random faults that are present on the slice of material. An entire circuit can now be made in about the same area which a single transistor occupied less than ten years ago. It is expected that this process of size reduction will continue, and that the rate of progress will be controlled by the degree of sophistication of the basic mask-making process.

The result of this and other technological improvements is a dramatic and continuing decrease in the cost of integrated circuits. For example, a typical digital integrated circuit, priced at about £5 in 1965, now costs approximately 10s. 0d., an order-of-magnitude reduction in price in about four years. This process is expected to continue to the point where such circuits will cost no more than a few pence, by the middle- to late-seventies.

Another probable development is new devices based on the planar technology. An example of such a device already in production and being seriously considered for many large-scale

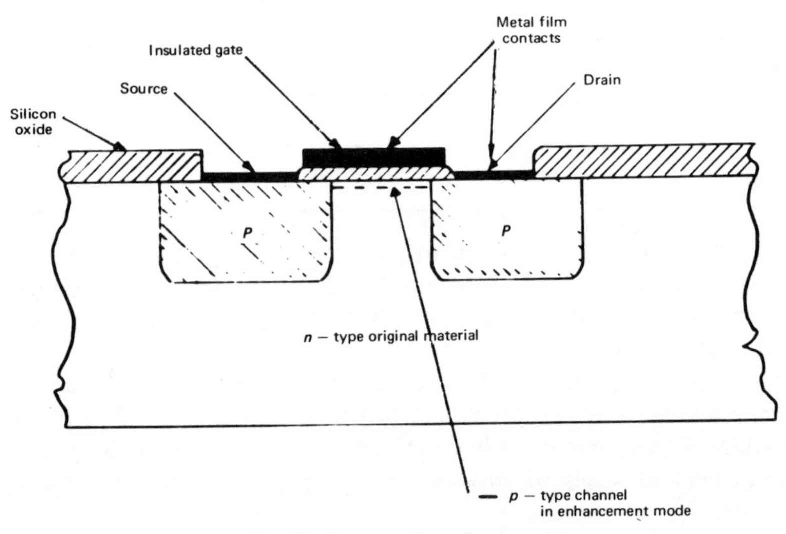

Fig. 10. Cross-section of an m.o.s.t.

applications is the metal:oxide:semiconductor transistor, or MOST[5]. Although radically different from the conventional transistor, the MOST owes its growing importance to the planar process, since only by this technique did control of surface effects lead to the successful development of a surface-controlled field-effect transistor in the early 1960s.

Fig. 10 shows a cross-section of a typical MOS transistor. The basic operation of a MOST is that electrical charges on the gate electrode control the conductivity of the channel between the drain and source regions, and in this way the device acts in a manner somewhat analogous to that of a thermionic valve.

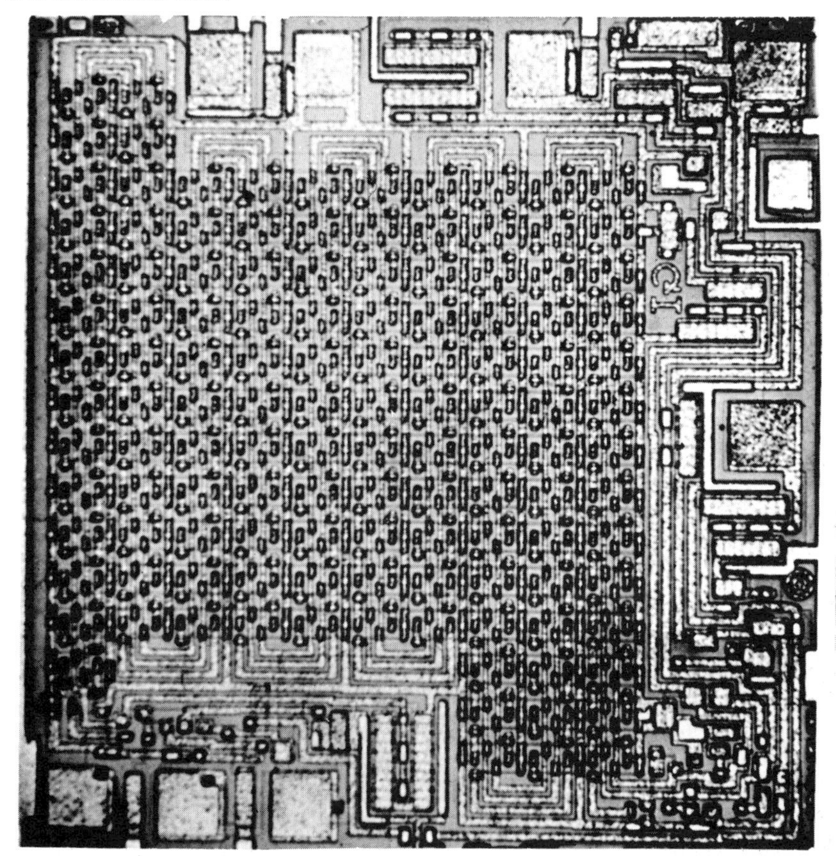

Fig. 11. Complex MOST device chip (128-bit shift register).

Outstanding features of MOS integrated circuits which promise further cost reductions are:

1 Fewer process steps are required
2 No diffused isolation areas are necessary between MOS components.

The second feature allows many more devices to be contained in a given area of silicon than is normal with conventional integrated circuits. Thus components can be very densely packed.

At present MOS circuits tend to be limited in their speed and high-frequency performance compared with conventional integrated circuits. However, they have compensating advantages. For instance, MOS logic circuits can be made which perform extremely complex functions and yet consume only a little power. One MOS integrated circuit already commercially available, for example, is a 128-bit shift register with a typical power dissipation of 2 mW/bit (Fig. 11).

This circuit is representative of another major trend in microelectronics, the development of chips of greater and greater electronic complexity, whether based on conventional (i.e. bi-polar) or MOS transistors. In order to classify the general complexity level of integrated circuits the terms M.S.I. (medium-scale integration) and L.S.I. (large-scale integration) have recently been introduced. Devices are called M.S.I. if they contain between ten and a hundred logic gates or their equivalent on one chip, and are fabricated generally using a large single-chip layout of high complexity. On the other hand L.S.I. devices, with more than a hundred logic gates per chip, are under development using a computer-designed 'discretionary wiring' technique to connect many smaller complex cells into the required final configuration. The L.S.I. 'chip' will thus be the significant part of the whole silicon slice and equivalent in area to a number of chips of M.S.I. complexity.

The foregoing examples of current technological trends in microelectronics are representative but do not by any means cover the full spectrum of progress. What is quite certain, however, is that the basic motivation for the bulk of research and development work in this field will continue to be reduction in the cost of electronic hardware. It is to be expected that much of the future growth of electronics will stem directly from the enormous cost-reduction benefits of microelectronics.

ACKNOWLEDGMENTS

The author has much pleasure in acknowledging the help of P. F. Guyton in the preparation of the paper. He also thanks Marconi Elliott Microelectronics Ltd for permission to reproduce Figs 2, 8 and 9, and General Instrument Microelectronics (U.K.) Ltd for permission to reproduce Fig. 11.

REFERENCES

1 I. M. MACKINTOSH Vicount Nuffield Memorial Paper. *Production Eng.* Mar. 1967, p.157.

2 P. E. HAGGERTY 'Integrated Electronics – a Perspective.' *Proc. I.E.E.E.* Vol. 52. Dec. 1964, pp. 1400–1405.

3 I. M. MACKINTOSH 'The Reliability of Integrated Circuits.' *J. Micr. and Rel.* Vol. 5. Jan. 1966. pp. 27–37.

4 J. ADAMS and W. WORKMAN 'Semiconductor Network Reliability Assessment.' *Proc. I.E.E.E.* Vol. 52. Dec. 1964. pp. 1624–1635.

5 R. A. HILBOURNE and J. F. MILES 'The Metal:Oxide:Semiconductor Transistor.' *Electronic Eng.* Mar. 1965, p. 156.

ANALYSIS AND OPTIMISATION OF COST AND PRODUCTION IN METAL REMOVAL

M. Field, N. Zlatin and A. Ackenhausen
Metcut Research Associates Inc.
Cincinnati

SUMMARY

The efficiency of machine-tool utilisation has been under study by many investigators for some time. In general their approaches have been based on considerations of either maximum production–minimum cost or maximum profit. Recently greater efficiency has been pursued by application of adaptive control to machine tools. Various ways of improving the efficient utilisation of machine tools are discussed. The bulk of the paper is devoted to a method for the determination and analysis of cost and rate of production in machining, utilising actual machining data. Detailed equations are presented for conventional as well as numerically controlled machine tools. Equations are derived for turning, milling, drilling, reaming, and tapping. The equations have been programmed so that, by means of a computer, one can analyse and determine the relative significance of each factor and its influence on the total cost and production rate. Optimised equations are also presented which are applicable when the relationship between tool life and cutting parameters can be mathematically expressed. Required machining data are obtained from either a machinability production laboratory or from machine shop records. All machining data are stored in a computer for systematic, rapid retrieval.

1.0 INTRODUCTION

The objective in manufacturing might be thought of as to produce hardware of specified quality at minimum cost.

Once a decision has been reached that a component is to be machined, the object of the industrial or manufacturing engineer is to select machining operations and a set of machining parameters that provide the specified quality at minimum cost. There usually exists a wide range of machine tools, cutters, and cutting conditions, all of which will satisfy the surface texture and surface-integrity quality specifications. The aim then is to select machining conditions such as cutting speeds, feeds, depths of cut, cutting fluids, tool materials, and tool geometry that will be optimal for the particular component. The optimisation criterion in machining has been at various times considered to be minimum cost, maximum production, or maximum profit.

Many investigators have derived analytical expressions for calculating optimised machining conditions. Representative approaches to this subject will be reviewed in the paper.

2.0 LITERATURE REVIEW

Professor Inyong Ham has well reviewed the economics of machining[1]. In his paper he referred first to Ernst's proposed equation for cost per piece based on the number of pieces between regrinds[2]. The procedure was simple and straightforward. The cost included machining, handling, cost per piece, total cost of changing, and regrinding the tool.

A more general analysis on the economics of machining, by Gilbert[3], was described in the same paper. Gilbert equated the cost per piece to the sum of the idle cost, the cutting cost, the tool change cost and the tool regrinding cost. Employing Taylor's equation, $VT^n = C$, he obtained the equation for minimum cost per piece by differentiating the total cost per piece with respect to cutting speed and then equating the result to zero. Here V is the cutting speed, T the tool life, and n and C are constants. Gilbert stated that the tool life for minimum cost was affected only by the exponent n and the ratio of the cost of labour to overhead.

Witthoff[4,5] analysed the economic problem in a manner similar to Gilbert's. He also based his analysis on Taylor's equation. Since feed and depth of cut were not considered by either Gilbert or Witthoff, analyses were applicable only for a given set of conditions. They assumed that the equation with a fixed value of n held over the range of cutting speeds involved.

Shaw, Cook, and Smith[6] proposed a different criterion for the analysis of the problem. Their analysis was based on the helical distance (L) travelled by a turning tool over a workpiece for a given amount of tool wear. The formula used was $VL^s = K$, where V is cutting speed, s an exponent, and K a constant. Although this analysis did not require extensive tool life tests or rely on tool life data like the others, it related to a given feed and depth of cut and was founded on similar assumptions.

Brewer[7] developed an analysis in which a more general expression of the tool life equation was employed. This equation included feed and depth of cut as variables, and wear was introduced as a variable in the analysis. Brewer also added a new cost element of premature tool failure cost per piece, and he separated tool depreciation cost per piece from the tool regrinding cost per piece.

Colding[8] also studied machining costs from various points of view. However, his equations did not take into account the effects of various feeds and depths of cut. In a later paper he showed how relatively simple cutting data relationships can be deduced from basic cutting parameters in turning, milling, grinding, and drilling[9]. He also showed how to adapt the theoretical cutting data expression to industrial needs, in particular for manuals to be used in programming numerically controlled machine tools. A flow-sheet for drilling was included in his paper. He claimed that tool life relationships were of the same general type in turning as in milling and grinding.

A more comprehensive approach, using a digital computer to analyse optimum cutting conditions in various machining conditions, was made by Weill and his co-authors[10]. The optimum number of cuts under various combinations of speed and feed was obtained through their analysis. Also, their analysis extended to non-cylindrical workpieces and multi-tooth machining operations.

In an attempt to simplify application of the analysis, work-sheet forms were developed by Siekmann[11] and Conn[12]. A special analogue computer was suggested by Gilbert and Weller[13]. Many nomographs have been published in terms of cost per piece *versus* cutting speed curves[3,6,7,14,15]. The effect of tool-changing and machining-cycle time have also been included in studies by Hoffmeister[16] and McCullough[17]. McCullough expanded Gilbert's formula for use with multi-tooth operations.

It was Ham's opinion that, while nomograms together with simplified formulas and work-sheets are easy to use, they provide an answer for a specific condition only and do not present the whole picture of the relations between the variables involved. He stated that this shortcoming is eliminated by using a digital computer. Otherwise it is impossible to consider the various combinations of machining elements and show their interrelationship and plot graphs showing trends. For analysing optimum machining conditions he used an IBM 7074 computer and Fortran[1]. He then applied his system to the equations developed by several of the investigators. His whole purpose was to show the application of computers to the economics of machining. As he stated, once the master programs have been prepared for a particular type of work, only input data for specific conditions (which are to be examined) are needed for a computation. The cost of computer time for analysis is relatively low.

Using Taylor's equation and the cutting time per part, Shaw[18] in 1965 obtained the derivative of the machining cost per part relative to cutting speed and determined the minimum unit cost per part. The objective was to show the added costs involved when the optimum cutting speed is not available on the lathe used. Since most machine tools are designed to operate at discrete feeds and speeds in a geometric progression, the speed for minimum cost may not be available on the particular machine used.

Armarego and Russell[19] developed a method based on maximum profit rate for selecting machining conditions for a single-pass turning operation. The profit rate was defined as one minus the ratio of machining cost per component to time to produce one component. Putting this definition into an equation involving cutting speed and feed, they then partially differentiated the equation, first with respect to cutting speed and then with respect to feed. The two equations were then set equal to zero. Since, as the authors state, the two equations could not be solved for a unique maximum, the curves represented loci of maximum profit rate for each of the two variables.

They concluded from the loci that profit rate increases as feed increases and speed decreases, and hence the maximum permissible profit rate could be achieved by using the highest feed and the corresponding speed required to satisfy the equation. The achievement of the maximum profit rate is thus limited by the maximum available feed, cutting speed, power, and required surface finish.

Okushima and Hitomi[20] appear to have been the first to present the concept of a cutting speed for maximum profit. In a so-called 'break even' chart they compared profits at cutting speeds for minimum cost and maximum production. They assumed that Taylor's tool life equation held for the machining conditions they used. Then the equation for the cutting speed for maximum profit was determined. The basic idea is good, but the originators limited themselves to a turning operation.

Using the same basic concept Wu and Ermer[21] determined the machining conditions for maximum profit by applying the principle that maximum profit occurs at the production rate for which the marginal revenue equals the marginal cost. They presented relationships between production rate, costs, revenues, profit, and cutting speeds. An example was given in their paper to demonstrate how the cutting speed for maximum profit can shift between that for minimum cost and maximum production, depending upon the selling price of the part. The effect of feed on maximum profit was also demonstrated by use of a modification of Taylor's equation. However, the entire analysis was for a turning operation. The assumption was that Taylor's equation is valid for the relevant cutting speeds and feeds. Also it was assumed that there is a linear relationship between cost and cutting speed. The authors stated that, if the relationship between cost and cutting speed is non-linear, the same equations hold.

In a later paper the same authors[22] commented that the above analysis was based on the assumption that for a given set of operating conditions the parameters in the tool life equations were constant. In reality, they now stated, the parameters in the tool life equations were empirical estimates, subject to uncertainties because of experimental error in tool life testing. The theoretical optimum cutting conditions were affected by the uncertainty in these estimates.

3.0 THE DILEMMA

The major deterrent against use of any of the aforementioned optimised equations is that they all depend on the use of an *accurate* mathematical *relationship* of tool life to cutting speed, feed, depth, and other machining parameters. Unfortunately no such accurate relationship exists. Most investigators assume the validity of Taylor's equation in the simplified form, $VT^n = C$, or the more advanced form, $VT^n f^{\alpha} d^{\beta} = C$. Unfortunately Taylor's equation does not always apply, and it is dangerous to assume that it does without checking[23]. We have found that the Taylor equation tends *not* to hold for milling, drilling, tapping, and reaming of aerospace alloys. It is also not applicable to many common commercial alloys. For many aerospace and commercial alloys the Taylor relationship applies at higher cutting speeds but tends to fail at the lower cutting speeds in the region of which these alloys are generally machined.

If one wants to optimise, the approach is to assume the Taylor relationship, calculate optimal speeds, feeds, and other cutting conditions, and then carefully check in the shop.

4.0 NEED FOR MACHINING DATA

It is apparent from the preceding discussion that accurate determination of machining cost and production depends on the existence of machining data relating tool life to the pertinent cutting parameters.

Machining data can be obtained in several ways. The first, and most general, is to obtain them from machining handbooks. The second is to develop experimental data on the particular material and operations involved in an individual company. The third is to record data in actual production. We feel that all three forms of data collection are necessary.

It is imperative that all machining data be collected, analysed, stored, and disseminated in a systematic fashion. In our laboratory we have developed tabular layouts for this purpose (Tables 2, 5 and 6). Historical shop data should likewise be collected in a systematic manner. It is necessary to devise a handling system, which might employ punched cards – and even a computer – for collection, storage, and dissemination of pertinent data.

5.0 ANALYSIS OF COST AND PRODUCTION RATE

Until it is possible mathematically to relate tool life with cutting parameters there exists an extremely useful and powerful method, namely to *analyse* costs and production rates from as little as *one* set of machining data. Specifically, the approach we suggest is to calculate all of the detailed cost and production rate factors which make up the total cost and total production rate. These details can be analysed to determine which are *significant* and which are *trivial.* Steps can then be taken to reduce the cost or the time of the factors which make up the greatest percentages of cost or time. It has been found, for example, that in many cases the cost of *producing chips* may only be 10 to 25% of total cost and that the predominating costs are those of tool reconditioning, loading and unloading, or setting up. In these circumstances, the logical approach to cost reduction (or optimising) is to reduce the high cost factors of the overall machining operation. A computer is essential for the long, tedious calculations.

5.1 *Cost and production rate equations for conventional machine tools*

Equations have been developed for determining the cost per piece, C, and the production rate in pieces per hour, P, for the common machining operations, namely, turning, milling, drilling, reaming, and tapping. Cost in \$/workpiece is given by eqns 1 to 4 inclusive, and production rate in workpieces/hour by eqns 5 to 8 inclusive. In the original papers[24], equations were further developed for detailed types of cutters, e.g. separate equations for cost are given for inserted tooth, throw-away insert, solid high-speed steel, and solid body-brazed carbide-tipped cutters.

Turning

$$C = M\left[\frac{D(e+L)}{3{\cdot}82f_r v} + \frac{2a+e+L}{r} + t_L + \frac{t_o}{N_L} + \frac{DLt_c}{3{\cdot}82f_r vT}\right] + \frac{DL}{3{\cdot}82f_r vT}\left[\frac{C_p}{(k_1+1)} + Gt_s + \frac{Gt_b}{k_2} + \frac{C_c}{k_3} + C_w\right] \tag{1}$$

Milling

$$C = M\left[\frac{D(e+L)}{3{\cdot}82Zf_t v} + \frac{2a+e+L}{r} + t_L + \frac{t_o}{N_L} + \frac{Lt_c}{ZT_t}\right] + \frac{L}{ZT_t}\left[\frac{C_p}{(k_1+1)} + Gt_s + \frac{Gt_b}{k_2} + \frac{ZC_c}{k_3} + C_w\right] \tag{2}$$

Drilling and reaming

$$C = M\left[\frac{D(e+L)}{3{\cdot}82f_r v} + \frac{2a+e+L}{r} + t_L + \frac{t_o}{N_L} + \frac{Lt_c}{T_t}\right] + \frac{L}{T_t}\left[\frac{C_p}{(k_1+1)} + Gt_s\right] \tag{3}$$

Tapping

$$C = M\left[\frac{mD(e+L)}{1{\cdot}91v} + \frac{2a}{r} + t_L + \frac{t_o}{N_L} + \frac{Lt_c}{T_t}\right] + \frac{L}{T_t}\left[\frac{C_p}{(k_1+1)} + Gt_s\right] \tag{4}$$

↑ M: \$/min; ↑ first term: Feeding time; ↑ second term: Rapid traverse time; ↑ t_L: Load and unload time; ↑ t_o/N_L: Set-up time; ↑ Lt_c term: Tool change time; ↑ $C_p/(k_1+1)$: Tool depreciation cost; ↑ Gt_s: Tool resharpening cost; ↑ Gt_b/k_2: Rebrazing or blade reset cost; ↑ C_c/k_3: Insert or blade cost; ↑ C_w: Grinding wheel cost

Turning

$$P = \frac{60}{\dfrac{D(e+L)}{3{\cdot}82f_r v} + \dfrac{2a+e+L}{r} + t_L + \dfrac{t_o}{N_L} + \dfrac{DLt_c}{3{\cdot}82f_r vT}} \tag{5}$$

Milling

$$P = \frac{60}{\dfrac{D(e+L)}{3{\cdot}82Zf_t v} + \dfrac{2a+e+L}{r} + t_L + \dfrac{t_o}{N_L} + \dfrac{Lt_c}{ZT_t}} \tag{6}$$

Drilling and reaming

$$P = \frac{60}{\dfrac{D(e+L)}{3{\cdot}82 f_r v} + \dfrac{2a+e+L}{r} + t_L + \dfrac{t_o}{N_L} + \dfrac{Lt_c}{T_t}} \quad (7)$$

Tapping

$$P = \frac{60}{\dfrac{mD(e+L)}{1{\cdot}91 v} + \dfrac{2a}{r} + t_L + \dfrac{t_o}{N_L} + \dfrac{Lt_c}{T_t}} \quad (8)$$

5.2 *Example of milling on conventional machine*

An example is given of the use of the face-milling equations for determining the costs and production rates in face milling on a conventional machine.

A 4340 steel block, quenched and tempered to 341 B.H.N., is face-milled, the cut taken being 2 in wide by 8 in long. The analysis is made for two types of cutter – a throw-away carbide insert and a solid high-speed-steel cutter. Both cutters are 4 inches in diameter. The pertinent tooling and time study information is given in Table 1.

TABLE 1 EXAMPLE OF CONVENTIONAL FACE-MILLING

OPERATION: Face-mill block, 2 in wide by 8 in long
Cutter: 4 in diameter face mill
Material: 4340 steel, quenched and tempered, 341 B.H.N.

Symbol		Description	Solid h.s.s. cutter	Throw-away insert
a	=	approach of cutter to work, in	9·0	9·0
C_c	=	cost of each inserted tooth, throw-away insert, or carbide tip, $	–	2·45
C_p	=	purchase cost of cutter, $	91·00	212·00
C_w	=	cost of grinding wheel for resharpening cutter, $/cutter	0·35	–
d	=	depth of cut, in	*	*
D	=	diameter of milling cutter, in	4·0	4·0
e	=	overtravel of milling cutter past workpiece, in	5·0	5·0
f_t	=	feed per teeth, in/tooth	*	*
G	=	labour and overhead cost on cutter grinder, $/min.	0·15	–
k_1	=	times cutter is resharpened before being discarded	20	9000
k_2	=	times cutter is resharpened before inserts (or blades) are reset (or rebrazed)	–	–
k_3	=	times blades (or inserts) are resharpened (or indexed) before blades (or inserts) are discarded	–	8
L	=	length of workpiece, in	8·0	8·0
M	=	labour and overhead cost on milling machine, $/min	0·15	0·15
N_L	=	number of workpieces in lot	100	100
r	=	rapid traverse rate, in/min	150	150
t_b	=	time to reset blades or to rebraze cutter teeth, min	–	–

t_c	=	time to change cutter or index all inserts in cutter, min	10·0	6·0
t_L	=	time to load and unload workpiece, min	3	3
t_o	=	time to set up milling machine for operation, min	60	60
t_s	=	time to resharpen cutter, min/cutter	80	–
T_t	=	tool life, measured in travel of work to dull one cutter tooth, in	*	*
v	=	cutting speed, ft/min	*	*
w	=	width of cut, in	2·0	2·0
Z	=	number of teeth in milling cutter	14	6

* These values are taken from tool life data, Table 2

The experimental relationship of tool life to cutting speed and other machining conditions is given in Table 2. Each data set of tool life *versus* cutting speed in Table 2 is numbered so that the corresponding calculations can be identified. The costs and production rates were determined using eqns 2 and 6 and the computer printout is reproduced in Fig. 1. Note that the computer is programmed to print out not only the total cost and the total production rate for each data set but also the detailed cost factors which make up the total. The lowest total cost

TABLE 2 TOOL LIFE DATA FOR FACE MILLING

Material	Condition and microstructure	B.H.N.	Tool mat'l: Trade name	Tool mat'l: Industry grade	Up or down milling	Tool geometry: AR (°)	RR (°)	CA (°)	TR (°)	INCL (°)	ECEA (°)	End rel. (°) / Cor. rel. (°)	Cutting fluid	Depth of cut (in)	Width of cut (in)	Feed in/tooth	Tool life end point (in)	Tool life/tooth (work travel, in) / Speed (ft/min)
4340	Quenched and tempered / Tempered martensite	341	–	T15 H.S.S.	Up	0	0	30	0	0	5	6 / 6	Sol. oil 1:20	0·100	2·0	0·010	0·060	(1) 17 / 93; (2) 22 / 76; (3) 32 / 62
4340	Quenched and tempered / Tempered martensite	341	370	C-6	Up	0	–7	45	–5	5	5	6 / 6	Dry	0·100	2·0	0·005	0·016	(4) 20 / 680; (5) 50 / 550; (6) 80 / 340

```
COST AND PRODUCTION RATE FOR MILLING

SOLID HIGH SPEED STEEL CUTTER

DATA*    WORK    *HARD*TOOL*    *CUT *FEED/*TOOL *    *FEED*RAPD*LOAD*SET-*CUTR*CUTR*CUTR*GRND*    **TOTAL**PROD*
 SET*            *NESS*MATL*    *SPD *TOOTH*LIFE *    *COST*TRAV*UNLD* UP *CHNG*DEPR*SHPN*WHL.*    **COST **RATE*
 NO.* MATERIAL *     *     *    *F/M *  IN  *IN/TH*   * $  * $  * $  * $  * $  * $  * $  * $  *    **$/PC.**PC/HR

  1 AISI 4340    341   T15        93 0.010   17.0     0.15 0.03 0.44 0.08 0.05 0.14 0.40 0.01        1.33  11.5
  2 AISI 4340    341   T15        76 0.010   22.0     0.19 0.03 0.44 0.08 0.03 0.11 0.31 0.00        1.23  11.2
  3 AISI 4340    341   T15        62 0.010   32.0     0.23 0.03 0.44 0.08 0.02 0.07 0.21 0.00        1.13  10.8
```

```
COST AND PRODUCTION RATE FOR MILLING

THROWAWAY INSERT

DATA*    WORK    *HARD*TOOL*    *CUT *FEED/*TOOL *    *FEED*RAPD*LOAD*SET-*INDX*BODY*INSERT*    **TOTAL**PROD*
 SET*            *NESS*MATL*    *SPD *TOOTH*LIFE *    *COST*TRAV*UNLD* UP *INST*DEPR* COST *    **COST **RATE*
 NO.* MATERIAL *     *     *    *F/M *  IN  *IN/TH*   * $  * $  * $  * $  * $  * $  *  $   *    **$/PC.**PC/HR

  4 AISI 4340    341   C-6       680 0.005   20.0     0.10 0.03 0.44 0.08 0.05 0.00  0.12         0.85  12.3
  5 AISI 4340    341   C-6       550 0.005   50.0     0.12 0.03 0.44 0.08 0.02 0.00  0.04         0.76  12.5
  6 AISI 4340    341   C-6       340 0.005   80.0     0.20 0.03 0.44 0.08 0.01 0.00  0.03         0.81  11.4
```

Fig. 1. Computer printout – cost and production rate for face-milling on conventional milling machine.

of \$1·13 for the h.s.s. cutter occurred with data set 3. Here the feeding cost was \$0·23, the loading and unloading cost was \$0·44, while the total cutter cost was \$0·30.

With the throw-away carbide insert the lowest cost of \$0·76 occurred for data set 5. Of this the feeding cost was only \$0·12, while the loading and unloading cost was still \$0·44; but the cutter cost was reduced to \$0·06. Further attack on cost should be directed toward reduction of the predominating loading and unloading costs.

5.3 *Cost and production rate equations for numerically controlled machine tools*

Cost, operation time per piece and production rate for numerically controlled machine tools are given by equations 9 to 20.

Turning

$$C = M\left[\frac{D(L+e)}{3{\cdot}82 f_r v} + \frac{R}{r} + t_i + \frac{DLt_d}{3{\cdot}82 f_r v T}\right] + \frac{DL}{3{\cdot}82 f_r v T}\left[\frac{C_p}{(k_1+1)} + Gt_s + \frac{Gt_b}{k_2} + \frac{C_c}{k_3} + C_w + Gt_p\right] \quad (9)$$

Milling

$$C = M\left[\frac{D(L+e)}{3{\cdot}82 Z f_t v} + \frac{R}{r} + t_i + \frac{Lt_d}{ZT_t}\right] + \frac{L}{ZT_t}\left[\frac{C_p}{(k_1+1)} + Gt_s + \frac{Gt_b}{k_2} + \frac{ZC_c}{k_3} + C_w + Gt_p\right] \quad (10)$$

Drilling or reaming

$$C = M\left[\frac{D(L+e)}{3{\cdot}82 f_r v} + \frac{R}{r} + t_i + \frac{Lt_d}{T_t}\right] + \frac{L}{T_t}\left[\frac{C_p}{(k_1+1)} + Gt_s + Gt_p\right] \quad (11)$$

Tapping

$$C = M\left[\frac{mD(L+e)}{1{\cdot}91 v} + \frac{R}{r} + t_i + \frac{Lt_d}{T_t}\right] + \frac{L}{T_t}\left[\frac{C_p}{(k_1+1)} + Gt_s + Gt_p\right] \quad (12)$$

Centre drilling or chamfering

$$C = M\left[\frac{D(L+e)}{3{\cdot}82 f_r v} + \frac{R}{r} + t_i + \frac{u_c t_d}{T_h}\right] + \frac{u_c}{T_h}\left[\frac{C_p}{(k_1+1)} + Gt_s + Gt_p\right] \quad (13)$$

Handling and setting-up

$$C = M\left[t_L + \frac{t_o}{N_L}\right] \quad (14)$$

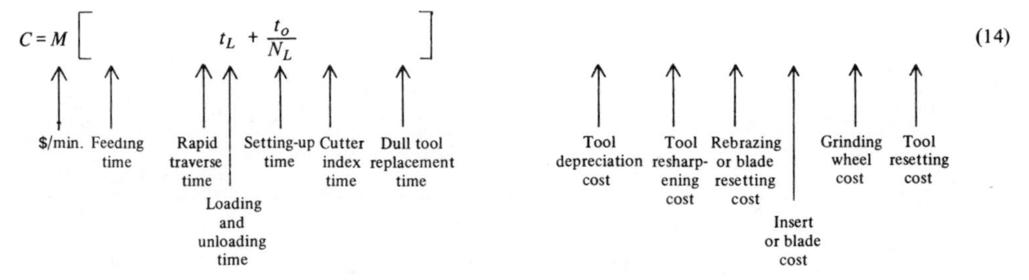

These equations differ somewhat from eqns 1–8. The cost equations, eqns 9 to 14 inclusive, contain cutter index time and tool presetting costs associated with numerically controlled machines. The cost equations are given for turning, milling (which includes face, end, and side milling), drilling, reaming, tapping, and centre drilling or hole chamfering. Note that the cost (and time) for work handling and setting-up are taken out of the individual operations and put into a separate equation, 14. All these equations are programmed into the computer. In numerically controlled machines, such as a lathe, it is common practice to use a series of machining operations on a given part: e.g. face, turn, centre drill, drill, then tap. The cost of each operation is calculated by the computer by successive application of eqns 9–14. The handling and setting-up equation is used just once for the component. The total cost is then the sum of the costs for all the operations plus the handling and setting-up costs.

For numerically controlled machines it is more useful to calculate the time for the individual operation. This can be done by applying eqns 15 to 20 inclusive. The production rate in pieces per hour can be obtained by dividing the total time for all the operations into 60. (See eqn 20.)

Turning

$$t_m = \frac{D(L+e)}{3{\cdot}82 f_r v} + \frac{R}{r} + t_i + \frac{DLt_d}{3{\cdot}82 f_r v T} \qquad (15)$$

Milling

$$t_m = \frac{D(L+e)}{3{\cdot}82 Z f_t v} + \frac{R}{r} + t_i + \frac{Lt_d}{ZT_t} \qquad (16)$$

Drilling and reaming

$$t_m = \frac{D(L+e)}{3{\cdot}82 f_r v} + \frac{R}{r} + t_i + \frac{Lt_d}{T_t} \qquad (17)$$

Tapping

$$t_m = \frac{mD(L+e)}{1{\cdot}91 v} + \frac{R}{r} + t_i + \frac{Lt_d}{T_t} \qquad (18)$$

Centre drilling or chamfering

$$t_m = \frac{D(L+e)}{3{\cdot}82 f_r v} + \frac{R}{r} + t_i + \frac{u_c t_d}{T_h} \qquad (19)$$

Production rate

$$P = \frac{60}{\Sigma t_m + \left(t_L + \frac{t_o}{N_L}\right)} \qquad (20)$$

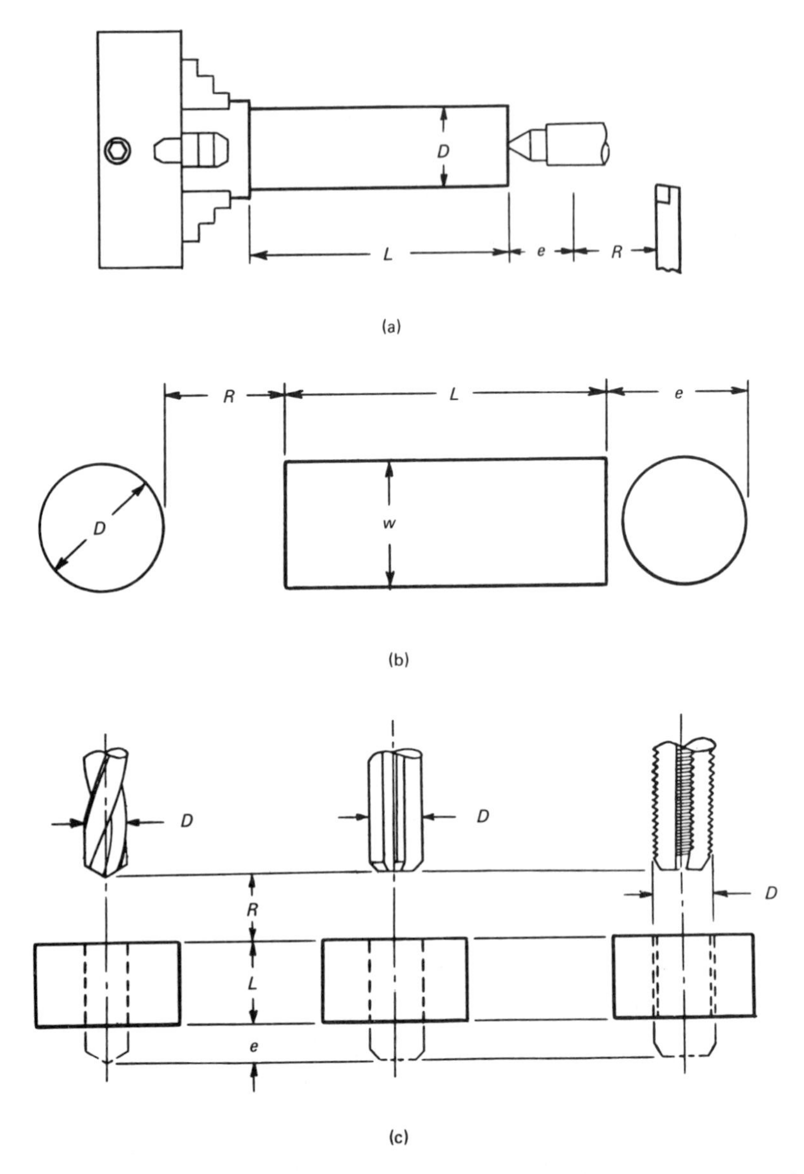

Fig. 2. Set-up for various machining operations. (a) Turning. (b) Milling. (c) Drilling, reaming and tapping.

The symbols for the cost and production rate for numerically controlled machining are given in Table 3. The tool and workpiece set-ups for the various operations are given in Fig. 2.

5.4 *Example: numerically controlled machining centre*

Consider the cost and production calculations for machining an 8 in × 2 in plate on a numerically controlled machining centre (Fig. 3). The material is 4340 steel, quenched and tempered to 341 B.H.N. The operations are to face-mill the top of the plate, then centre drill, drill, and tap the six holes. Tooling and time-study data for the operations are shown in Table 4.

TABLE 3 SYMBOLS FOR COST AND PRODUCTION RATE EQUATIONS FOR NUMERICALLY CONTROLLED MACHINING

Symbol	Definition	Applies to operation: Turn	Mill	Drill and ream	Tap	Centre drill
C	cost for machining one workpiece; $/workpiece	√	√	√	√	√
C_c	cost of each insert or inserted blade; $/blade	√	√	No	No	No
C_p	purchase cost of tool or cutter; $/cutter	√	√	√	√	√
C_w	cost of grinding wheel for resharpening tool or cutter; $/cutter	√	√	No	No	No
d	depth of cut; in.	√	√	No	No	No
D	diameter of work in turning, of tool in milling, drilling, reaming, tapping; in	√	√	√	√	√
e	extra travel at feed rate (f_r or f_t) including approach, over-travel, and all positioning moves; in	√	√	√	√	√
f_r	feed per revolution; in/rev	√	No	√	No	√
f_t	feed per tooth; in/tooth	No	√	No	No	No
G	labour + overhead in tool reconditioning department; $/min.	√	√	√	√	√
k_1	times lathe tool, or milling cutter, or drill, or reamer or tap is resharpened before being discarded	√	√	√	√	√
k_2	times lathe tool or milling cutter is resharpened before inserts or blades are rebrazed or reset	√	√	No	No	No
k_3	times blades (or inserts) are resharpened (or indexed) before blades (or inserts) are discarded	√	√	No	No	No
L	length of workpiece in turning and milling or sum of length of all holes of same diameter in drilling, reaming, tapping; in	√	√	√	√	√
m	threads per inch	No	No	No	√	No
M	labour + overhead cost on lathe, milling machine or drilling machine; $/min.	√	√	√	√	√
n	tool life exponent in Taylor's equation	√	√	√	√	No
N_L	number of workpieces in lot	√	√	√	√	√
P	production rate per 60 min hour; workpieces/h	√	√	√	√	√
r	rapid traverse rate; in/min	√	√	√	√	√
R	total rapid traverse distance for a tool or cutter on one part; in	√	√	√	√	√
S	reference cutting speed for a tool life of $T = 1$ min; ft/min	√	No	No	No	No
S_t	reference cutting for a tool life of $T_t = 1$ in; ft/min	No	√	√	√	No
t_b	time to rebraze lathe tool or cutter teeth or reset blades; min	√	√	No	No	No
t_d	time to replace dull cutter in tool changer storage unit; min	√	√	√	√	√
t_i	time to index from one type of cutter to another between operations (automatic or manual); min	√	√	√	√	√
t_L	time to load and unload workpiece; min	√	√	√	√	√
t_m	time (average) to complete one operation; min	√	√	√	√	√
t_o	time to set up machine tool for operation; min	√	√	√	√	√
t_p	time to preset tools away from machine (in tool-room); min	√	√	√	√	√

t_s	time to resharpen lathe tool, milling cutter, drill, reamer or tap; min/tool	√	√	√	√	√
T	tool life as time to dull a lathe tool; min	√	No	No	No	No
T_h	number of holes per resharpening	No	No	No	No	√
T_t	tool life as travel of work or tool to dull a drill, reamer, tap or one milling cutter tooth; in	No	√	√	√	No
u_c	number of holes centre-drilled of chamfered in workpiece	No	No	No	No	√
v	cutting speed; ft/min	√	√	√	√	√
w	width of cut; in	No	√	No	No	No
Z	number of teeth in milling cutter or number of flutes in tap	No	√	No	√	No

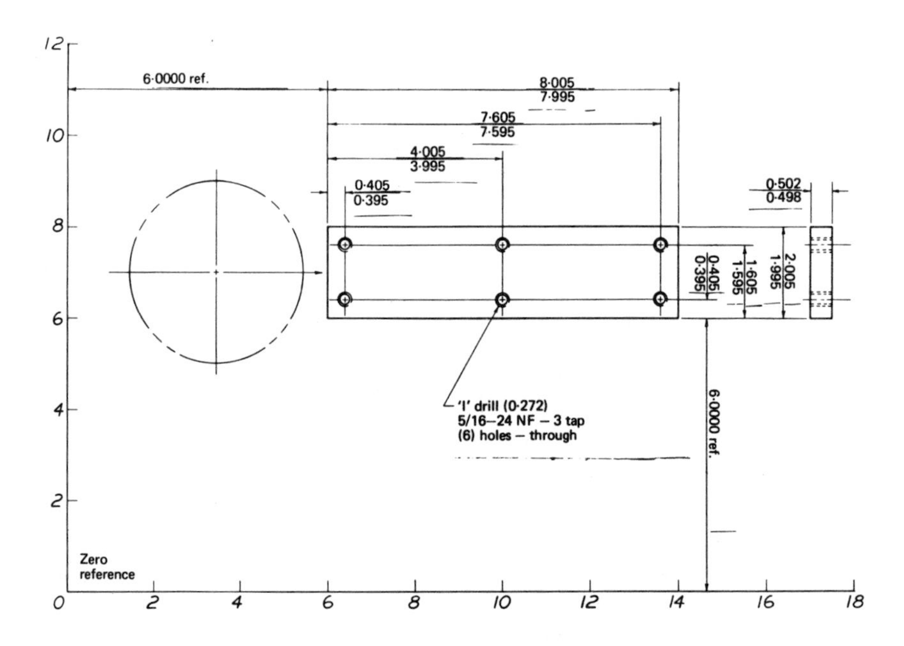

Fig. 3. Part machined on numerically controlled machining centre.

The face milling, operation 10, will be evaluated for both high-speed steel and throw-away carbide face mills. The remaining operations – centre drill, operation 20; drill, operation 30 and tap, operation 40 – will be done with high speed steel tools. The tool life and cutting speed and other pertinent machining conditions pertaining to these operations are given in Tables 2, 5 and 6.

Costs and machining time for individual operations were computed using the pertinent equations (see eqns 9–20). The computer printout is reproduced in Fig. 4. This printout gives not only the total cost and operating time for each operation but also the detailed cost for each element of the total cost.

TABLE 4 EXAMPLE - NUMERICALLY CONTROLLED MACHINING CENTRE

OPERATION: Face mill, drill, and tap
Material: 4340 steel, quenched and tempered, 341 B.H.N.

		OPERATION				
		10 Face mill		20 Centre drill	30 Drill	40 Tap
		H.S.S.	T.–A.			
C_c	cost of each insert or inserted blade; $/blade	–	2·45	–	–	–
C_p	purchase cost of tool or cutter; $/cutter	91·00	212·00	1·50	0·70	1·40
C_w	cost of grinding wheel for resharpening tool or cutter; $/cutter	0·35	–	–	–	–
d	depth of cut; in	*	*	–	–	–
D	diameter of tool in milling, drilling, and tapping; in	4·0	4·0	0·188	0·272	0·312
e	extra travel at feed rate (f_r or f_t) including approach, overtravel, and all positioning moves; in	0·400	0·400	0·600	2·250	2·250
f_r	feed per revolution; in/rev	–	–	0·002	*	–
f_t	feed per tooth; in/tooth	*	*	–	–	–
G	labour + overhead in tool reconditioning department; $/min	0·17	0·17	0·17	0·17	0·17
k_1	times milling cutter, or drill, or tap is resharpened before being discarded	20	9000	2	12	–
k_2	times milling cutter is resharpened before inserts or blades are rebrazed or reset	–	–	–	–	–
k_3	times blades (or inserts) are resharpened (or indexed) before being discarded	–	8	–	–	–
L	length of workpiece in milling or sum of length of all holes of same diameter in drilling, reaming, tapping; in	8·00	8·00	1·5	3·00	3·00
m	threads per inch	–	–	–	–	24
M	labour + overhead cost of machining centre; $/min	0·85	0·85	0·85	0·85	0·85
N_L	number of workpieces in lot	25	25	25	25	25
r	rapid traverse rate; in/min	150	150	150	150	150
R	total rapid traverse distance for a tool or cutter on one part; in	18·00	18·00	30·50	33·65	28·40
t_b	time to rebraze cutter teeth or reset blades; min	–	–	–	–	–
t_d	time to replace dull tool or cutter in tool changer storage unit; min	3	3	3	3	3
t_i	time to index from one type of cutter to another between operations (automatic or manual); min	0·1	0·1	0·1	0·1	0·1
t_L	time to load and unload workpiece; min	2	2	2	2	2
t_p	time to preset tools away from machine (in tool room); min	20	20	12	12	12
t_o	time to set up machine tool for operation; min	45	45	45	45	45
t_s	time to resharpen milling cutter, drill, reamer or tap; min/tool	80	–	5	5	–
T_h	number of holes per resharpening	–	–	200	–	–
T_t	tool life as travel of work or tool to dull a drill, reamer, tap or one milling cutter tooth; in	*	*	–	*	*
u_c	number of holes centre-drilled or chamfered in workpiece	–	–	6	–	–
v	cutting speed; ft/min	*	*	100	*	*
w	width of cut; in	2·00	2·00	–	–	–
Z	number of teeth in milling cutter or number of flutes in tap	14	6	–	–	2

*These values are taken from tool life data, Tables 2, 5 and 6

TABLE 5 TOOL LIFE DATA FOR DRILLING

Material	Condition and microstructure	B.H.N.	Drill mat'l: Trade name	Drill mat'l: Industry grade	Type of drill	Drill size: Dia. (in)	Drill size: Length (in)	Drill size: Flute length (in)	Drill geometry: Type of point	Drill geometry: Helix angle (°)	Drill geometry: Point angle (°)	Drill geometry: Lip relief (°)	Cutting fluid code*	Depth of hole (in)	Feed (in/rev)	Drill life end point (in)	Drill life (number of holes) v Speed (ft/min)			
																	(8) 25	(9) 50	(10) 75	(11) 100
Alloy steels– *(cont.)* 4340	Quenched and tempered / Tempered martensite	341	–	M2 h.s.s.	Twist	0·250	4·0	2·75	Standard	29	118	7	31	0·5 through	0·002	0·015	98	84	76	70
																	(12) 25	(13) 50	(14) 75	(15) 100
4340	Quenched and tempered / Tempered martensite	341	–	M2 h.s.s.	Twist	0·250	4·0	2·75	Standard	29	118	7	31	0·5 through	0·005	0·015	80	85	56	50

* 31–sulphurised mineral lard oil, light duty

TABLE 6 TOOL LIFE DATA FOR TAPPING

Material	Condition and microstructure	B.H.N.	Tap material	Tap size	Number of flutes	Tap style	Fraction of thread (%)	Cutting fluid code*	Depth of hole (in)	Tap life end point (in)	Tap life (number of holes) v Speed (ft/min)	
											(16) 50	(17) 200
Alloy steels 4340	Quenched and tempered / Tempered martensite	341	M1 h.s.s.	5/16-24NI	2	Plug	75	52	0·5 through	Tap breakage	100	80

* 52 sulpho-chlorinated mineral lard oil, medium duty

N/C MACHINING COSTS AND OPERATION TIMES
FOR
PART NO.-32198765-1 • PART NAME-PLATE • LOT SIZE- 25
MATERIAL-AISI 4340 - QUENCHED AND TEMPERED • HARDNESS- 341

DATA SET NO.	OPER. NO.	MACHG OPER.	TOOL MATL	SPEED SFM	FEED	TOOL LIFE	FEED COST $	RAPD TRAV $	LOAD UNLD $	SET-UP $	TOOL INDX $	TOOL REPL $	TOOL DEPR $	TOOL SHPN $	BLAD RSET $	INST COST $	GRND WHL $	TOOL PRST $	TOTAL COST $	OPER. TIME MIN.
40001	N010	FM-HSS	T15	93.	0.010	17.	0.57	0.10			0.08	0.08	0.14	0.45			0.01	0.11	1.57	0.99
40002	N010	FM-HSS	T15	76.	0.010	22.	0.70	0.10			0.08	0.06	0.11	0.35			0.00	0.08	1.51	1.12
40003	N010	FM-HSS	T15	62.	0.010	32.	0.86	0.10			0.08	0.04	0.07	0.24			0.00	0.06	1.48	1.28
40004	N010	FM-TA	C-6	680.	0.005	20.	0.36	0.10			0.08	0.16	0.00			0.12		0.22	1.07	0.85
40005	N010	FM-TA	C-6	550.	0.005	50.	0.45	0.10			0.08	0.06	0.00			0.04		0.09	0.84	0.83
40006	N010	FM-TA	C-6	340.	0.005	80.	0.73	0.10			0.08	0.04	0.00			0.03		0.05	1.05	1.13
40007	N020	CTR-DRL	M2	100.	0.002	200.	0.43	0.17			0.08	0.07	0.01	0.02				0.06	0.87	0.91
40008	N030	DRILL	M2	98.	0.002	12.	1.62	0.19			0.08	0.61	0.01	0.20				0.48	3.21	2.95
40009	N030	DRILL	M2	84.	0.002	25.	1.89	0.19			0.08	0.30	0.00	0.10				0.24	2.82	2.90
40010	N030	DRILL	M2	76.	0.002	37.	2.09	0.19			0.08	0.20	0.00	0.06				0.16	2.80	3.02
40011	N030	DRILL	M2	70.	0.002	50.	2.26	0.19			0.08	0.15	0.00	0.05				0.12	2.87	3.17
40012	N030	DRILL	M2	80.	0.005	12.	0.79	0.19			0.08	0.61	0.01	0.20				0.48	2.38	1.97
40013	N030	DRILL	M2	65.	0.005	25.	0.97	0.19			0.08	0.30	0.00	0.10				0.24	1.91	1.83
40014	N030	DRILL	M2	56.	0.005	37.	1.13	0.19			0.08	0.20	0.00	0.06				0.16	1.85	1.89
40015	N030	DRILL	M2	50.	0.005	50.	1.27	0.19			0.08	0.15	0.00	0.05				0.12	1.87	1.99
40016	N040	TAP	M1	100.		25.	0.17	0.16			0.08	0.30	0.16	0.00				0.24	1.13	0.85
40017	N040	TAP	M1	80.		100.	0.21	0.16			0.08	0.07	0.04	0.00				0.06	0.64	0.63
LOAD, UNLOAD AND SETUP TIME AND COST									1.70	1.52									3.22	3.80

NOTE – FEED UNITS ARE IPR FOR TURNING, DRILLING, REAMING, AND CENTREDRILLING OR CHAMFERING
FEED UNITS ARE IPT FOR MILLING

TOOL LIFE UNITS ARE IN. FOR MILLING, DRILLING, REAMING, AND TAPPING
TOOL LIFE UNITS ARE MIN. FOR TURNING
TOOL LIFE UNITS ARE NO. OF HOLES FOR CENTREDRILLING OR CHAMFERING

Fig. 4. Computer printout – cost and operation time on numerically controlled machining centre.

In the face-milling, operation 10, cost elements are given for three T15 high-speed-steel cutter conditions and three throw-away carbide conditions. The minimum cost (and minimum operating time) occurred for data set 40005 using the carbide throw-away cutter at 550 ft/min and 0·005 in/tooth feed. Note that the feeding cost was \$0·45, or 54% of the total cost of \$0·84 for the milling.

The costs and times of the remaining operations can likewise be examined. The most expensive operation was drilling, which had a minimum cost of \$1·85. Also note that the centre drilling operation cost was \$0·87, which was more expensive and took more time than the milling. The loading–unloading and setting-up operation cost was \$3·22, which exceeded any of the machining operation costs and also took more time per piece than any of the machining operations.

6.0 OPTIMISATION

Taylor's equation can be written, relating the tool life to cutting speed –

for turning $$vT^n = S \qquad (21a)$$

or $$vT_t^{\,n} = S_t \qquad (21b)$$

for milling, drilling, reaming, and tapping.

If these simplified Taylor equations can be assumed to hold, the cost for the various machining operations can be minimised. This has been done by inserting the appropriate Taylor equation into the cost equation, differentiating the cost with respect to cutting speed, and equating the derivative to zero.

Cutting speeds for minimum cost, $v_{\text{min. cost}}$, and for maximum production, $v_{\text{max. prod}}$, for the conventional machining operations are given by eqns 22 – 29 inclusive.

For turning

$$v_{\text{min. cost}} = \left\{ \frac{nM(e+L)}{(1-n)L\left[Mt_c + \dfrac{C_p}{k_1+1} + Gt_s + \dfrac{Gt_b}{k_2} + \dfrac{C_c}{k_3} + C_w\right]} \right\}^n S \qquad (22)$$

$$v_{\text{max. prod.}} = \left\{ \frac{n(e+L)}{(1-n)Lt_c} \right\}^n S \qquad (23)$$

For milling

$$v_{\text{min. cost}} = \left\{ \frac{nMD(e+L)}{3{\cdot}82 f_t L\left[Mt_c + \dfrac{C_p}{k_1+1} + Gt_s + \dfrac{Gt_p}{k_2} + \dfrac{ZC_c}{k_3} + C_w\right]} \right\}^{\frac{n}{n+1}} S_t^{\frac{1}{n+1}} \qquad (24)$$

$$v_{\text{max. prod.}} = \left\{\frac{nD\,(e+L)}{3{\cdot}82 f_t L t_c}\right\}^{\frac{n}{n+1}} S_t^{\frac{1}{n+1}} \tag{25}$$

For drilling and reaming

$$v_{\text{min. cost}} = \left\{\frac{nMD\,(e+L)}{3{\cdot}82 f_r L\left[Mt_c + \dfrac{C_p}{k_1+1} + Gt_s\right]}\right\}^{\frac{n}{n+1}} S_t^{\frac{1}{n+1}} \tag{26}$$

$$v_{\text{max. prod.}} = \left\{\frac{nD\,(e+L)}{3{\cdot}82 f_r L t_c}\right\}^{\frac{n}{n+1}} S_t^{\frac{1}{n+1}} \tag{27}$$

For tapping

$$v_{\text{min. cost}} = \left\{\frac{mnMD\,(e+L)}{1{\cdot}91L\left[Mt_c + \dfrac{C_p}{k_1+1} + Gt_s\right]}\right\}^{\frac{n}{n+1}} S_t^{\frac{1}{n+1}} \tag{28}$$

(tap resharpened)

Note: $Gt_s = 0$ when tap not resharpened

$$v_{\text{max. prod.}} = \left\{\frac{mnD\,(e+L)}{1{\cdot}91Lt_c}\right\}^{\frac{n}{n+1}} S_t^{\frac{1}{n+1}} \tag{29}$$

(tap resharpened
and not resharpened)

By similar application of the Taylor equation, the optimised cutting speeds for numerically controlled operations are given by eqns 30 – 37 inclusive.

For turning

$$v_{\text{min. cost}} = \left\{\frac{nM\,(L+e)}{L\,(1-n)\left[Mt_d + \dfrac{C_p}{k_1+1} + Gt_s + \dfrac{Gt_b}{k_2} + \dfrac{C_c}{k_3} + C_w + Gt_p\right]}\right\}^{n} S \tag{30}$$

$$v_{\text{max. prod.}} = \left\{ \frac{n(L+e)}{(1-n)\,Lt_d} \right\}^{n} S \tag{31}$$

For milling

$$v_{\text{min. cost}} = \left\{ \frac{nMD(L+e)}{3{\cdot}82 f_t L \left[Mt_d + \dfrac{C_p}{k_1+1} + Gt_s + \dfrac{Gt_b}{k_2} + \dfrac{ZC_c}{k_3} + C_w + Gt_p \right]} \right\}^{\frac{n}{n+1}} S_t^{\frac{1}{n+1}} \tag{32}$$

$$v_{\text{max. prod.}} = \left\{ \frac{nD(L+e)}{3{\cdot}82 f_r L t_d} \right\}^{\frac{n}{n+1}} S_t^{\frac{1}{n+1}} \tag{33}$$

For drilling or reaming

$$v_{\text{min. cost}} = \left\{ \frac{nMD(L+e)}{3{\cdot}82 f_r L \left[Mt_d + \dfrac{C_p}{k_1+1} + Gt_s + Gt_p \right]} \right\}^{\frac{n}{n+1}} S_t^{\frac{1}{n+1}} \tag{34}$$

$$v_{\text{max. prod.}} = \left\{ \frac{nD(L+e)}{3{\cdot}82 f_r L t_d} \right\}^{\frac{n}{n+1}} S_t^{\frac{1}{n+1}} \tag{35}$$

For tapping

$$v_{\text{min. cost}} = \left\{ \frac{mnMD(L+e)}{1{\cdot}91 L \left[Mt_d + \dfrac{C_p}{k_1+1} + Gt_s + Gt_p \right]} \right\}^{\frac{n}{n+1}} S_t^{\frac{1}{n+1}} \tag{36}$$

$$v_{\text{max. prod.}} = \left\{ \frac{mnD(L+e)}{1{\cdot}91 L t_d} \right\}^{\frac{n}{n+1}} S_t^{\frac{1}{n+1}} \tag{37}$$

As previously discussed, the validity of the optimised determination depends on the validity of the constants n and S or S_t in the Taylor equation. The most accurate values of these constants can, of course, be determined by experiment, i.e. actual cutting tests. It is possible at the same time to determine the range of cutting conditions over which Taylor's equation applies. The least reliable procedure is to pick an average value for the Taylor constants from a handbook. Some people actually go so far as to assume there is a single constant for each type of cutting tool material for turning.

We suggest that, if one assumes Taylor's relationship and proceeds to determine the optimised cutting conditions, these conditions be verified by actual shop tests.

7.0 ADAPTIVE CONTROL DURING MACHINING

Attempts are being made to apply adaptive control during actual machining to achieve optimisation. The adaptive control approach has as its end-point the machining of a component at the lowest cost subject to power limitation, cutter stiffness or strength, and quality requirements.

The adaptive control systems being developed embody various approaches to the problem. Some involve an attempt to machine at the highest feed rates within the constraints of power or forces available in the machine tool or the cutter. Some are being developed to control the temperature rise between the tool and the cutter and others to control chatter or vibration. The more sophisticated systems attempt automatic control of the speed and feed so as to minimise overall cost.

A considerable amount of work still has to be done before adaptively controlled machines can achieve the goal of optimality on a basis of minimum cost and maximum production or maximum profit.

8.0 CONCLUSION

It has been the hope of all industrial and manufacturing engineers to optimise analytically and determine minimum cost and maximum production or maximum profit in any machining operation.

Although the mathematics for optimisation exists, one major ingredient is unfortunately lacking: there are no accurate mathematical equations relating tool life to the pertinent cutting parameters such as speed, feed, depth, tool material, tool geometry, cutting fluid, etc. In view of this disturbing situation the results of optimisation calculations should be carefully checked by shop tests.

However, one significant approach toward optimisation can be utilised. Experimental and historical machining data can be gathered to calculate, by computer, the total cost and production rate as well as the individual factors which make up the totals. Analysis of the computer printout of these cost and production details provides an extremely valuable guide to manufacturing and management people in their quest for cost control.

REFERENCES

1 INYONG HAM. *Economics of Machining: Analyzing Optimum Machining Conditions by Computers.* American Society of Tool and Manufacturing Engineers. Paper No SP64–60. 1963.

2 HANS ERNST. *Economics of Machining* Report from Cincinnati Milling Machine Co., Vol. 13, No 1, 1956.

3 W. W. GILBERT. 'Economics of Machining'. *Machining – Theory and Practice.* American Society for Metals. 1950.

4 J. WITTHOFF. 'Die Rechnerische Ermittlung der Gungstigsten Arbeitsbedingungen bei der Spanabhebenden Forming'. *Werkstatt und Betrieb.* Vol. 80. 1947.

5 J. WITTHOFF. 'Ermittlung und Betriebeswirtschaftliche Bedeutung der Werkzeugkosten'. *Werkstatt stechnil und Maschinenbau.* Vol. 39. 1949.

6 M. C. SHAW, H. H. COOK, and P. A. SMITH. 'Putting Machinability Data to Work'. *Tool Engineers.* August 1955.

7 R. C. BREWER. *On the Economics of Basic Turning Operation* American Society of Mechanical Engineers. Paper No. 57–A–58. Abstracted in *Mechanical Engineer,* Vol. 80, No 110, February 1958.

8 B. N. COLDING. 'Machinability of Metals and Machining Costs'. *International Journal of Tool Design and Research.* Vol. 1. 1961.

9 B. N. COLDING. *Machining Economics and Industrial Data Manuals* C.I.R.P. Annual Meeting,

10 R. WEILL, DORIS, SAVOYE, GUILLAUME and MEGRELIS. The Use of Electronic computers for the Determination of Optimum Machining Conditions'. *Proceedings of the Third International M.T.D.R. Conference,* University of Birmingham, September 1962.

11 J. SIEKMANN. 'Now, An Easier Way to Find Best Cutting Speed'. *American Machinist.* 10 February, 1958.

12 H. CONN. 'Tomorrow's Machining Concept – Optimization'. *Automatic Machining.* May 1957.

13 W. W. GILBERT and E. J. WELLER. 'Application of a Machinability Computer'. *American Society of Tool Engineers Annual Collected Papers.* Paper No 24T26. 1956.

14 A. O. SCHMIDT, I. HAM, W. I. PHILLIPS, and G. F. WILLSON. 'Ceramic Tooling Tests at the Kearney and Trecker Corporation'. *Machinery.* Vol. 6. No 5. 1957.

15 A. O. SCHMIDT and J. R. ROUBIK. 'Milling Practice Today'. *American Society of Tool Engineers Annual Collected Papers.* Paper No 60. 1958.

16 G. HOFFMEISTER. 'Die Werkzeugwechselzeit' *Werkstatt und Betrieb.* May 1961.

17 E. M. McCULLOUGH. 'Economics of Multi-Tooth Lathe Operations'. *American Society of Mechanical Engineers Journal of Engineering for Industry.* Series B. November 1963.

18 M. C. SHAW. 'Optimum Selection of Machine Tool Speeds and Feeds'. *Int. J. Mach. Tool Des. Res.* Vol. 5. 1965.

19 E. J. A. ARMAREGO and J. K. RUSSELL. Maximum Profit Rate as a Criterion for the Selection of Machining Conditions, *Int. J. Mach. Tool Des. Res.* Vol. 6. 1966.

20 K. OKUSHIMA and K. HITOMI. 'A Study of Economical Machining: An Analysis of the Maximum-Profit Cutting Speed'. *Int. J. of Prod. Res.* Vol. 3. No 1. 1964.

21 S. M. WU and D. S. ERMER. 'Maximum Profit as the Criterion in the Determination of the Optimum Cutting Conditions'. *Journal of Engineering for Industry.* November 1966.

22 D. S. ERMER and S. M. WU. *The Effect of Experimental Error on the Determination of the Optimum Metal-Cutting Conditions.* American Society of Mechanical Engineers. Paper No 66–WA/Prod–2. 1966.

23 N. N. ZOREV. 'The Effect of Tool Wear on Tool Life and Cutting Speed'. *Russian Engineering Journal.* Vol. XLV. Issue No 2. P.E.R.A., U.K., 1965.

24 M. FIELD, N. ZLATIN, R. WILLIAMS, and M. KRONENBERG. *Computerized Determination and Analysis of Cost and Production Rates for Machining Operations* – Part I, A.S.M.E. Paper No 67–WA/Prod–18, and Part II, A.S.M.E. Paper No 68–WA/Prod–17.

ADVANCED MANUFACTURING TECHNOLOGY IN THE AERO–ENGINE INDUSTRY

A. H. Meleka
Rolls-Royce Ltd, Bristol Engine Division

SUMMARY

The introduction of modern design concepts involving the use of advanced materials requires corresponding development of manufacturing methods. The conventional techniques of metal cutting, metal forming, and fastening and joining processes are compared with electrochemical machining and electron-beam welding, both of which typify advanced processes of manufacture. The problems associated with the economics of such processes are considered.

1.0 INTRODUCTION

The great strides made by the aviation industry in increased aircraft speed, payload and range are the product of advancement in many fields. These include the evolution of aerodynamic design and of airframe configuration, and the introduction of lighter structures, for example the use of honeycomb stiffened panels. There can be little doubt, however, that advances in power plant performance make a primary contributing factor. Basic performance characteristics such as specific fuel consumption and thrust-to-weight ratio have shown continued improvement, as can be seen in Fig. 1. This has been primarily due to the introduction of advanced design concepts such as turbine blade cooling and the application of large fans. Other major contributing factors have been the introduction of advanced materials like the titanium alloys used extensively in the compressor, and the introduction of heat-resisting materials like the Nimonic series of alloys in the turbine.

The demands of modern design concepts and advanced materials require a corresponding development of manufacturing methods. It is clear that the methods which have served well in the past are in many cases no longer adequate. An essential part of the gas turbine operates at such high temperatures that it requires materials of extreme toughness. These materials cannot be cut by conventional methods. Even grinding is inadequate, for the rate of wear of the grinding wheel is of the same order as the rate of metal removal. There are also questions of geometry; how can a hole with an aspect ratio of 200:1 be drilled in a material as tough as Nimonic 15? What if the hole is not round in cross-section? It may also be curved!

New processes had to be found, developed and economically applied. But the materials themselves are complex alloys that have to be handled with knowledge of their structure and properties. For example, a process requiring some heating will have to be performed within well defined limits of temperature. Some of the alloys acquire their strength from a controlled amount of mechanical working. A serious drop in strength may result if additional work is introduced. Then there is the question of surface properties. Most parts in an aero-engine are

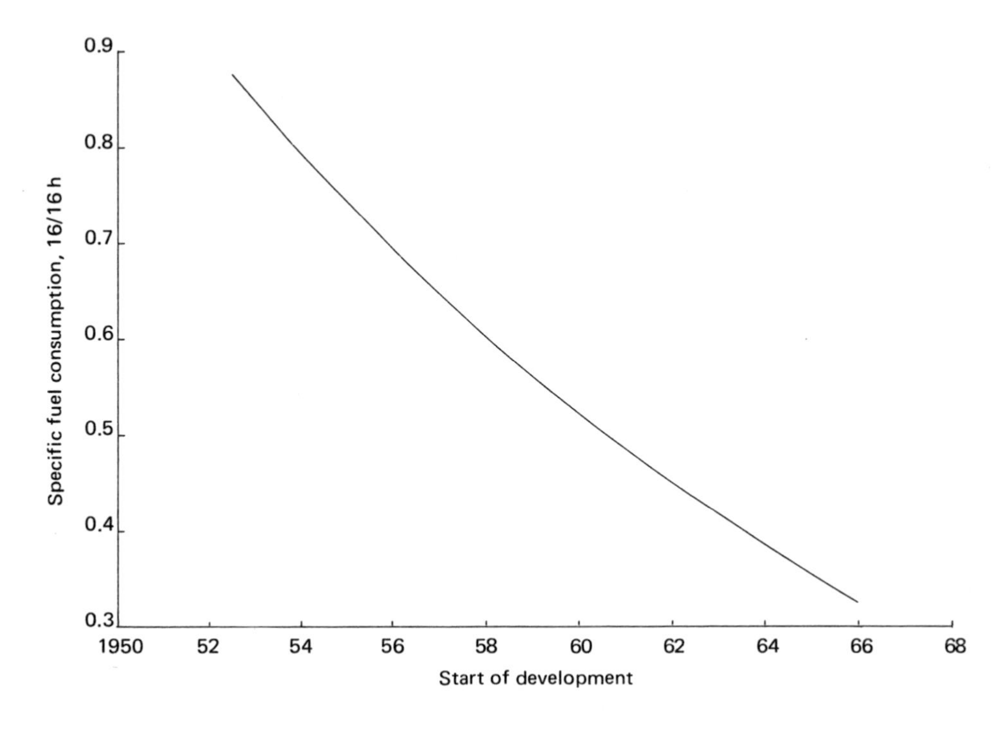

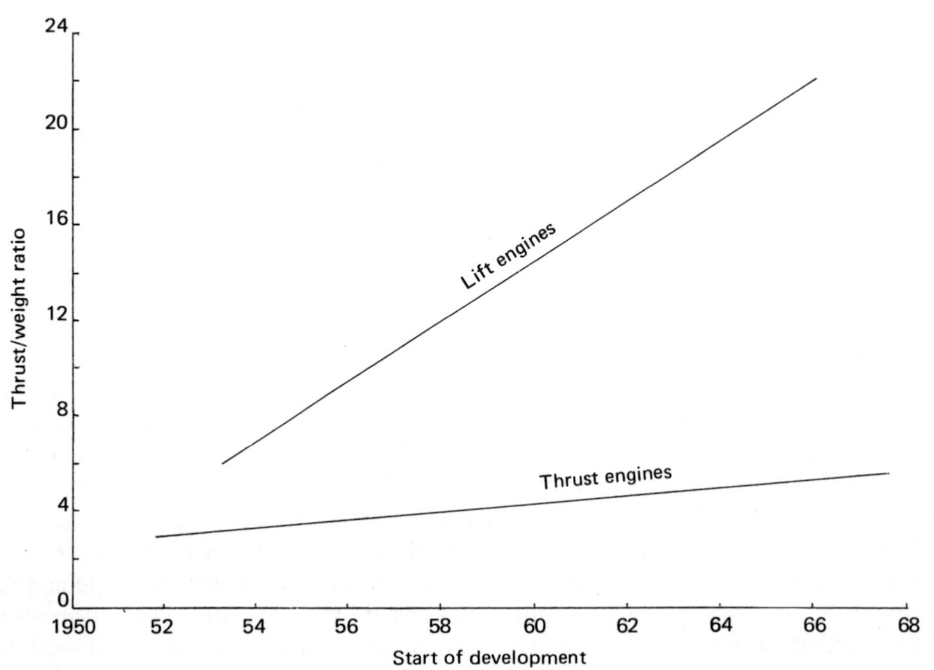

Fig. 1. Above – How specific fuel consumption has improved with time. Below – How thrust weight ratios have grown.

highly stressed under fatigue conditions, and the surface properties have to be adequate. It is well known that fatigue cracks are often initiated at the free surface. Thus chemical and electrochemical processes have to be watched closely as they may introduce undesirable surface texture.

It is clear therefore that those responsible for the development of new methods have to be fully aware of the likely detrimental effects of these processes on material properties. Their work should be conducted in close collaboration with that of their metallurgical colleagues.

2.0 CONVENTIONAL MANUFACTURING PROCESSES

2.1 *Metal cutting processes*

The limitations of conventional processes will now be examined in the light of the above considerations.

Machining is a process which is used more extensively than any other in the engineering manufacturing industries. The time-honoured machining process is to use a tool that is tougher and harder than the metal to be cut. There are two basic limitations, one due to the increase in mechanical strength of the material relative to that of the cutting tool, the other geometrical. Reference has already been made to the very tough materials being used in modern jet engines.

As these materials are also difficult to manipulate, it is not possible to produce precision parts by forging and thus to eliminate machining altogether.

Again, although precision casting has advanced considerably, it is not always possible to cast a complex part with all regions within the required tolerances. Some areas have priorities, for example the aerofoil form of a blade. This leaves other regions with additional material that will have to be removed by some form of machining.

An example of geometrical limitations is the drilling of cooling passages in turbine blades and other hot parts in the turbine or exhaust system. There are, however, less challenging requirements which, although they can be conventionally met, carry a heavy cost penalty. This applies particularly to the machining of intricate forms that require the use of fine cutters. Such tools wear quite rapidly. This is reflected in time for machining and in eventual cost.

2.2 *Metal forming processes*

Metal forming has not received as much attention in engineering manufacturing industries as its potential justifies. This has not been the case in Russia, where metal forming is reputed to be applied quite extensively in such sectors as the motor-car industry.

The advantages of metal forming are: material conservation, substantial reduction in the cost of machining, and possibly an improved product because of beneficial grain flow. The deciding factor is the quantity required, since the cost of design and manufacture of dies has to be justified. There are, however, certain limitations owing to material properties and the need for truly massive presses if large parts have to be formed.

2.3 *Fastening and joining processes*

Joining parts by bolting or riveting carries penalties of weight, cost and endurance. Joining two parts directly by fusion (welding) has obvious attractions. The electric arc has shown itself to be a heat source capable of producing joints with good metallurgical structure in a wide range of materials. Arc welding, however, suffers from a number of basic limitations. Penetration is limited since heat is conducted away, and a weld zone with a depth-to-width ratio of the order of one is the result. Also heat dissipation is considerably greater than is strictly required for the joining operation. This leads to undesirable metallurgical effects and to a degree of distortion in the parts to be joined.

3.0 ADVANCED MANUFACTURING TECHNOLOGY

The last decade has seen the development and application of new methods that are radically different from the conventional ones. Progress continues to be made but two examples have been selected for discussion here, particularly as they have made direct impact on manufacturing technology in the aero-engine industry.

3.1 *Electrochemical machining*

The contribution of electrochemical machining (e.c.m.) has been substantial. Metal is removed by electrolysis, but interest is focused not on the cathode, as in electroplating, but on the anode, from which metal is removed.

The process is particularly attractive when large volumes of metal have to be machined, although there are special cases where intricate work can be best performed by e.c.m. The process is in full production, and many millions of pounds have been spent on plant during the last few years by engine manufacturers on both sides of the Atlantic.

The machines are generally of high current capacity, up to 30 000 A, though the voltage is low, in the range 12 to 24 V (Fig. 2). Unlike electroplating, e.c.m. involves high current densities

Fig. 2. Typical 20 000 A electrochemical machine.

up to 500 A/in^2 or even higher, compared with only a few A/ft^2 in electroplating. The copper cathode is placed quite close to the workpiece, leaving only a small gap some 0·010 in across (Fig. 3). The smaller the gap, the more accurately is the shape of the cathode reproduced on the workpiece. However, narrow gaps may resist the flow of electrolyte, thus requiring powerful pumps.

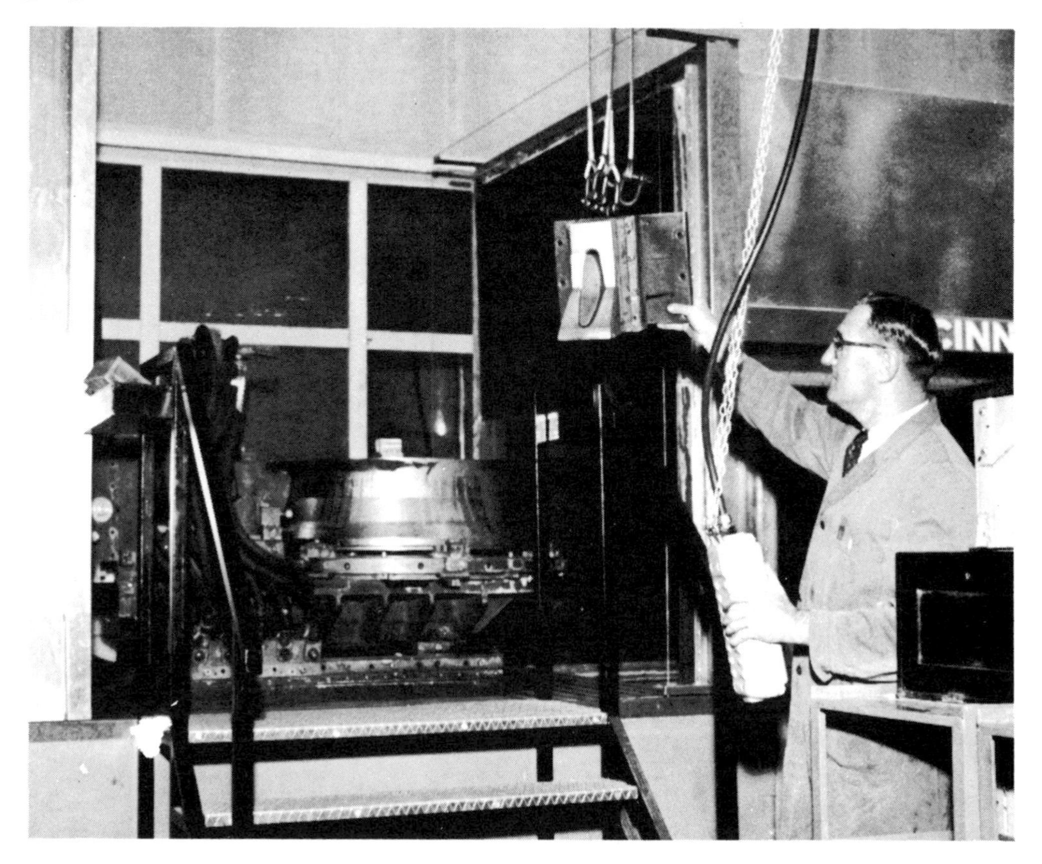

Fig. 3. Copper cathode tool, to be used in machining an engine casing, placed in machine enclosure.

Electrolyte has to be pumped through the gap to provide a fresh supply to take part in the electrochemical reaction. The electrolyte also carries away the dispersed reaction products, which are, in most cases, metal hydroxide particles. Simple salt electrolytes are adequate for most applications, for example a water solution of some 10% concentration by weight of sodium chloride or sodium nitrate. Titanium alloys, however, require special electrolytes because of the rapid passivation of the surface.

Electrochemical machining has been applied in its forming mode as can be seen in Fig. 4. This is by far the most widely used variation of the process. Other variations are also being utilised, e.g. drilling, turning and grinding.

3.2 *Electron beam welding*

The effect of electron-beam welding (e.b.w.) on joining methods has been far-reaching. This

Fig. 4. A casing 'sculptered' by e.c.m.

has been primarily due to its penetration capabilities and the low distortion resulting from minimum heat input. The designer is now in a position to introduce fusion welding where it would have been impossible in the past. There is the added advantage of the vacuum environment in which e.b.w. has to be done. This results in chemically pure welds, thus avoiding the

Fig. 5. A typical electron-beam welding machine incorporating a large vacuum chamber.

contamination which is a hazard in non-vacuum methods. Fig. 5 shows a typical e.b.w. plant.

The source of heat is a well-focused beam of electrons. As the beam is intercepted by solid material, the kinetic energy of the beam is transformed into heat which fuses the metal. If the power density is sufficiently high, evaporation in the centre of the molten pool takes place and a capillary is formed which is filled by metal vapour and surrounded by a molten layer. Thus the welding action of an electron beam is a combined cutting and fusion operation, not unlike the passage of a hot wire across a block of ice. Fig. 6 shows an example of an electron-beam-welded compressor drum.

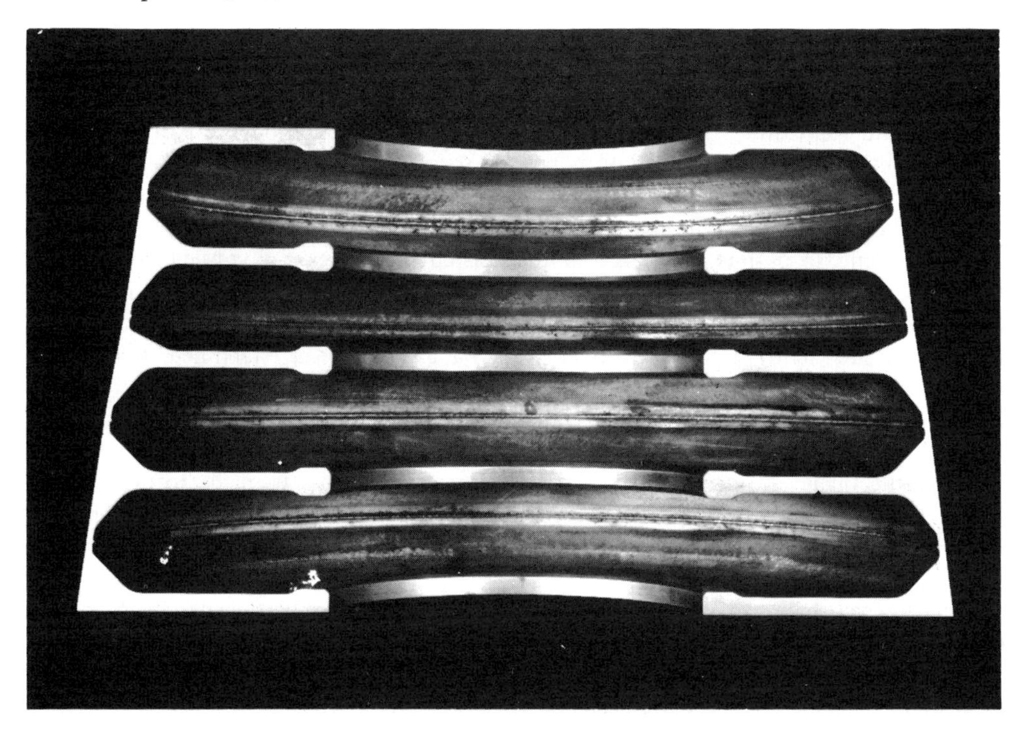

Fig. 6. A cross-section of a compressor drum after electron beam welding.

One remarkable characteristic of e.b.w. is the ability to reach regions which are inaccessible to other heat sources. This has been made possible owing to the fact that the beam is in the form of a fine pencil which can be as small as 0·020 in at its widest point and as long as a few feet. Also remarkable is the ability to weld simultaneously a number of layers. After the beam passes through the first layer, and provided there is sufficient energy available, it can penetrate a second or even a third layer.

There are numbers of limitations to e.b.w. Cost is high because the equipment operates at high voltages, of the order of 30/150 kV. There is also the need for a vacuum chamber to house the components and for some remotely controlled manipulation of parts inside the vacuum chamber. In the preparation of the abutment surface attention must be given to their accuracy, since if gaps exist the beam will go through them without heating, as it would not be intercepted by solid material. Alignment of the abutment surfaces during welding is also critical. The beam is only 0·010 in in diameter, and the accuracy of alignment has to be of the same order.

Because of the evaporation mechanism of e.b.w. and the vacuum environment, certain metals that are volatile near their melting point, or alloys containing such metals, will suffer some loss during the welding operation. Such evaporation can also lead to complications, for metal vapours may condense on the filament and so lead to erratic gun behaviour.

4.0 ECONOMIC ASPECTS OF ADVANCED MANUFACTURING TECHNIQUES

So far only the technical aspects of new methods have been considered. Economic considerations have also to be satisfied.

There is a further important and possibly more difficult problem: the 'human element' in innovation. There is an understandable reluctance on the part of most people to accept new and largely unknown methods, especially if their own experience with known techniques has been adequate and successful. There is also understandable reluctance on the part of industrial organisations to provide large sums of money for speculative work. Skill is therefore required on the part of those responsible for the evaluation and introduction of new methods in dealing with such human and financial matters.

It is difficult to outline a universal approach as circumstances vary considerably from one organisation to the other. However, it is essential that those who are likely to apply a new technique, either in design teams or manufacturing teams, are made aware of such developments at a sufficiently early stage, once basic viability has been established. It is only by collaboration over the period of development that that understanding and cooperation can be cultivated which will ultimately lead to a successful introduction. There can also be no doubt that accumulated experience in older methods can have considerable relevance to the new ones.

As to the financial aspects of innovation, every attempt must be made to overcome the 'White Elephant Invasion'. It is most discouraging to see complex and costly equipment lying idle because it has not been developed to a satisfactory production stage. Substantial sums are wasted in such unfortunate cases.

An element of risk has to be accepted but has to be kept within narrow margins. Some form of risk-sharing could well be evolved between the user and the manufacturer of plant. After all, the potential user often feeds valuable information to the manufacturer. Only by using equipment over an adequately long period can one establish its true virtues or drawbacks.

COMPUTER-AIDED PRODUCTION ENGINEERING AT ROLLS-ROYCE

S. B. L. Wilson
Rolls-Royce Ltd, Derby

SUMMARY

The fundamental objective of management is to optimise and maintain strict control over the 'design concept to finished product' process. Numerically controlled (n.c.) machines provide valuable management tools to help achieve this control over the manufacturing part of this process. Computer aids to assist in their efficient and effective use have been available for several years. The author of this paper, tracing the history of computing support for n.c. machines in the Aero-Engine Division of Rolls-Royce Ltd, suggests however that real computer-aided production engineering is yet to be born. Looking to the future he shows how the computer, together with the newer associated devices available, e.g. the graphical display screen, can provide another management tool not only to assist and control the design and manufacture of the product but to bridge the gap between design and production.

1.0 INTRODUCTION

For over a decade the computer has provided a powerful tool to ease the solution of problems in many technical and commercial fields. The aerospace industries in particular, and engineering in general, have utilised its calculating power with ever-increasing effect since the mid-1950s. If one looks at the situation a little more closely, however, one soon realises that this calculating power has been harnessed to provide assistance primarily in two main areas: performance and mechanical analysis of the *designed* product or component, and test analysis of its *manufactured* version. In contrast the computer has had relatively little impact on the physical design and manufacturing processes themselves. Computer-aided design, to be discussed in other papers at this conference, is *in its truest sense* an innovation, owing its birth in the late 1960s to advances in teleprocessing and the development of terminal devices including, in particular, the graphical display screen.

The computer used as a production or planning engineer's tool is not an innovation: its calculating power has been to some extent exploited in this area since the late 1950s. An added fillip to its use was provided by the advent of numerically controlled (n.c.) machine tools, i.e. machine tools operating under the control of highly detailed 'numerical' information pre-recorded on a medium such as magnetic tape, paper tape or punched cards. During the 1960s, largely owing to the availability of better-designed and more sophisticated n.c. machine tools, use of computers to aid preparation of control tapes has increased significantly.

In general, however, the real power of neither the n.c. machine tool nor the computer has yet been harnessed. I submit, in fact, that computer-aided production engineering in *its* true sense has not yet been born, only conceived. To substantiate this view I should like to outline the situation in the Rolls-Royce Aero-Engine Division and offer some views on the future.

2.0 DEVELOPMENT OF COMPUTER SUPPORT

2.1 *Computer preparation of control tapes*

The development of computer aids to production engineering in our Aero-Engine Division has to a large extent been influenced by the growth of its n.c. machine tool population (Fig. 1). Though the computer had previously provided a useful calculating tool it was not until 1962 that our first major system for computer preparation of control tapes, Cocomat (Fig. 2), became fully operational.

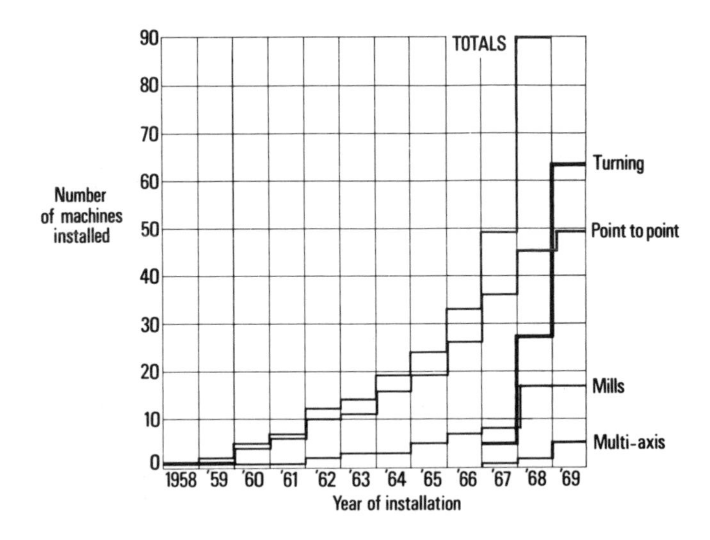

Fig. 1. N.C. machines at Rolls-Royce (excluding Bristol division).

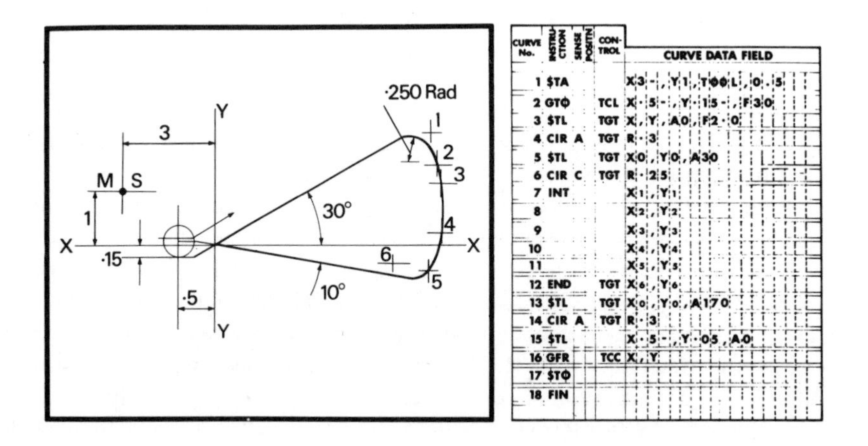

CURVE No.	INSTRU-CTION	SENSE	POSITN	CON-TROL	CURVE DATA FIELD
1	$TA				X3-, Y1, TΦΦL, 0.5
2	GTΦ			TCL	X·5-, Y·15-, F30
3	$TL			TGT	X, Y, A0, F2·0
4	CIR	A		TGT	R·3
5	$TL			TGT	X0, Y0, A30
6	CIR	C		TGT	R·25
7	INT				X1, Y1
8					X2, Y2
9					X3, Y3
10					X4, Y4
11					X5, Y5
12	END			TGT	X6, Y6
13	$TL			TGT	X0, Y0, A170
14	CIR	A		TGT	R·3
15	$TL				X·5-, Y·05, A0
16	GFR			TCC	X, Y
17	$TΦ				
18	FIN				

Fig. 2. Example of Cocomat part-program.

Designed to support some of our three-axis milling operations, Cocomat introduced the concept of the computer part-programming language whereby the planning engineer, using a mnemonic type of language (Fig. 2), is easily able to specify the geometry and machining requirements of his workpiece. He leaves the computer to interpret his instructions and convert them into the highly detailed form necessary for the machine tool, finally producing this information in the format and on the medium (for example magnetic tape) required by its control unit.

However, like its contemporaries (e.g. Apt or Profiledata), Cocomat is a 'geometrical only' type of system. For while the user or 'part-programmer' can leave the determination of geometric details (e.g. exact location of blend points) to the computer system, he must explicitly supply such technological details as the cutting tool to be used, feed rate, etc. (TΦΦL, F respectively in Fig. 2).

Nevertheless, it has been determined that for 1967 Cocomat showed net *tangible* savings of £36 000 in respect of production engineering personnel, and that much greater benefits accrued from increased accuracy, slashed lead times, etc.

2.2 *'Technological' n.c. computer systems*

Until mid/late 1966 Cocomat, together with some 'special-to-product' systems developed by the Division, met our requirements. Possibly more important, however, the systems gave production engineering personnel confidence in the computer. This not only enabled them fully to utilise the potential of the relatively simple three-axis machines, but also to become the first organisation in the U.K. to install multi-axis machining centres, for example Sunstrand Omnimills (Fig. 1).

Confidence proved even more vital in 1966, when the Division changed its machine tool policy. The change was brought about in particular by two major developments in the machine tool field:

- The availability of n.c. turning machines of the type required
- The transfer-line concept (e.g. Molins Sytem 24)

The former development in itself led to the decision to accelerate the growth, not only of n.c. turning machines but of our whole n.c. machine tool population (Fig. 1). The transfer-line concept had a more profound effect: it emphasised that the n.c. machine tool was not merely a replacement for several manually operated machines but a vital element in maintaining management control of the manufacturing process.

As a result of this policy decision it has been estimated that the Rolls-Royce Aero-Engine Division will, by the end of 1969, have by value 10% of all n.c. machines in the U.K., and much higher percentages in the particular fields of turning and multi-axis machines. The *average* of 50% saving in machining time resulting from these n.c. installations will, it is estimated, produce, in direct savings alone, economies of £0·5m per annum by the end of 1969 after deducting depreciation and interest on capital. It is perhaps interesting to note that there is a very high proportion of n.c. machining read into the factory cost of the RB 211 engine for the Lockheed Tristar Airbus.

The implications of the policy change on computing software requirements were obvious to both our production engineering and computing functions. Together, we took a critical look at our n.c. computing policy. One of the major decisions which emerged from the discussions was that the computer must be used to assist in determining technological details (i.e. tools, feeds, speeds, etc.) in addition to geometrical details. Various considerations led to this decision, including:

a Experience gained from some self-written 'special to product' n.c. computer systems
b The success of 'automation' and 'auto-planning' in the Division
c The necessity for continuity of expertise, despite manpower changes
d The need to modify the conventional planning engineer's conservatism in order to optimise n.c. machining conditions
e The need to enforce standards both within the Division and in respect of sub-contractors and suppliers, e.g. cutting-tool manufacturers
f The (intuitive) view that economic 'adaptive' control will require a good first approximation.

In 1967 Rolls-Royce committed itself to 'geometrical/technological' n.c. computer systems by joining the Exapt Association, an international society devoted initially to the development of three such systems: Exapt 1 for drilling machines etc., Exapt 2 for turning machines, and Exapt 3 for mills. A trivial Exapt 1 part-program is shown in Fig. 3 where 'technological' statements or definitions are displayed in the block headed *Machining statements.* Here TAP 1

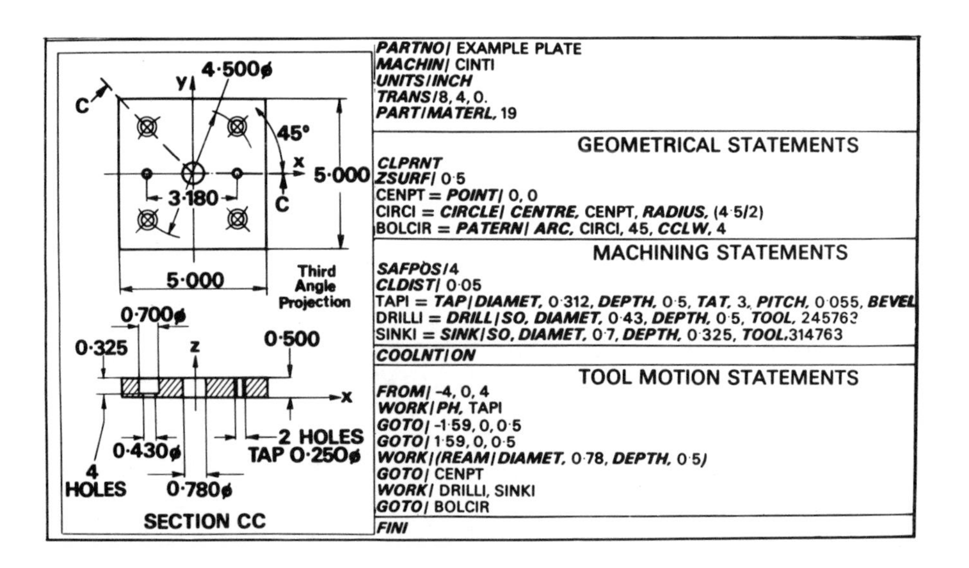

Fig. 3. Example of point-to-point part-program (Exapt 1).

is the name given by the part-programmer to a tapping operation (TAP) by which he wishes to produce a tapped hole of diameter 0·312, depth 0·5, with a thread of type 3 having 0·055 pitch. His addition of the modifier BEVEL indicates that he wishes the pre-drilled hole to be chamfered before the tapping tool is used. In the computer this statement will cause the Exapt 1 system to choose from its tool library the appropriate drilling tool (for the pre-drilling operation), chamfering tool, and tap. Meanwhile, using the material characteristics procured from its materials library on the basis of the PART/MATERL, 19 statement, the computer will determine the feed and speeds appropriate for each operation. Finally, following the simple TOOL MOTION (i.e. WORK, GOTO) statements, it will detail actual tool position and movement.

It is worth emphasising here that the Exapt system, like most other n.c. computer program systems, is user-oriented in that it is a tool which the part-programmer can use as he desires. On this point note that the part-programmer (Fig. 3) has explicitly specified the cutting tools he wishes to use for drilling (DRILL) and countersinking (SINK), leaving the system to determine only feeds and speeds. Had he desired (because of say, rigidity considerations) to specify feeds and speeds explicitly, he had freedom to do so by merely stating his values after the modifying words FEED and SPEED.

The first operational versions of Exapt 1 and Exapt 2 were made available to our various machining centres in May 1969. Fig. 4 shows both sides of a typical turbine wheel turned on an n.c. lathe using control tapes produced *via* an Exapt 2 part-program. It is early yet to comment in general on the cost savings produced since we anticipate a learner period of about six months. The wheel in Fig. 4 was part-programmed by one of my own staff as a test, and tape preparation costs up to the 'ready for proofing' stage were of the order of 60% of corresponding manual figures. The Exapt 2-produced tape did machine the part correctly first time! We anticipate that Exapt 3 will be made available in early 1971.

Fig. 4. Typical turbine wheel turned on n.c. lathe part-programmed *via* Exapt 2.

2.3 *Bridging the design-production gap*

Though the step from geometrical-only systems to those with technological capability is great, it attacks only the problems of manufacture and not the associated major problem area, the gap between the design engineer and the production engineer.

It is somewhat out of keeping that the geometry of a component be decided by Design Engineering, using various computing aids, transmitted to Production Engineering in the form of a detail drawing from which the actual geometry is extracted, or tool geometry determined, and put *back* into the computer *via* an n.c. computer system. In that way we feed back to the computer that geometrical information which it was instrumental in determining in the first place.

There are of course good historical reasons why this is so, e.g. the lack of proper computing facilities and the slow initial growth in the use of n.c. machine tools, but these reasons are now becoming invalid. In the near future the production engineer is going to demand information in a form more suited to his *numerically* controlled cutting and inspection machine tools. The computer, with its massive, random-access storage and graphical display ability, already provides the hardware necessary to act as the error-free transfer medium.

The concept of trapping the vital geometrical manufacturing information at its source, i.e. in design, is not new. In our Aero-Engine Division the Proconsel computer system

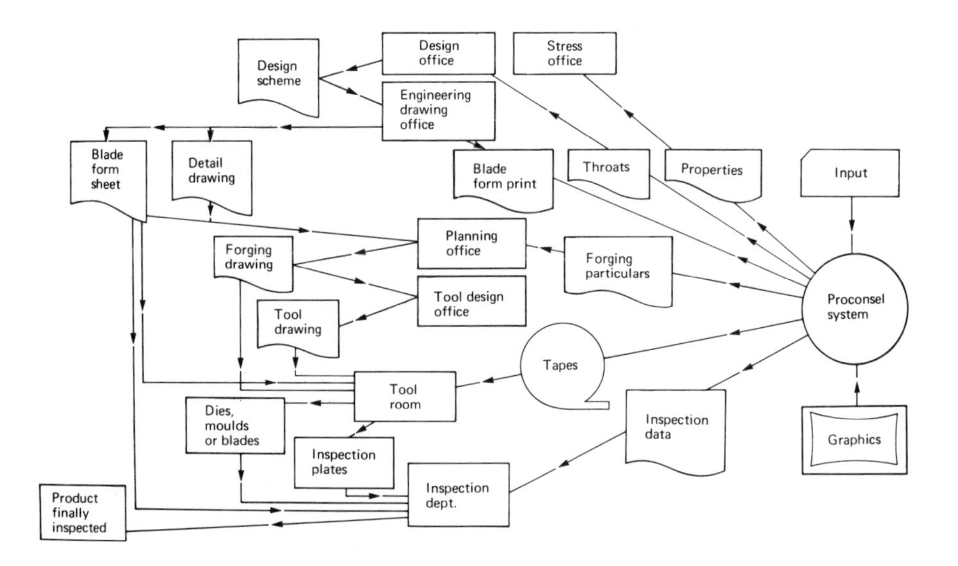

Fig. 5. Proconsel and work areas.

for blade and/or die-block manufacture (Fig. 5) has for the last five years bridged the gap between design engineering and production engineering by requiring the basic geometrical information to be extracted from the *design scheme drawing.*

The Proconsel system itself:

a conducts all the detailing calculations necessary for accurate and full definition of blade shape
b designs, in accordance with rules supplied by our production engineering organisation, the manufacturing tools (e.g. die-blocks, moulds, anodes and cathodes, including the flash gate necessary for the required metal flow from the dies and incorporating allowances for forging contraction effects)
c optionally chooses cutters and feed rates
d produces control tapes for n.c. manufacture of forging, casting or electrochemical machining tools, or, if desired, the blade itself
e produces inspection data, and, *via* an n.c. draughting machine, inspection graticules to check both the manufacturing tools and the finished blades

It is perhaps interesting to note that Proconsel has proved to be by far the most successful n.c. computer system so far used by Rolls-Royce. There are numerous examples of lead times slashed from months to days, and even hours. A prime example of such slashing occurred shortly after the first full-scale Proconsel system became operational in 1965, when a decision was made by our design organisation to change the blading on the compressor of one of the variants of the Spey engine. The forging dies for the new blades were being n.c.-machined in the tool room within twenty *clock* hours of the design decision! If this had not been possible many engines would have left the plant during the succeeding weeks and would each have required expensive re-blading on first overhaul.

Considering its pure calculating power, and its ability automatically to produce information in the form required respectively by designers, detailers, production personnel and inspectors, we have determined that, for 1967, Proconsel produced net tangible savings of £87 000 of which £29 000 applied to design and detailing.

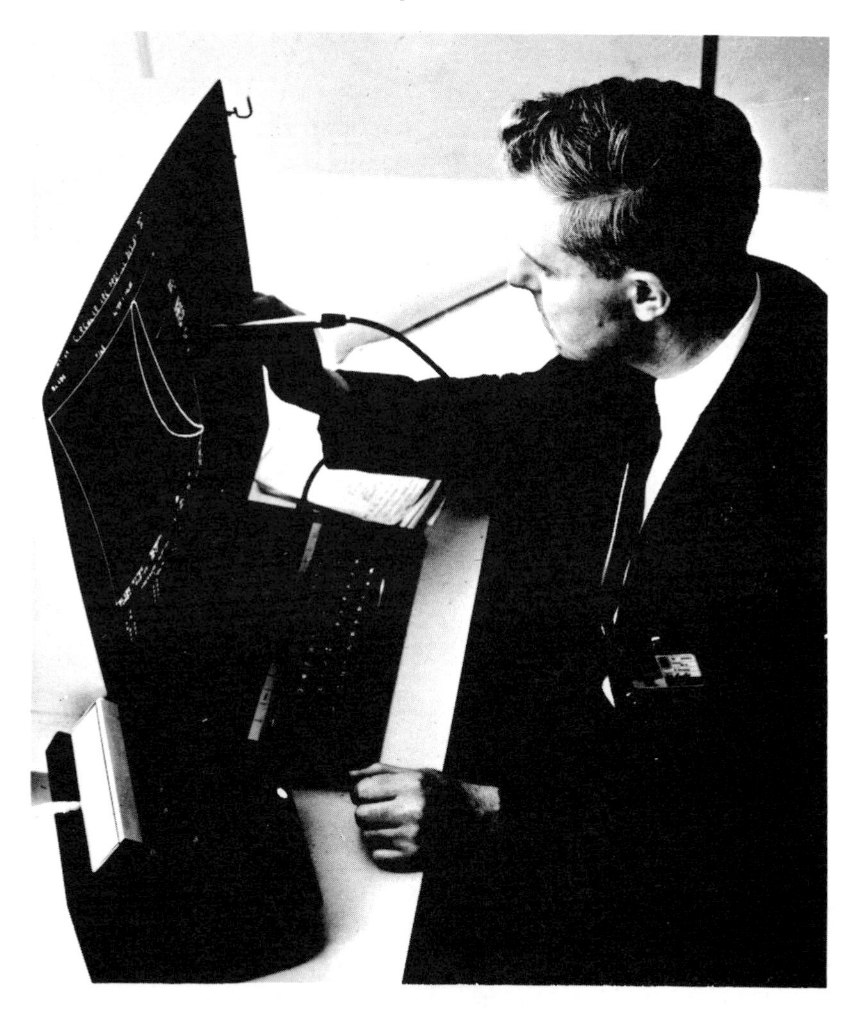

Fig. 6. Designer's graphical display.

With the help of our computer-aided design team the system has recently been extended backwards into the design office itself. Here use is made of the graphical display screen (Fig. 6). On it, at the touch of a button, the design engineer can cause his aerofoil sections to be displayed pictorially. He can likewise modify them on the screen to take regard of stress, vibration and positional information determined and displayed for him. When finally satisfied, he can automatically store his design in the computer file ready for Proconsel itself.

While this system will be further extended to provide assistance to our aerodynamicists, work is also proceeding to bridge the gap for other types of component. In particular, a graphical computer-aided turbine-disc design system is already operational. We hope to link this to the technological part of Exapt 2 in 1970 and produce optimised control tapes for n.c. turning of discs.

3.0 ON-LINE COMPUTER CONTROL

What of the future? An immense amount of work will certainly continue on development of n.c. machine tools and on the general-purpose (e.g. Exapt) and 'special-to-product' n.c. computer systems necessary for their fullest economic utilisation. No matter how good these systems in themselves become, they will not solve all the problems which exist. Among the latter could be listed:

a Switching a component from one machine to another size-compatible, but dynamically incompatible, machine at short notice, owing e.g. to break-down, overload etc. (Note that a control tape normally contains data apt for the particular machine tool-control system combination for which the machining operation was planned. Only in certain circumstances can this same control tape be used to produce the part on another machine tool-control system combination, even though the latter has the necessary physical capability.)

b Dynamic alteration of machine tool controlling information to take account of real time and such local conditions as cutting-tool wear and workpiece material inconsistencies

c Physical movement of parts between machines

To cater for b requires initially the development of appropriate sensing devices. The remaining problems listed could be overcome by a relatively new method: on-line computer control (Fig. 7).

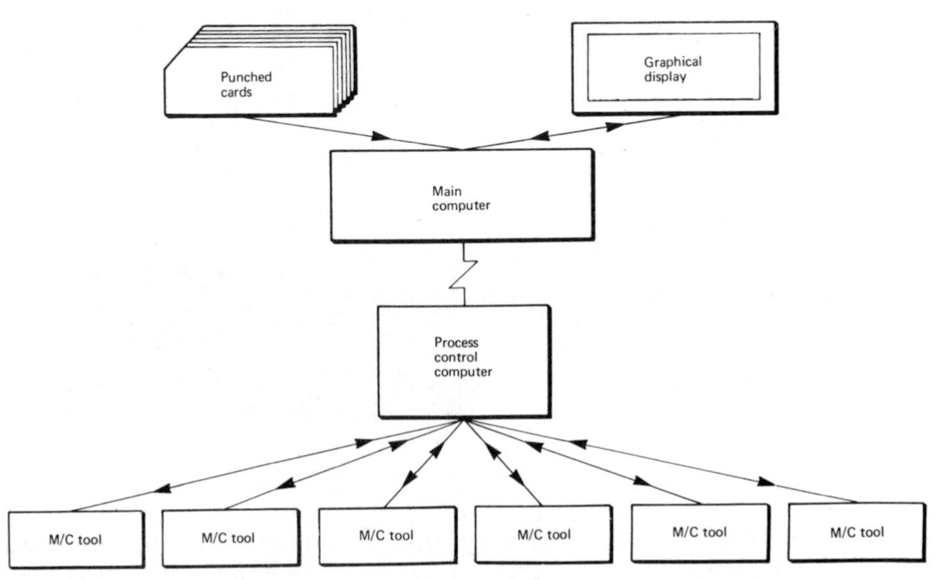

Fig. 7. Scheme of direct computer control.

Here the physical movements of machine tool slides are controlled by information communicated direct from a shop-floor computer. The computer has the power to alter controlling information rapidly to suit an alternative machine tool, and to elicit the necessary response from sensing devices recording local machining conditions. With the addition of automatic mechanical handling, and workpiece pallet or other locating equipment, all under the control of the shop-floor computer, each part can be automatically routed to and from each of the machines required for its manufacture. This is what is now 'affectionately' known as the 'on-line manufacturing complex' (e.g. Molins system 24).

In short, on-line computer control offers the possibility of the fully automated *batch production* machine shop!

But the automated machine shop is only part of the story. The real objective of any company is to turn a design concept into finished hardware as quickly and economically as possible, but under strict management control at all times. The computer could be used to achieve this objective because:

a *via* the graphical display screen or other devices it could help design, detail, and part-program the requisite components in accordance with computer-produced design and production engineering schedules

b on completion of the scheduled 'proofing' stage, the n.c. machine tool controlling information could be automatically merged with production control data produced by the computerised production control system

c the requisite components will be produced automatically in accordance with the resulting manufacturing schedules under the control of the shop-floor process-control computer

This is not 'pie in the sky'. Development work is going on in several parts of the world NOW! Computer-assisted management control in the fullest sense is technically feasible NOW! The time scale for its full implementation depends largely on economics, but more fundamentally on the degree of management (design and manufacturing) involvement.

BIBLIOGRAPHY

1 ANON. *Programming of Numerically Controlled Machine Tools,* NEL Report No 187 National Engineering Laboratory, East Kilbride, Scotland May 1965.

2 H. OPITZ, W. SIMON, G. SPUR and G. STUTE. 'The Programming of Numerically-Controlled Machines with EXAPT'. *Machinery and Production Engineering.* Vol. 111 (2857). pp. 329 – 336. 16 August 1967.

3 S. B. L. WILSON. 'The Computer and Numerically Controlled Machine Tools'. *Machinery and Production Engineering.* Vol. 114 (2948). pp. 769 – 778 14 May 1969.

4 F. E. TAYLOR. 'Towards Integrated Systems for Design Automation'. *Data Systems.* pp. 22 – 25, 48 May 1968.

5 E. HUGGINS. 'How to Fail with Automation'. *Management Today.* pp. 93 – 94 December 1968.

TECHNICAL COMPUTING IN A DESIGN AND PRODUCT DEVELOPMENT ENVIRONMENT

S. Matthews
formerly with
Ford Motor Co. Ltd, Basildon

SUMMARY

The introduction of technical computing into the Ford Motor Co. in the United Kingdom and in Germany is reviewed and an indication is given of the hardware configuration (utilising a time-sharing computer) to be made available by early 1970. Applications of computer-aided design, automatic drafting, numerical control and other types of technical computation using analogue/ hybrid computer systems are described.

1.0 INTRODUCTION

Culminating in 1962, we at the Ford Motor Co.* had made a study of the advantages of providing an 'in house' technical digital computer service for the product development and design activities of the then-separate Ford of Britain structure.

The result of this survey was overwhelmingly in favour of such a venture. As a pilot scheme a Mark II 40 k core storage IBM 1620 digital computer was immediately installed. In addition the installation included a CalComp 12 in wide, continuous-roll $x-y$ incremental plotter driven on line to the above machine. Initially effort was concentrated on training some 250 selected design engineers to program in Fortran. Of these, approximately 25% demonstrated outstanding aptitude. Small groups from the top stratum, each representing as wide a spectrum of activity as possible, were then, in turn, seconded for advanced training to the newly formed Computer Consultant's Office. This secondment was for three months. In addition, special computer-appreciation courses were provided for management and higher executive grades.

It was considered mandatory that all supervisors be included in the more detailed courses so that they could exert the desired influence on their subordinates. This decision made a valuable contribution to minimisation of the time taken to change from manual calculation (using normal desk aids) to computer solution of design problems.

Finally, mathematics courses orientated to the use of a digital computer, and covering in sufficient detail the following subjects, were established:

- Matrix algebra and its applications
- Co-ordinate geometry
- Numerical analysis
- Vector analysis

---

* Mr Matthews is now at Cambridge University.

An interesting side-effect of this effort was the competition which developed between different design and development areas to head the lists of successful applications. These were published in a series of newsletters which also presented in detail new mathematical techniques and suggestions as to how they could be applied. A bibliography for further reading was appended.

By the end of the first year some three hundred computer programs had been written and were in regular use. Upon such a sound foundation there has been built up an impressive Computer Services Department. During this period the Ford of Europe concept was imple-

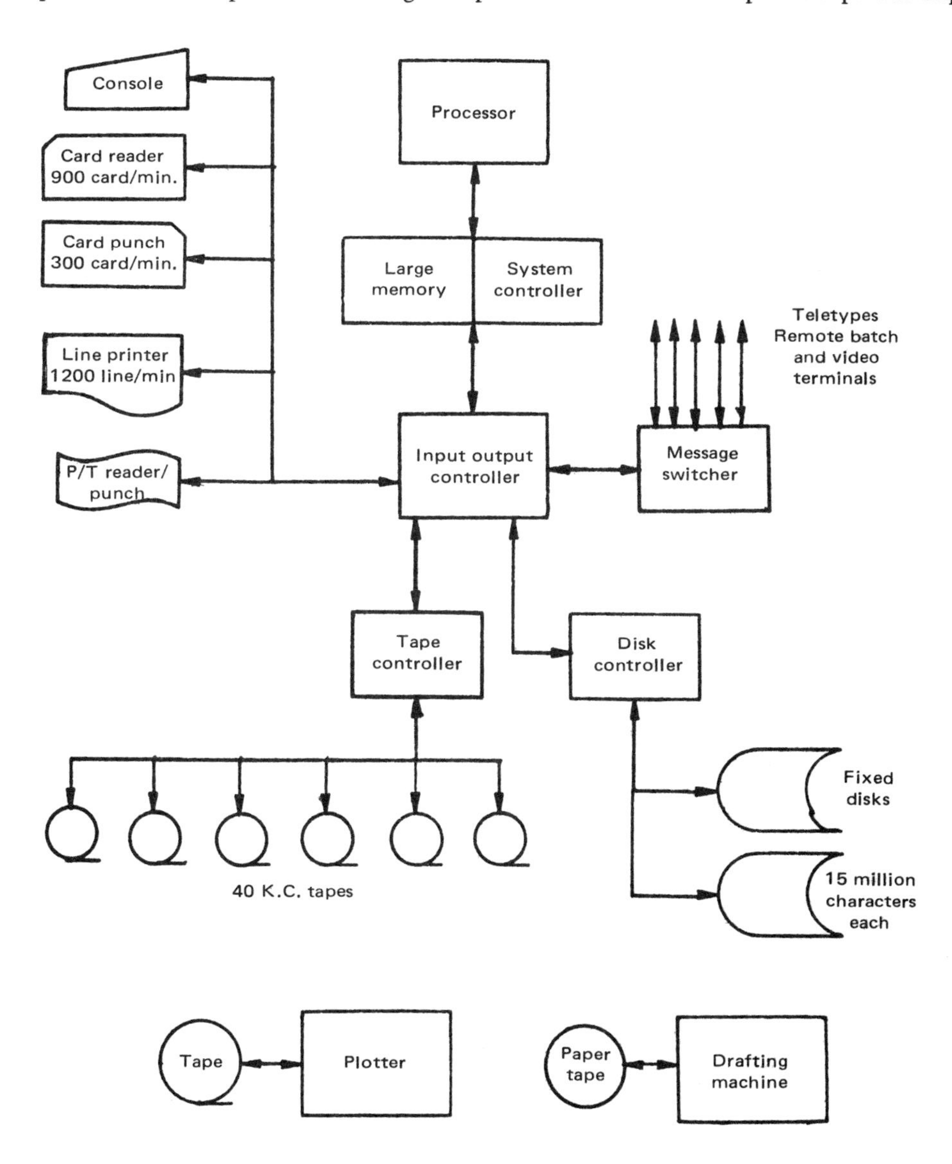

Fig. 1. Hardware configuration for time-sharing computer – a system available by 1970.

mented and now there are two main research and engineering centres, the first at Dunton, U.K., and the second at Merkenich, Germany.

In the course of time the original IBM 1620 computer was replaced by an IBM 1130 3C at Dunton and an identical configuration at Merkenich. The two systems are linked, and there is a daily time slice allocated for data and page transmission. Further digital computer support using a Univac 1108, is purchased externally.

The hardware system which will be available between the time of writing and early 1970 is shown in Fig. 1.

2.0 TIME-SHARING ACTIVITIES

The provision of a time-sharing facility was early recognised to be highly desirable.

The group was particularly fortunate in that it had a dedicated line to the time-sharing computer at Ford's U.S.A. headquarters in Dearborn. A single link was established for approximately six months during 1966 and was used essentially for educational purposes. Many engineers were trained in 'Basic'. The teletype terminal was sequentially placed in all main areas for a period, to provide the engineers with practical experience in the use of such equipment. This service was then discontinued pending the installation of a GE 265 time-sharing computer at the Southampton Row bureau of De La Rue Bull.

No doubt the following chronological data will be of interest.

June 1967	A teletype terminal was installed in the Computer Services Department, Dunton.
July 1967	Twelve terminals were strategically placed in the newly occupied Research and Engineering Centre, Dunton. These were shared by four available channels to the GE 265 at the above bureau.
August 1967	The first group of engineers received formal advanced training in Basic and the use of the facility as a commercial venture. (By the end of 1967 some 200 engineers had successfully completed training.)
September 1967	A Users' Group was set up to act as a clearing house for computer problems and to link the computer user with the Computer Services Department. (Throughout 1967 the accent was on implementation and general evangelising.)
March 1968	A time-sharing program library was formed, with company-wide distribution. The number of teletype terminals was increased to fourteen. Fortran was included in the available languages. Five terminals were placed in the Merkenich Design Centre.
April 1968	The number of available channels was raised to six.
June 1968	A CalComp continuous-roll plotter was demonstrated with one of the time-sharing terminals (this is now a permanent feature). On-line trial connection was established with Dearborn, *via* satellite. Nine channels were operational between 08.00 and 13.00 hours. This venture has now been discontinued. A teletype/teletype link was made between the Research and Engineering Centres at Dunton and Merkenich. This was used for data and page copy transmission.
July 1968	A complementary Users' Group was established at Merkenich.
September 1968	Some 160 extra engineers received training.
November 1968	Programs were evaluated in order to: • reduce soaring expense by encouraging tape storage and more efficient programming. • improve access to the time-sharing program library with respect to function and versatility.
January 1969	The number of terminals was increased to eighteen.

Figs 2 and 3 show how the use of the teletype terminals progressed.

From the above notes it will be seen that there is an element of remote batch processing in addition to true time-sharing. With the introduction of a large time-sharing computer, normal working hours will be devoted to time-sharing and all batch processing will be done at night.

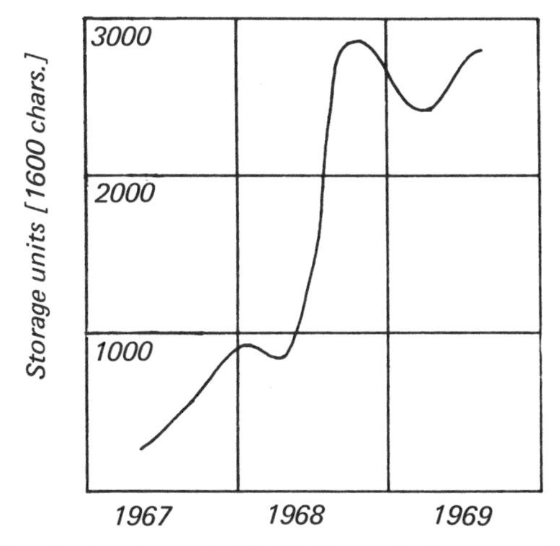

Fig. 2. Time-sharing storage 1967–69. Usage of teletype terminals (1).

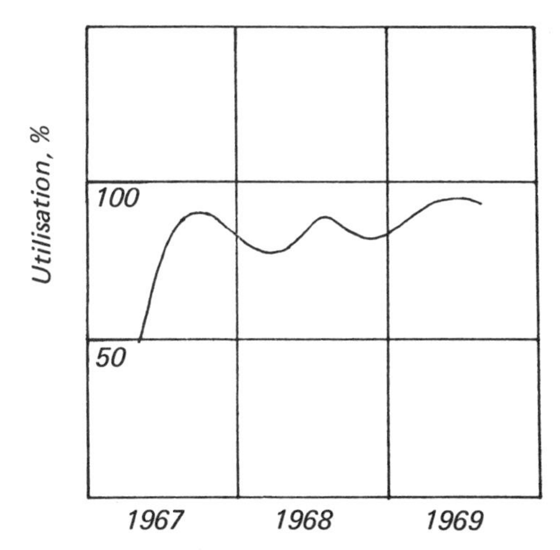

Fig. 3. Time-sharing storage 1967–69. Usage of teletype terminals (2).

3.0 APPLICATION RESEARCH

Computer-aided design (c.a.d.) is a term much in use. Unfortunately it can have different meanings to different people, depending on their experience and discipline. Broadly speaking, design calculations by a digital computer constitute c.a.d. in so far as the user is achieving desired results in a much reduced time. However, only a much narrower connotation of c.a.d. is understood here, namely the use of computers and peripheral equipment supported by software and programs with emphasis on design optimisation; or at least provision for rapid and preferably visual means of assessing the effect of modifying design parameters.

It is also expedient at this time to clarify the term *design automation*. The term implies that design engineers will become obsolete. Nothing of course could be further from the truth: in fact their value will be enhanced. The author therefore prefers to use the phrase 'toward design automation'. The engineer must initiate the entire design process by defining the design parameters. In many cases the system must provide the opportunity for him to intervene at any time in the design process and modify the parameters.

A typical example of this concept of c.a.d. is the company's system of automotive gear design. This system covers spur, spiral, helical, spiral bevel and hypoid gears. This program permits, where relevant, a specified number of mating gears to be designed simultaneously with the original gear. In addition, certain calculated parameters such as gear life are used to optimise mating gears on the criterion that other components in the complete gear system shall have equal life, thus minimising the possibility of premature failure of any component during service. At selected stages of the design process intermediate results are displayed. Manual intervention is allowed for at these stages. The quick look permits modification of relevant parameters should it be deemed advisable by the design engineer. On completion of the design process the complete manufacturing data are produced. Normally, an enlarged view of the generated tooth form is automatically drawn for reference purposes (see Fig. 4).

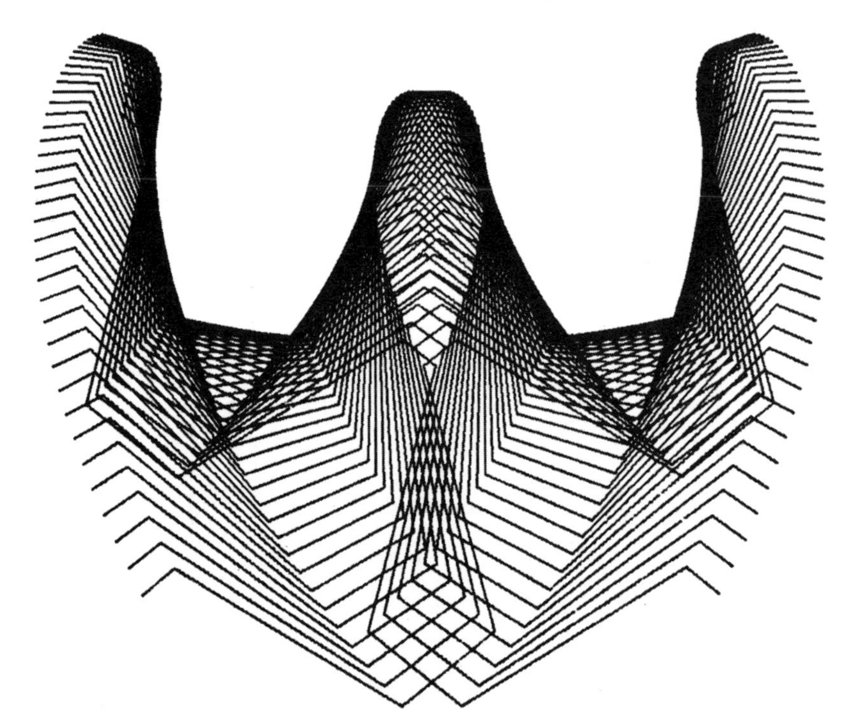

Fig. 4. Enlarged generated tooth form.

Other typical products of successful c.a.d. are:

- steering systems
- suspension systems
- other multi-link mechanisms, e.g. side-window regulators
- windshield wiper mechanisms (by calculating and displaying the wipe pattern)
- main crankshaft bearings and polar diagrams for reference and reporting purposes

It will be noted that many of the above examples are based on three-dimensional co-ordinate geometry problems. This selection was made in order to emphasise that this type of work is ideally suited to the use of an interactive graphical terminal operating in a time-sharing environment. The work is rapidly being extended to surface definition, interrogation and modification. Typical non-controversial examples of these studies are:

- The swept surface generated by a vehicle front wheel during the complete operational movement of the wheel, i.e. through maximum bounce and rebound and maximum steer and other controlling factors.
- the design of, initially, vehicle inner surfaces
- packaging problems

Many such applications extend automatically to numerical control of machine tools. This advance will be made possible because, once surface equations are established, the co-ordinates of incremental cutter paths will emerge automatically.

A complementary research was commenced some years ago to provide a drafting system which would support, and in fact complete, a sophisticated design system. The initial specification of the drafting system was:

a Minimise user training
b Free format so that system can accept data from all anticipated sources
c Provide complete set of data-manipulation routines, as transformation matrices
d Provide range of curve-fitting routines
e Provide curve-fairing routine
f Provide full complement of surface routines
g Provide surface-fairing routine
h Provide adequate annotation routines
i Output compatible with plotters and numerically controlled drafting machines

The following describes the current state of the drafting system, which has been in use for approximately two years. It will be noted that the system does not fully satisfy the specification. Where this is so it may be assumed that rectification of the omissions is in an advanced stage.

4.0 AUTOMATIC DRAFTING SYSTEM

4.1 *Basis of operation*

The system is basically constructed of two main executive programs which control several smaller modules, some of which function according to selected options.

The first, and larger, executive program directs control to the data reading, interrogation and printing routines and general mathematical routines. The data-checking module, apart from producing a formal listing of input data, also indicates any errors which result from its extensive interrogation, and causes a program abort. Where errors do not exist, control is directed to the mathematical section, which contains all the necessary curve-fitting routines. Fit having been effected, interpolated points which describe the curves are stored on magnetic disk together with appropriate annotation. These are accessed by the second executive program.

The second executive program essentially comprises plotting and drawing sizing routines. Since the incremental plotter can only accommodate a drawing of at most 27 in in the y direction, a drawing size check is essential. It having been established that the drawing may be accommodated, the curves are plotted; otherwise a message is passed to the operator and the program terminates.

4.2 *First executive program*

In an attempt to avoid errors the program system was written so that it was 'user orientated'. Such orientation eliminates need for heavy training of users in computer science, and requires that the input data be kept as nearly as possible in the form with which the user is familiar for manual solution. Thus the amount of data was kept to a minimum and information not supplied was implied by the method in which the data was presented.

All general options are listed on one card which is divided into two parts:

1 the views required, i.e. plan, end elevation, side elevation
2 three-dimensional projections, i.e. perspective, axonometric or orthogonal.

A 1 is entered in the appropriate field to request any particular option.

So that the draughtsman can readily identify the curves produced by the program, a label can be attached to each curve, this being printed on the output graph. For example, SECTION AT 300 BS indicates a section through the object at a constant x value of 300 mm (z plotted against y). To permit lines of unlimited length (in the plotter x direction only) curves are annotated CONTINUE or CONTINUE SMOOTH. The former would produce discontinuous joins and the latter smooth, continuous boundaries. For these cases no annotation is written on the output graph.

In addition to three-dimensional co-ordinate data, tangent vectors which dictate the slope of curve boundaries may be input. A suitable option parameter indicates whether first, last, both or no end-point tangency conditions are required. For example, consider the transverse roof line of a car. A flat, smooth curve is desired to pass through the centre-line. Therefore it is required that a unit tangent vector be supplied in the transverse direction only.

Experience showed that, because of the unfamiliarity of the tangent vector concept to draughtsmen, it was necessary to introduce a certain amount of automatic tangent selection into the executive program. However, if a general space curve were under consideration, the tangent vectors could be used as input data by the option already described.

The following checks on three dimensional co-ordinate data are made:

1 no alphabetic or special characters are included in a numeric field
2 only one decimal point
3 not more than one sign

It is important to note that if any errors are detected the program is terminated before the mathematical routines are entered. Comments may be added to describe each point if required, these being edited and written alongside the data point on the formal listing. As already mentioned, it is possible to select a three-dimensional projection by a suitable entry in the general option card. The type of projection is selected by means of further codes. Data, after interrogation for errors, are operated upon by an appropriate transformation subroutine. The transformed co-ordinate data are then processed, curve by curve, as previously described.

4.2.1 *Orthogonal projections*

Any combination of three views, end, front elevations and plan, may be user-selected together with angles of rotation. The angular rotational increment may be either in the form of a number of degrees about the x, y and z axes or direction cosines of any two of a new set of x, y and z axes. Also specified is the number of angular increments, i.e. the number of complete sets of rotated orthogonal projections.

Initial tangent vectors, if they are required, are automatically rotated by the system.

4.2.2 *Axonometric projections*

This is a family of projections of which isometric and oblique are members. As with the orthogonal routine, a rotation may be effected by supplying the appropriate code and angle.

4.2.3 *Perspective projections*

Perspective projection is obtained from a simulation of the way in which light rays, after reflection from an object, build up an image on photographic film in a camera. A picture plane is constructed and the relative position of a viewing point determined from input data, this point being the distance of an observer from and above the object. To obtain the perspective view, points and lines of the object are projected onto the picture plane from the viewing point.

Again, the object may be rotated (around the vertical axis only).

4.3 *Second executive program*

As already described, the first function of this executive program is to size and frame drawings. Instructions are issued to the computer operator as to the size and number of drawings he is to expect. This enables the operator to check that there is enough paper on the plotter drum.

Each drawing has a set of axes to identify the relative positions and directions of the curves drawn. For example, axes labelled BS (bridge station) and HT (height) in the x and y directions would indicate a side elevation. The origin is indicated and is rounded down to the nearest 100 mm.

Complete annotation is produced by this executive program.

5.0 ANALOGUE AND HYBRID ACTIVITY

Ford's have had an analogue computer facility for the solution of scientific and engineering problems since 1960, when a medium-size, hundred-amplifier, AEI 955 machine was installed at the Birmingham Research Establishment. This machine was a non-patchboard machine and had limited bandwidth. It subsequently became evident that the limitations of this machine were severe, and in August 1968 it was replaced by a newer, more sophisticated, medium-size, 142-amplifier, general-purpose, EAL 680 machine that is capable of being extended into a full hybrid system. It is envisaged that this hybrid computer facility will be extended in early 1970 by the purchase of an interface to link it to the IBM 1130 digital computer to form a fully hybrid system which will be made available by the introduction of a new time-sharing machine.

With the formation of the Ford of Europe organisation, the analogue/hybrid systems groups in both Germany and Britain joined to form a single integrated service to the Product Development Group, Ford of Europe. In addition to the existing EAL 680 hybrid computer and its ancillary output equipment (such as a display console, x–y plotter, and an ultra-violet recorder) in Dunton, the facilities include three EAL TR 20 analogue computers, and their associated output peripherals, in Cologne.

The greater sophistication and patchboard facilities of the new machine have greatly decreased the turn-round time for problems, and significantly increased the number of problems handled and the types of application.

With the introduction of the new machine, a series of presentations and lectures on the applications of analogue and hybrid computation techniques were given to product development areas in an effort to ensure that maximum use was made of the new facility. Training courses, both internal and external, were also run for the benefit of product development area personnel. With the aid of this publicity and training program, which is continuing, it is envisaged that the engineers with the problems will be able to use the machine themselves to solve their problems, with aid where necessary from computer services personnel.

This use of the facility on a bureau basis will, it is realised, take some time to develop, but signs of success are already becoming evident. At present the machine is run on a one-shift basis and utilisation of 80–90% is being achieved. It may be necessary to go into two-shift working in the future.

The present applications of the hybrid computer may be conveniently considered in three categories, described respectively in Sections 5.1, 5.2 and 5.3.

5.1 *Simulation of vehicle dynamic systems*

Systems are simulated or modelled on the computer. The models may be readily modified to optimise engineering requirements and evaluate the resulting performance without recourse to costly and time-consuming physical test and build. Examples of this type of application are dynamic suspension studies, simulations to predict the performance of a vehicle in the design stage, dynamic simulation of a wind-shield wiping system to predict maximum loads, and simulation of a starter-motor cranking a cold engine in order to determine the optimum battery-starter combination.

5.2 *Processing of vehicle and rig test results*

Outputs from analogue or digital transducers (fitted to test rigs or carried in test vehicles) are edited, analysed and suitably recorded, either on line or by using magnetic tape recordings of the data. Such applications of the hybrid computer introduce a high degree of automation into data analysis and show great advantages over the previous dependence on optical and manual analysis methods.

5.3 *Development of special-purpose instrument systems*

Instances occur in which it is economic to construct instrumentation systems for specific test applications. Such systems usually involve lengthy development times and, during this development, the use of general-purpose instruments. It has been found that this development and instrument utilisation period may be reduced by using a hybrid computer to plan, develop and prove an optimum special-purpose system before any construction begins. Examples of such applications are the development of special-purpose systems for use in performance testing of a vehicle, and for the analysis of the interior noise level in a test vehicle.

When the present hybrid computer is linked, by an interface, to a digital computer to form a full hybrid system in 1970, further applications – and extensions of present applications – will be possible. When dealing with dynamic system analysis requiring complex logical decisions, full advantage may be taken of the scope of a digital machine, e.g. great data storage, high-precision calculations and the ability to select the next computation stage from a number of alternatives. This will permit applications in each of the three categories to be treated in greater depth and with shorter turn-round time and greater efficiency.

A fully hybrid system will also allow studies to be done on test process control by monitoring the output data of a given test sequence and then, by processing and computation, obtaining various pre-programmed alternatives, and so defining the most desirable test sequence. The chosen test sequence may then be transmitted from the computer by electrical signals direct to a test rig, etc.

It is envisaged that work will be done, in conjunction with an academic establishment, on the computer control of an engine test cell. Initially the dynamic behaviour of an engine dynamometer system will be simulated on the hybrid computer. The simulation will be controlled using the digital computer and interface. In this manner there can be a considerable amount of development on the system without the expense involved in 'tying up' a complete engine test cell.

Since its installation the hybrid computer has been used for many applications that were not foreseen before its purchase. It would seem certain that, with the introduction of a fully hybrid system in 1970, and with increased experience in hybrid techniques, there will be many applications other than the large number envisaged at this moment. It is certain that the fully hybrid system will permit many of the present constraints and limitations to be overcome and will contribute to the improved quality of the company's products.

6.0 NUMERICAL CONTROL

Numerical control was introduced into the Research and Engineering Centre at Dunton in 1967 to expedite the manufacture of prototype vehicles. A Sundstrand four-axis Omnimill was installed. Today it is used exclusively to machine all prototype and new-concept engine and transmission castings. This project is supported by a team of part programmers using Apt plus special assistance in post-processor development. There is a similar but not identical activity in the Research and Engineering Centre at Merkenich.

As a point of interest, the Ford Motor Co. in the U.S. has been involved in large-scale machining of press-forming dies, templates and wood models. These are used both in vehicle body manufacture and for reference purposes.

The software and computer programs are unique to the company and are sophisticated to a high degree.

The author trusts that this paper has indicated the essential part that computers and their application play in the technical development of the products of the Ford Motor Co. in a world-wide context. It is suggested that the advent of time-sharing computers in the U.K., and the undoubted reliability of remote-access terminals, now provide a facility that should be more generally employed in British industry.

ACKNOWLEDGEMENT

Sincere appreciation is expressed to the Ford Motor Co. for permission to prepare and present this paper.

SESSION 2. DISCUSSION ON THE PAPERS BY M. FIELD, A. H. MELEKA AND S. MATTHEWS

Dr A. H. MELEKA (*Rolls-Royce*): Would Dr Field tell us, has the computer been fed with information relating to the rigidity of the machine tool and the relative rigidity of the part itself?

Dr M. FIELD: We have been spending our energy on the use of machining data. Other companies are applying constraints and so forth to the same thing. Ling Temco Vought is using this type of approach, but adding to it information to control effective rigidity, size of tools, vibration, surface finish. There is a company called Abex in the United States doing something similar. They are adding to this all the other pertinent factors which you have to use as constraints in a machining process. If you pick the wrong speed of feed you might get into vibration problems, you might exceed the rigidity of the cutter and get too much cutter deflection.

So this is one part of the overall subject. We have not applied the constraints or restraints associated with rigidity of workpiece or cutter, but other people have done so.

B. DAVIES (*Birniehill Institute*): How are the formulae derived, analytically or from data? How often are they updated and how do you check off the optimisation formulas?

Dr M. FIELD: The formulas are derived quite simply. They are all in terms of measurable parameters, diameters, length of cut, feed per tooth or feed per revolution. These are the parameters which we chose to put in, things which you can preset or measure.

The formulas for optimisation are only in there for the simplified Taylor relationship VT^n = a constant, which we do not think holds very often. We just put it in there because all the investigators in Europe seem to want it, and this is also true of the university community in the United States. You can put in the more advanced Taylor relationship, velocity multiplied by time to the one exponent multiplied by feed to another and depth exponent is a constant.

We prefer to work with raw data. The computer does not give a darn whether you have an equation or raw data. It will work either way just as quickly. We have other things going on. We would like to know the relationship between the various machining parameters. We can very quickly and fairly cheaply determine some of these relationships. We can do a limited amount in the laboratory or in the shop. We would then like to know how we can extrapolate this information to other situations.

The things that have to be updated are the data, not the equations. I am excluding the optimised equations. The equations remain the same: the data change. You have to put in the pertinent data.

N. ZLATIN (*Metcut Research*): Would Dr Meleka comment on the machining of metallic composite materials: for example, boron composites?

A. H. MELEKA: We have not attempted to machine this type of material electrochemically, but I think there will be problems because the electrochemical characteristics of the component materials will be different.

We have been confronted with this type of situation in conventional alloys which contain inter-metallics and solid solutions and so on. This can be quite a problem, even with conventional alloys, because of the relative rate of metal removal. Probably the electrochemist has to devote some attention to the development of electrolytes that would reduce the gap between the characteristics of the two materials.

We have not really had a great deal of experience with conventional machining of metallic composite materials.

B. DAVIES (*Birniehill Institute*): Would Mr Matthews tell us, do Ford's still employ a method of making clay models and copy from the model?

S. MATTHEWS: Yes. Only, we make rather more accurate ones. We have now tried to get the clay model within 1/32 in of actual size. We use better material, better clays.

P. P. LOVE (*Glacier Metal Co.*): You refer to main crankshaft bearings and the production of fuller load diagrams for reference and reporting purposes as a typical example of successfully applied c.a.d. In working out the load diagrams, how do you take into consideration the effect of interactive stiffness of the crankcase, housings and crankshafts?

S. MATTHEWS: These are fed in as data. We are designing the main bearing on the crankshaft. We are not designing the crankshaft, we are designing the bearings. We know the properties of the crankshaft, we know the stiffnesses.

P. P. LOVE (*Glacier Metal Co.*): How about the crankcase itself?

S. MATTHEWS: The answer is no, not on the crankcase.

G. R. FRANKLIN (*W. E. & F. Dobson*): Within what limits do you modify the shapes of your clay models and at what stages do the internal space utilisation exercises come in?

S. MATTHEWS: We start off by doing a survey of public opinion. Then the styling people, together with the ergonomic group, set out a standard package. We design for say 95% of the population.

We package four features into the space. We have a program for this. We consider the driver operating and his elbow sweeping if he is doing a floor change, or a column change. What is the swept shape that his elbow goes through? All this is taken into consideration – the packaging of the instruments, safety aspects, etc.

We arrive at certain 'hard points'. These hard points in the system are specially coded and will not change.

P. GALLOWAY (*I.C.I.*): The Ford Motor Co. obviously believe that this sort of graphic use of a computer is valid and viable for carrying out a very large design job: basically, one very large design job for a very large company. Do you consider that it would be equally viable for a much smaller organisation which wanted to carry out a number of related but really very different design jobs?

S. MATTHEWS: Yes, I think so. We originally bought *computers*. We still buy *time* on the GE265, and we time-share with that computer. You can buy time and use it for the short periods that you want. I think that even moderately-sized firms should have these things. This is the way in which smaller firms can in fact go in for computer-aided design. This must be the trend in Britain.

SESSION III

Manufacturing Technology II

Chairman: Mr W. Gregson
Assistant General Manager
Ferranti Ltd.
Edinburgh

AUTOMATED ASSEMBLING IN PERSPECTIVE

R. Iredale
'Metalworking Production'

SUMMARY

The benefits which accrue from the introduction of automated assembly techniques are not being reaped by British industry over a wide enough front. Managing directors have the major responsibility in ensuring that this situation is corrected. Given automated assembly, product design can be materially improved, leading to cost reductions. The assembly stage is considered to be the main area in which cost reduction can be achieved. Opportunity exists for the establishment of a viable assembly-machine industry in Britain.

1.0 INTRODUCTION

The state of the art in automated assembling can be described in one word, and that word is – *inadequate.* Inadequate, that is, when it is considered that the assembly function represents by far the most fruitful area for cost reduction with which to counter the ever increasing cost of labour and materials. And the only reason it is inadequate is that the motive power has not yet been applied. Though there is tremendous interest and an air of expectancy, medium- and large-batch producers in the metalworking industries have not yet experienced the economic compulsion that should be now driving them to a sustained programme of development in automated assembling.

2.0 LONG-TERM ECONOMICS

At the present time it is often difficult to demonstrate the economic benefits of installing assembly machines in a metalworking plant. There is a scarcity of instances of long-term economic gains achieved. This is pretty obvious at the many conferences which have been held, in the demands by would-be users at these conferences for concrete proof of projects that have paid, and in the notable failure of more experienced users to provide this proof.

Recently the author carried out some investigations to try and fill this gap with some authentic economic data gathered over a sufficiently long period to show, one way or the other, whether automated assembling is an economic necessity for medium- to large-batch metalworking industries. The metalworking industries themselves could not provide it, so some time was spent gathering first-hand information in the specialist mass-production industries making tin cans, dry batteries, electric lamp bulbs and cigarettes (Fig. 1). The author found there the most compelling arguments for general metalworking industries to get to grips with automated assembling.

In these industries one can look back over thirty years and see the economic effects of a gradual progression towards product simplification, product rationalisation and a high level of auto-

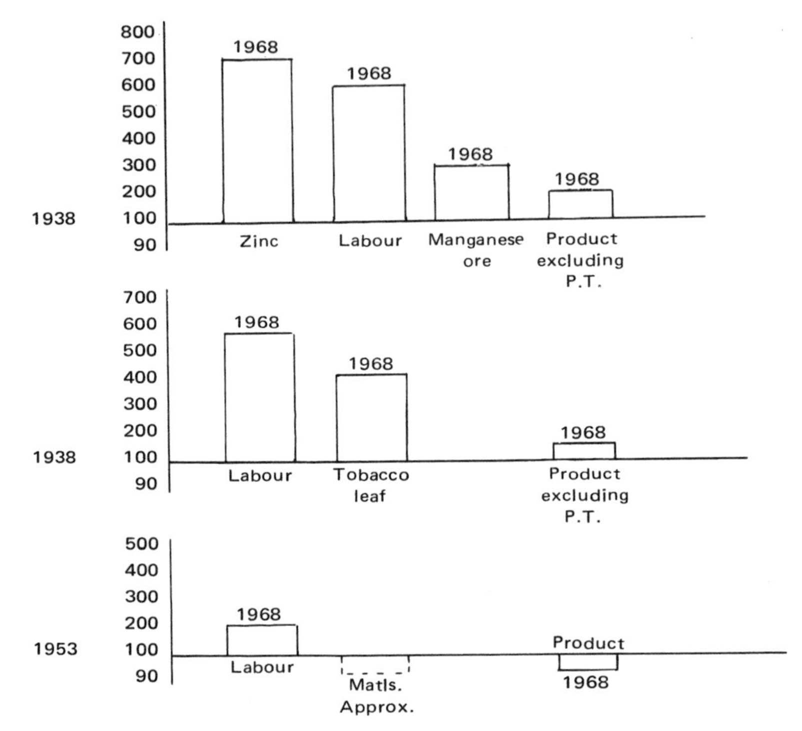

Fig. 1. Cost comparisons. Top – Ever-ready U2 single-cell battery, price 4d in 1938, 8d in 1968. Centre – ten Woodbines, manufacturer's price 4½d in 1938, 7d in 1968: not accounted for are the greater cost of financing increased tobacco duty and the trends in the prices of paper and board for rolling and packaging. Bottom – Osram/G.E.C. tungsten-filament domestic lamps. Figures go back to 1953 only. Reduction of materials costs really due to reduced costs of material processing when lampmakers took it over.

mation. The industries are now paying up to seven times as much for material as they were thirty years ago, and the hourly wage rate is about six times what it was, and yet there is hardly one of the industries that during these thirty years has more than doubled its total manufacturing cost! *Increased efficiency* has absorbed the material and wage increases, and has also absorbed the high capital investment that created it.

In each of the industries product assembly accounts for somewhere between 60 and 80% of the manufacturing effort. So the increased costs have been offset mainly by *assembly automation.*

Now it is known that the large quantities of fairly stable designs of product in these specialist industries lend themselves to the high degree of technical know-how and high capital investment that make assembly automation possible. The important thing, however, is not the apparent dissimilarity between their operations and those in the metalworking industries, but the spirit in which their projects were tackled.

3.0 TECHNICAL DIFFICULTIES

In metalworking industries the need to assemble such a variety of discrete parts in relatively low-volume products makes the creation of the right environment for automated assembling and the provision of the equipment more difficult both technically and financially. It *does* raise a higher order of problems of organisation and control of the total manufacturing process. But the metalworking industries are not unaccustomed to the additional burden of a greater engineering challenge. Success in breaking new ground in areas *outside* the assembly shop is due to the fact that they have always produced the men to deal with the situation. The author believes that the men who can blaze the way across this last frontier exist now both in our colleges and in industry.

4.0 THE CASE FOR METALWORKING

Despite the greater variety of technical difficulties, there is no denying the striking parallel in the economic situation between high-production industries and the medium- to large-batch metalworking industries where about *60%* of the manufacturing effort is on the assembly function.

Ministry of Labour statistics are difficult to trace back thirty years, but some digging and allowance for changes in engineering categories show that the rise in hourly rates for workers in the metalworking industries over the last thirty years has been about sixfold and it is rising latterly at an increasing rate (Fig. 2). The prices of materials used in the engineering industries

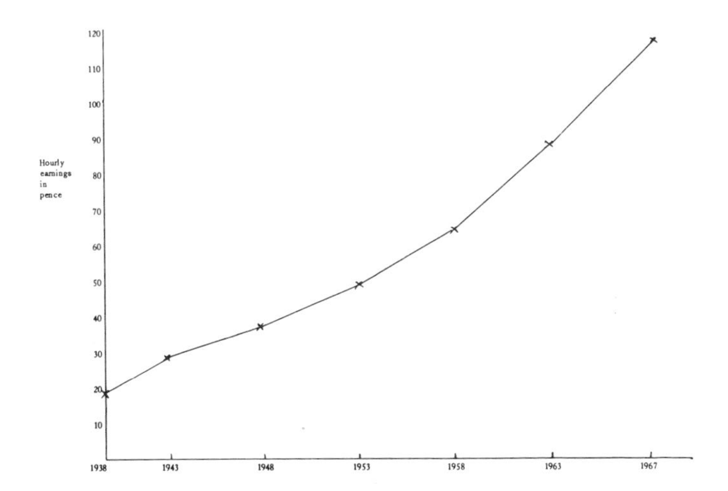

Fig. 2. Hourly earnings on average for workers in metal, electrical, engineering and shipbuilding industries. Inaccuracies of a few pence are possible because in 1953 electrical industries took the place of metal processing industries in official statistics.

are available only for the years between 1954 and 1965, and the price rise in these eleven years for the metals in major use – steel, aluminium and brass – has been between 25 and 35%. Significantly, the price of plastic materials is dropping (Fig. 3). These materials can play the vital role in the consideration of product design for automated assembling.

If these trends continue during the next thirty years, and there is no reason to suspect that they will not, then they suggest a very strong economic compulsion on Britain's metalworking industries to start now on the task of absorbing the price changes and remain competitive in world markets (Fig. 4) by attacking the one remaining area for large-scale cost reduction. Unfortunately, however, one does not absorb this sort of cost by flirting with automated assembling. And one cannot assess its value from such isolated attempts as the author's.

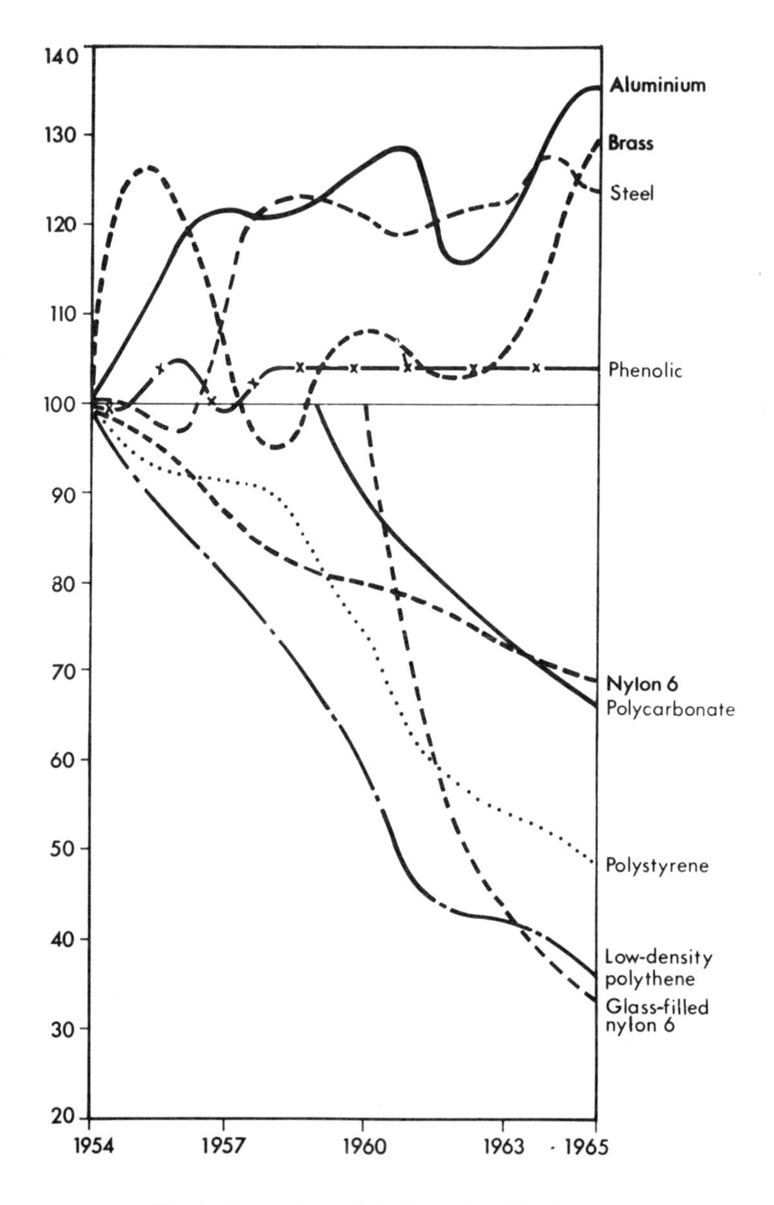

Fig. 3. Comparison of plastics and metal prices.

5.0 THE MANAGING DIRECTOR'S RESPONSIBILITY

It is doubtful if any other manufacturing philosophy cuts so completely across the design, pre-production and selling activities of a manufacturing organisation as does automated assembling. Departmental self-interest will therefore be the greatest source of obstacles which, by discouraging initial attempts to establish a satisfactory environment, will threaten the achievement of total productive economy.

Its successful implementation in industry, more than any other technique, needs the

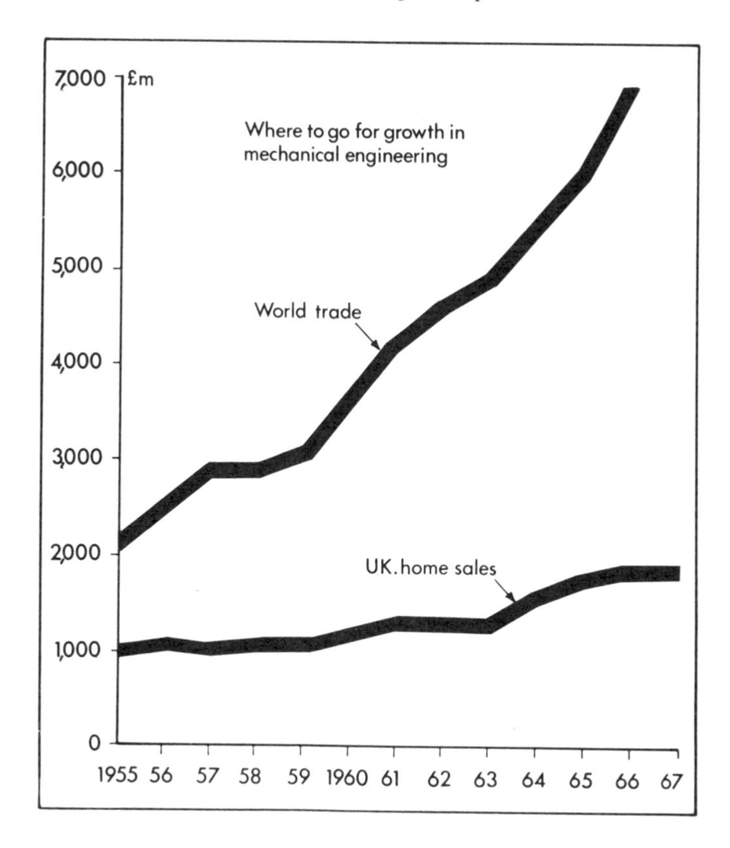

Fig. 4. Comparison of world trade with U.K. home sales.

enthusiastic support – no, more: the sustained personal interest of the one man who can override the interests of each little empire – to ensure that all departments cooperate in the venture. That man is the managing director.

All the production engineers the author has spoken to in those companies which have blazed the trail in automated assembling attribute their progress to top-level support. But the author also knows a good many production engineers who feel that progress in their companies, in terms of total penetration into the manufacturing operation, over a period of ten to fifteen years, is inadequate. Progress has lost impetus when the company has started trying to equate the long-term value of automated assembling to the not always favourable micro-economic value of the initial projects. And these are two economic values which cannot always be equated, for the following reason.

The installing of one or two assembly machines generally is tantamount to introducing an oddity into the manufacturing process. Those few machines raise unusual considerations in the marketing department, in the design office, in the pre-production department and in the machine shop. As such they are unable to inspire that total commitment which is the wellspring of real economies through automated assembling.

The emphasis shifts completely in favour of the machine only when it becomes the normal method of assembly in an environment conditioned by its requirements.

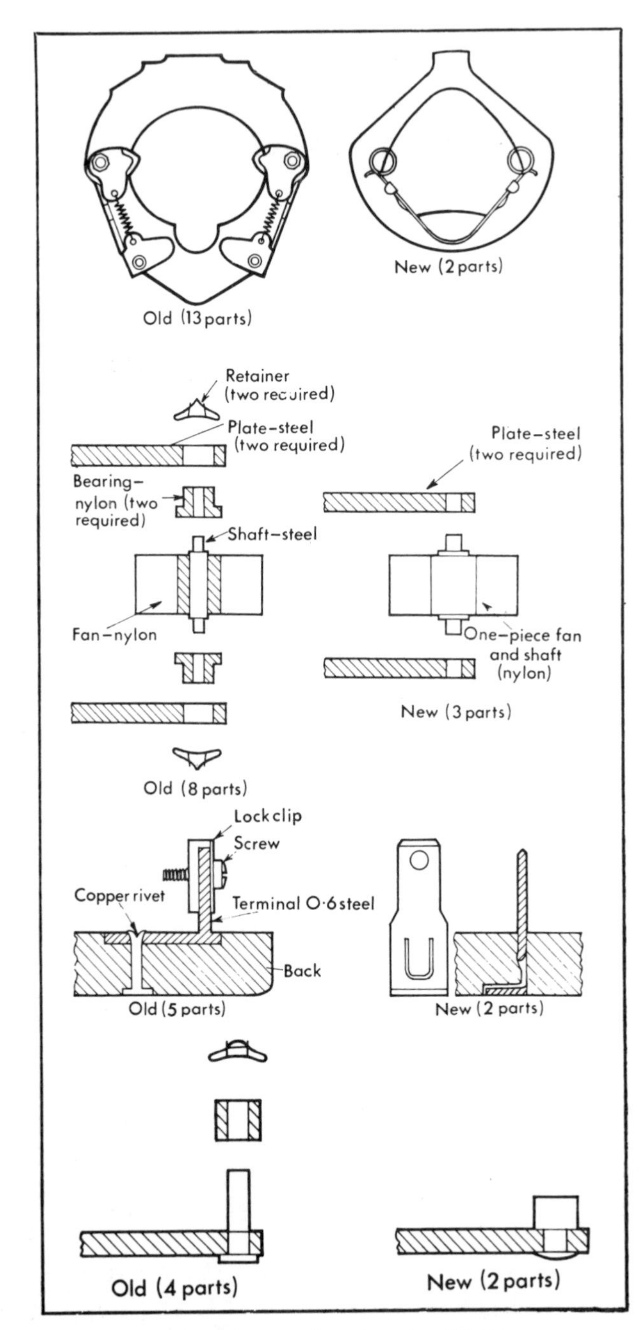

Fig. 5. Examples of product simplification.

The product design and parts-manufacturing question is at the core of the problem: how to create the right environment for automatic assembly? That question will be considered in the next section.

6.0 ONE BEST DESIGN

The more product design schemes for medium- to large-batch production items the author observes in the process of visiting metalworking companies, the more he is convinced that there exists but one best design of a product in terms of its ability to meet functional requirements at lowest cost, and that there is close correlation between that design and the design that is most easily assembled! (See Fig. 5.)

Consider again the balance of labour costs in a product, i.e. parts manufacture 40%, assembly 60%. Depending on the product these proportions vary, but there can be no doubt that in the majority of products the cost of assembly is disproportionately high.

The next major breakthrough in manufacturing costs will come through reducing the cost of the assembly process and it will come to those who *completely transfer the accent* from the way in which piece parts are manufactured to the way in which they are assembled (Fig. 6).

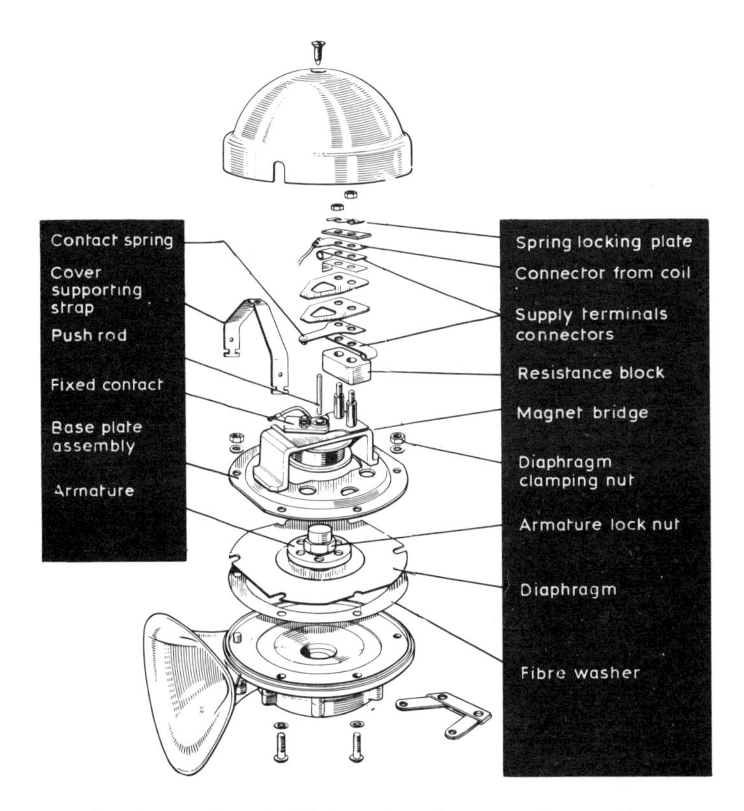

Fig. 6. Redesign of a Windtone horn for automatic assembly.

7.0 PART MANUFACTURE HIGHLY DEVELOPED

It must be emphasised that the high-production non-metalworking industries are not alone in having absorbed rising costs. Over the past thirty years the metalworking industries have also borne the brunt of increases in material and labour costs. But, where these increases have been offset by improved manufacturing efficiency, it has been almost totally in the manufacture of piece parts.

The result is that technological developments in piece-part manufacturing techniques have reached the stage where transfer of accent to the assembly operation is opportune. The materials, the forming techniques and the quality control procedures creating the right environment for automated assembling of parts exist now.

By and large, parts can be produced without need for any real development work on the materials, on the processes themselves or on the control of their quality. It is largely a matter of realising the availability and evaluating the relative merits of this wealth of materials and processes to evolve an acceptable product which can be easily put together.

There will be optional courses, and maybe some slight cost increase will be incurred in part manufacture by following the predominant aim of making assembly easy. Such an increase will be dwarfed by the total savings. However, companies which have torn a product apart and rebuilt it for simple assembly have often found that piece-part manufacturing costs have dropped.

8.0 TOWARDS SIMPLE MECHANISMS

If the author were asked to look at the design of a product and seek lowest-cost manufacture he would take the assembling stage for his main consideration, whether or not automated assembling was to be contemplated.

This determined attack on design and manufacturing considerations with the *predominant* aim of making assembly easy and reliable also has the merit of paving the way for automated assembling by allowing assembly by relatively simple mechanisms, thus putting the metal-working industries on the road to some of the economic benefits now being achieved among the *mass*-production industries.

9.0 MACHINES

Now to the assembly machines themselves. Today the development of what could be a viable assembly-machine industry is being seen in this country. And almost all the participants in this development are pinning their hopes on a range of standard pieces of equipment which can be put together to make an assembly machine in which special engineering is limited to those machine features and that tooling which make contact with or control the behaviour of the components and assemblies (Fig. 7).

One reason for this line of development is that a standard piece of equipment can be manufactured at a lower, more predicatable cost than an equivalent special-purpose item. The cost of the machine should therefore be lower and more predictable, providing a better basis for the customer's consideration of capital expenditure. But there will still be special engineering because of the variation in customers' products, and this will dictate that the assembly machine must always to a great extent remain a 'customised' piece of equipment.

Another reason for suppliers to develop standard pieces of equipment is that, as more and more users become proficient at tooling their own machine modules, these standard pieces could provide a bread-and-butter off-the-shelf selling line whose predictable and relatively high profit margin would help to offset the less predictable profit on a fully engineered machine.

The failure of at least two large machine-tool manufacturers to advance from their initial move into assembly-machine building is probably due to the fact that they have found it to be a more troublesome, far less rewarding field of activity than they have been conditioned to expect from their machine-tool-building activities.

Fig. 7. Bodalex standard indexing table.

In the past it has been even less rewarding, as shown by the number of assembly-machine builders who bore the brunt of the unpredictable excess engineering costs (which were the inevitable accompaniment of earlier attempts at automatic assembly) and died by the wayside. However, as an investment in the future, assembly-machine building is a sound proposition, as is shown by the existence of a fairly prosperous industry in the U.S.A.

In recent years there have been visits to the U.S.A. by representatives of companies with a developing interest in assembly-machine building. The opinions of all these people are extremely useful as guidelines for the development of an assembly-machine industry in Britain. They have discovered what expertise, what attitudes and what equipment went into the making of a successful assembly-machine industry. A great deal of experience does lie on the other side of the Atlantic, where there are 56 companies connected with assembly-machine building.

In the U.S.A. it is generally reported that the smaller companies are the real experts. Some of these companies operate by producing a limited field of standard equipment, such as a chassis or feeder system, and applying what has been described as a highly personalised approach to its application and customer liaison.

Some of the companies which have sponsored visits are introducing American equipment into this country, either by importing or manufacturing under licence, to supplement their own ranges of equipment (Fig. 8).

One of the most valuable sources of information on current practice in designing assembly machines in user industries and on a range of proprietary equipment available is now in the process of compilation. This is the set of data memoranda being compiled by the Institution of Production Engineers and financed by the Ministry of Technology.

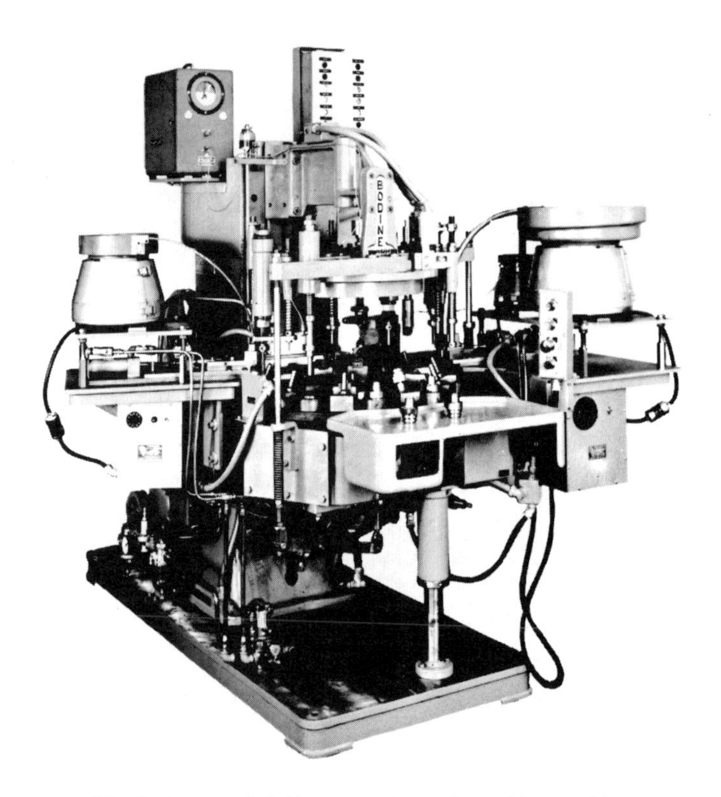

Fig. 8. Automatic ball-race gauging and matching machine.

The availability of these data memoranda should provide an impetus for accelerating the development and use of assembly machines. The author considers it important to remember that most of the assembly equipment developed to date is based on the Detroit concept of automation, i.e. it employs relatively inflexible mechanisms

10.0 NEW THINKING NEEDED

The field of application for automated assembling, particularly in medium-batch production industries, can be extended by developing equipment with the flexibility to adapt to different assemblies (Fig. 9). This opportunity for a vaster market than hitherto suspected lies in the grasp of the machine developer who is not content to follow accepted concepts of assembly-machine design. New concepts of control including computer participation (Fig. 10) are also likely to play an important part. The author thinks it is time for a new wave of thinking to sweep through the assembly-machine departments in this country.

People who have been concerned with assembly-machine development have worked on the assumption that the machine is inferior to the human assembler it is about to replace. They have prejudged the issue. They have limited development by designing from the premise that, without inordinate ingenuity and cost, the machine cannot be made to have the dexterity of the human hand or the ability to sense sub-quality in components and reject accordingly. *And* to some extent they are right – of course it cannot. But this is a very negative attitude.

Fig. 9. Flexible storing machine between fixed indexing machines.

What is now needed is a consideration of the *superiority* of the machine over the human assembler, leading to product design which will take advantage of the superior features.

A machine can *apply greater force* for press fits, riveting, swaging and upsetting. It can *handle dangerous parts or processes.* It can perform multiple operations. For any one manual assembly operation only one pair of hands can be applied: a machine can apply many – all left hands if need be. How, for instance, would one design an operation or product if all human beings had six hands? It would be very different from today's products. A machine *has no preferred orientation.* It may be a mistake to design a machine in which gravity is used to feed parts, as it usually is. It may be better to take advantage of a machine's ability to work in any orientation, instead of just standing upright as a man does. A machine can work at speeds set

Fig. 10. Computer-controlled assembly line.

only by mechanical limits – faster than a human operator. Gravity feed of components has limited the speeds to which present-day machines have been developed. A machine has a short reaction time and it can work very near to the part-manufacturing process, thus eliminating the need to put parts in bins, store them, and then put them through the whole process of unscrambling and re-orientating for assembly.

The author is sure that the future development of the assembly machine must begin with study of these *superior* characteristics of the machine and design of products accordingly.

ACKNOWLEDGEMENT

This paper is adapted from a survey paper presented at the Second Discussion held on Automated Assembling by the Institution of Production Engineers, 10–11 September 1968.

MECHANISATION OF MANUAL OPERATIONS IN INDUSTRIAL ASSEMBLY

E. Cappuccio
Ing. C. Olivetti & C.S.p.A., Ivrea

1.0 CLASSIFICATION OF AUTOMATIC ASSEMBLY MACHINES

Automatic assembly machines are systems composed of elements which can be classified as follows:

- Feeding, orientating mechanisms and escapements.
- Systems for transfer of an assembly, or of a fixture on which components have to be positioned, to successive stations (basic machine).
- Mechanism for picking up and positioning components.
- Inspection devices.
- Operating units.

Each element calls for examination and presents specific problems. As very deep examination is impossible in this paper, only the general principles and considerations which seem to the author to be relevant are discussed.

1.1 *Feeding, orientating mechanisms and escapements*

For a clear classification and accurate description of the elements one can consult *Production Engineering Data Memoranda,* published by the Institution of Production Engineers, London. This is a very important publication which is intended to cover the full area of automatic assembly. When it is finished it will supply a really complete panorama of the entire field. So far the first five volumes have been issued. The first one deals with hopper-feeders of different kinds, with reference to the difficulties presented by the different shapes of the components to be fed, and indicates the best ways for overcoming these difficulties. The other four volumes cover the vast field of orientating mechanisms, both inside and outside the bowl, and escapements.

The problem of regular feeding of parts is not exclusive to assembly machines. It is encountered whenever one wants to replace a manual operator with a mechanical device. To start with loose components, and then to orientate and to isolate them for input to a machine, presents many difficulties. It can be convenient to overcome the problem in a different way.

A first method is direct linkage between a machine which produces a component and another machine which assembles a group of components. In this way parts never become loose. A typical example of the principle is a spring-forming machine linked to a machine which fits that spring to a group of components. Another case is a press which feeds to an assembly machine a strip of blank parts which maintains a very thin connection between the machines. The main difficulty is in the fact that the follow-up link forces the first machine (the spring-forming machine and the press in the examples) to go at the same speed as that of the assembly machine, which usually is slower, with consequent loss of productivity.

A second method is to obtain the components from a normal machine tool, gathered in a magazine, and to keep their order for the loading of the succeeding operation. This system is quite usual at Olivetti, particularly for the gathering of flat parts from sheet steel under the blanking presses (Fig. 1), according to the procedure normal for the laminations of small

Fig. 1. Gathering of flat parts from sheet steel.

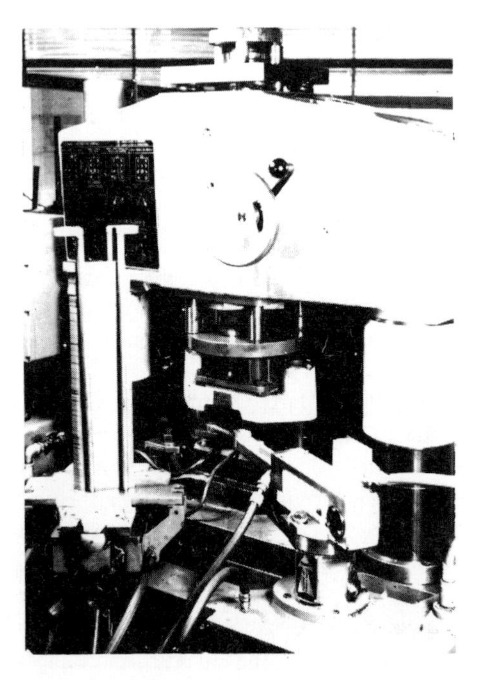

Fig. 2 Magazine of flat parts for feeding press.

electric motors. The column of parts thus formed can be transferred as a magazine to feed a press, tooled up with a mechanical arm, for a second operation. This system goes very well, and has been applied to a considerable number of second-operation presses (Fig. 2). In many cases the column of parts can be automatically recomposed after the operation.

Fig. 3. Magazine of flat parts for feeding an assembly machine.

The column of parts can also be used for feeding an assembly machine (Fig. 3). What often jeopardises this system is the fact that one is forced to break the order of the parts for operations which require loose parts (i.e. heat treatment or plating). Obviously the system of keeping components in ordered columns cannot be used if the parts are far from flat.

Another system has been used at Olivetti's quite successfully in the case of components manufactured on an automatic screw machine. It consists in avoiding a complete cut and leaving a very thin connection between the components along their axes. (Fig. 4). It is possible to obtain in this way sticks of screws which, if of reasonable length, can go through the usual processes of heat treatment and plating while connected. In the case of a stick of screws with hexagonal heads, a pneumatic screwdriver can be fed. In the case of a stick of rivets, an automatic riveting machine can also be fed. The method is limited only by a certain weakness of the stick, which can easily be deformed.

Other methods worth mention are those enjoying extensive development for electronic assembly, like special magazines of peculiar shapes, the gluing of components to special tapes, and so forth. It is not difficult to invent solutions of this kind. The difficulty is entirely in their standardisation because the organisation of production is greatly affected.

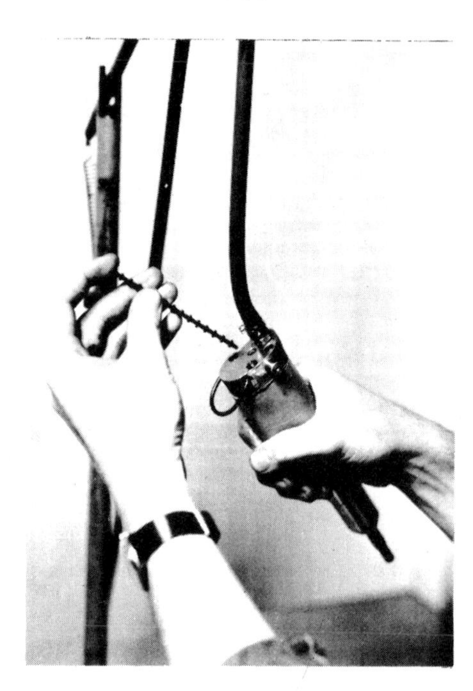

Fig. 4. Feeding 'stick' of screws to pneumatic tool.

1.2 *Basic machine*

The basic machine is a device for binding together the different elements which compose an assembly machine. Usually the basic machine includes a system for the transfer of either assemblies or a fixture which receives the different components to successive stations. For this reason the basic machines can be classified according to the kind of transfer adopted.

1.2.1 *Fixed-position-machines*

These are machines in which transfer is not provided for. The different components arrive automatically from individual feeding devices and position themselves in an immobile fixture.

With a machine of this kind one can assemble only a few different parts. This is because access to a single spot (the fixture) is limited by the dimensions of the different mechanisms. But they can be very useful when a certain assembly is composed of many equal components. For instance, an assembly of pinions on a shaft, fixed with two screw-nuts at the end of the shaft, has few different sorts of component (shaft, pinion and nut) but many actual components (for instance ten pinions of the same shape and two nuts), and a machine can be justified. The fixed-position machine can also have simple movements of the main component or the fixture, in order to facilitate the work. Usually there is a slider with two positions for the unloading of the finished assembly and for easier manual feeding of the components, out of the area where the automatic units operate. With the stated limitations, which are due to overcrowding in a limited area, these machines suit many applications, particularly for semiautomatic work, since their cost can be kept reasonable.

1.2.2 *Indexing rotary tables*

These are assembly machines of wider application. In them the fixture is transferred along a circumference by means of a circular or rigid-ring table, with a number of stops within 360°.

Such machines are by no means exclusively for automatic assembly. On the contrary, they have a very long tradition, and are quite widespread in industry. However, it is worth discussing them with particular reference to the requirements of automatic assembly.

They can be operated with different systems (pneumatic, hydraulic, mechanical), depending on the performance required. Mechanical drive, with mechanical linkage and synchronisation with the different operating units, is the most secure system for the speeds common in automatic assembly (cycles under three seconds). Indexing has to be fast, and table accelerations can alter the positions of components in fixtures when they have not yet been fastened. Thus it is often necessary to control the acceleration of an indexing movement, and this can be done with a variable-pitch screw or a Geneva-cross. These considerations, mentioned here in connection with indexing tables, keep their importance for machines with linear transfer, fixed indexing and high speed, as will be seen later. Also, the utility of rotary tables is limited by the risk of overcrowding, and by restricted accessibility for random manual interventions on the fixtures.

The number of different components which can be assembled on such a machine is quite limited. If many different components are to be assembled, many stations are needed around the machine. The sector for each station thus diminishes. The arc per station can be increased if the diameter of the table is increased, but then the peripheral speed during indexing increases and the accuracy of the position of the fixture is diminished, and this can be dangerous even if one takes for granted the use of floating fixtures and of pins for precise location of the fixture at each station.

It is difficult to give data of a general value, but Olivetti (Ivrea) never go above eight or nine different components to be assembled and above twelve to fourteen stations. The most used standard rotary table for assembly operation at Olivetti is shown in Fig. 5. The maximum

Fig. 5. Olivetti standard rotary table.

diameter of the plate is 1·400 mm. It is a ring table and has a central column which rotates in synchronism with the indexing movement. This column drives the operating unit by means of a system of chains. It is mechanically operated by a variable-pitch screw and the minimum cycle time obtained is 2·5 s.

For very high production rates rotary tables with much higher speeds can be built. They do not stop at all at the stations for the different operations. The problems involved in the design and manufacture of this kind of equipment are outside the author's direct experience.

1.2.3 *Linear transfer and fixed indexing machines*

These are machines which present a sequence of pallets, moved one step at a time through a distance which is equal to, or a multiple of, the distance between the pallets themselves. Movement takes place along a closed circuit which is defined by the structure of the machine. The pallets can be connected by chains, flexible belts, metallic cords, etc.

The most used and secure drive is again mechanical, and the author's earlier comments about the control of acceleration and the advantages of mechanical linkage with operating units in all stations if high speeds are required are still valid.

Linear transfer machines offer the possibility of avoiding overcrowding, and thus allowing the best distribution of stations when there are many different components to be assembled. But they are very expensive because of their general complexity, especially when one needs the mechanical linkage and synchronism with all stations. Therefore, when the cycle time is above 4 – 5 s, it is better to forget the mechanical link and to use electropneumatic connections which can be synchronised with a cyclical distributor, mechanically linked to the indexing machine.

Linear transfer machines may have oval or other shapes. The pallets can go in reverse either under or beside the main channel.

1.2.4 *Power and free lines*

These are machines with linear transfer. The pallets can be driven or left standing by the transferring element (chain, belt or other). The single pallet can be disconnected from the moving element by a fixed stop or another standing pallet.

Some of these machines can be quite complicated, having a friction clutch for connection with the transfer element. Others are very elementary, merely having the pallet supported and moved by frictional contact with a continuously running belt. In the latter case, if a single pallet is stopped its successors stop against it, sliding on the belt. Thus the movement of each pallet is independent, within certain limits, of the movement of the others.

Power and free machines are very useful for the assembly of many different components at not very high cycle speeds. They allow easy introduction of manual stations between automatic stations without imposing a very strict rhythm on the worker. It is unnecessary to have mechanical linkage with the machine, but each automatic station can start on a signal originated by the arrival of the pallet.

An original machine, designed and developed at Olivetti's, which combines the advantages of a power and free line with the low cost of a rotary table, will now be described. The principle has been adopted for many assembly machines. This one (Fig. 6) is an automatic hot-riveting machine in which one jig can be loaded while the other is in operation, even when there is a difference in the cycle time of each operation.

The mechanical group consists of two sectors, each of 120°, made of insulating material. On each sector is mounted a jig on which are positioned manually the pieces to be riveted. The

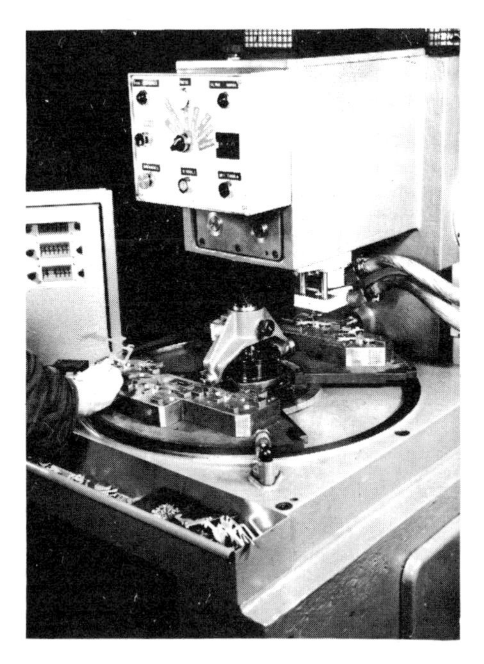

Fig. 6. Automatic hat-riveting machine.

sectors are driven by a central shaft which is in continuous rotation. The connection between the sectors and the shaft is a power and free type. If one of the two sectors is stopped, the other one continues to rotate until it stops against the first one. The sector for each work phase is positioned by insertion of pins into holes on the underside of the sector. This means that each group to be assembled has its own sectors and its own particular arrangement of locating holes. The result is that the sectors can assume many, defined, angular positions. The movement of the sectors is correlated with that of the electrode is by means of microswitches. The electrode moves along a radial line in 'point-to-point' fashion over a range of about 130 mm, and vertically for the actual riveting.

The electrical control cabin is in two parts. The first transmits impulses to control the movement of the electrode, and the second determines the technical characteristics of the riveting process, e.g. heat, duration, etc.

While the operator loads one of the jigs, the other one moves to different positions where the parts are riveted one by one. When the riveting is finished, the sector waits until the operator completes loading and restarts the cycle, using a pedal. When the finished assembly reaches the operator it is automatically expelled before the operator starts loading again.

Coming back to the 'in-line' power and free machine, the author is firmly convinced that it is the one which will have the widest use in mass production. In fact, Olivetti's are making significant efforts in its development. One of the advantages is that it can be built up gradually. If the line is a pure conveyor, it can be installed at the start for manual operations only. Every assembly line for mass production requires a conveyor. Instead of buying a mere conveyor, one can install a power and free machine that is long enough for mechanisation as forecast. The extra cost of this line compared with a manual conveyor is not very large, and its return can be justified by the operator's increased freedom to balance the variation of his rhythm of work.

Later on, station by station, automatic devices can be introduced. They will replace one by one the operations formerly introduced after careful evaluation of the return on each investment. A mechanised line can, for instance, be detached from the programme for the launching of a new product. In this way more time can be allowed for the mechanisation of an assembly line.

1.2.5 *Compound tables*

Compound tables, with numerical control of two axes, are being developed. Their use is more particularly in the electronic industry, for inserting electronic components on printed circuit boards. Automatic assembly in these industries will certainly benefit from the introduction of integrated circuits, of which standardisation is going ahead well, and which are handier than the discrete components previously used.

1.2.6 *Special-purpose assembly machines*

These are assembly machines designed, even to the basic unit, for the solution of a particular problem, and cannot be classified in any way. Their limit comes only from the ingenuity of the engineers and from calculations for their economic justification.

1.3 *Mechanisms for pick-up and positioning of components*

These mechanisms collect components one by one after escapements have isolated them, and which position them either on the fixture of the basic machine or on other components previously loaded. They can have different shapes and various functional principles which are not worth listing. Everybody can have suppliers' catalogues for these orientation devices. Many different models have been used at Olivetti's. Now standardisation is to limit the number of these elements in connection with the different basic machines in greatest use. For each rotary ring table a small rotating head with a vertical movement along its axis is used. This head can be easily driven through a system of chains from the central column of the basic machine (Fig. 7).

Fig. 7. Rotating heads with vertical movements.

A few words about so-called robots are appropriate in the context of pick-up mechanisms. They are big, automatic arms, with numerical control on four or five axes, which can lead a head with fingers to many positions in space. For the kind of assembly done at Olivetti's these robots are too big, but perhaps they are useful for automatic assembly in other industries. Olivetti's plan to use these robots for unloading die-casting machines and big moulding presses, and have bought both models on the British market.

1.4 *Operating units*

These are mechanisms contributing to the fastening of an assembly. They can be automatic screw-drivers, riveting heads, hot-sticking heads, projection welding units, pin drivers, etc. There are many specialised suppliers to whom anybody can refer.

Generally speaking there is less need for unassembled or dismantled groups of parts because the cost of automatic assembly is low. Once the cost of an assembly has been greatly reduced it can be less expensive to replace the assembly than to replace only a single part of it. Hence the spreading use of permanent fastening operations. Among these operations hot sticking and welding are quite expensive compared with simple riveting. Now one can find on the market very good riveting heads which enable many riveting units to work together on an assembly machine without excessive noise.

1.5 *Inspection devices*

Inspection of the functioning of each concurrent operation on an assembly machine is extremely important.

If an operation has not been performed properly, the finished assembly has to be rejected automatically if inefficiency and expenditure on manual quality control are to be avoided. For example, a missed fastening operation can leave loose components in fixtures and components can end up in places where they can be dangerous to the integrity of a machine. Incorrect positioning of a component can equally endanger the integrity of a machine as well as the quality of the finished assembly. On these grounds, and in order to reduce manual work, any assembly machine always includes a more or less complex net of signals. Depending on the kind of inspection required, signalling stations with different kinds of probe can be provided, or signals can be taken at certain points in the path of a single mechanism.

Here, instead of describing specific solutions, we shall discuss inspection in a general way.

In a high-productivity automatic system each automatic operation has to be checked. One has to verify, after each automatic positioning of a component, that it is exactly where it should be. If part loading is manual, automatic inspection is no longer necessary. The operator can be given the responsibility of verifying that previous automatic positionings have been correct, to the degree permitted by the distance between the operator and the previous automatic station.

Automatic unloading of the finished assembly has always to be checked. This is usually done at a station where probes inspect the fixture after the automatic unloading, checking whether the nest of the fixture is really empty. As far as the operating heads are concerned, it is usually enough to take a signal which confirms that the run of the head is complete.

What is the result of all these signals? First of all, during automatic unloading, scrap is selected from the good assemblies. A failure, encountered for instance at station No 3, is signalled to a 'memory' so that the assembly is switched on to the scrap channel when it arrives at the unloading station, which can be station No 12. Unloading mechanisms can also be designed to collect bad assemblies in different channels according to the nature of the defects.

The control system can be designed in such a way that the machine and all stations stop as soon as a fault signal is issued, or so that it can provide for the selection of only the defective assemblies at the unloading station. In the latter case it is usually established that the machine has to be stopped after so many defective assemblies have been encountered. This system is most advisable when a machine is well run in, well after the debugging period. During the initial debugging stage, on the other hand, it is advisable to stop the machine each time a fault occurs.

2.0 THE PRESENT STATE OF AUTOMATIC ASSEMBLY

The author considers it very useful for anyone who has to face the problems of automatic assembly to know the state of the art throughout the world. In the last four or five years almost continual contact has been maintained between many people who work in this field, especially in the United States, and the results of up-to-date experience can be provided.

A complete panorama of all the firms with significant successes cannot be given here, only a concise list of the firms which have most impressed the author by the amplitude of their efforts and the wide use of automatic assembly in their factories. The list will certainly be useful to people who want to organise a tour for first exposure to the problems, taking advantage of the courtesy which these firms always extend to visitors.

It is almost impossible to describe in detail what these firms have made, and therefore only very brief notes are given. Reference to British firms will be avoided, first because they can be very easily contacted by anyone in British industry, and secondly because some firm may be forgotten. The examination is almost entirely devoted to the American scene and to the section of industry of personal interest to the author, i.e. metalworking, to the exclusion of other sections like packaging, lampmaking and many others which have a very long tradition and experience in automatic production.

2.1 *American manufacturers of assembly equipment*

These are quite numerous and are of various sizes, and they are dedicated to different aspects of automatic assembly. Some of them manufacture and sell only operating units, others feeding devices, others design, debug and sell entire systems, even of high complexity. A very interesting and complete survey is the one in the magazine *Automation*, April 1966, where 56 firms are listed which operate in the U.S.A.

It is important to consider also the equipment developed by users themselves. This examination, however, is limited to manufacturers for the market and to those who produce complete assembly systems. The firms mentioned are ones with which the author has had contact.

2.1.1 *Gilman Engineering and Manufacturing Co. Inc. Janesville, Wisconsin*

Perhaps Gilman's is the biggest firm. It sells entire assembly systems, using both rotary tables and linear transfer machines. It has experience over more than twenty years and claims that more than 400 of its systems are installed in sixty different big clients' premises.

The main basic machine produced by Gilman is an 'in-line' transfer machine with the 'go and return' rows parallel and very near to each other (Fig. 8). The central idea of the machine is free access to one of the fronts of the machine for manual loading or other manual operations and to have all automatic stations at the back of the return row, out of the way of the operator's hands but easily accessible from the front in the case of a jam. This machine is of modular construction and many different lengths can be obtained. The connection between the indexing mechanism, the automatic loading stations and the operating units is a direct and mechanical

Fig. 8. Gilman 'in-line' transfer machine.

one, by means of a camshaft which runs all along the machine. The machine is very good for automatically assembling groups, even of many different components, with high productivity. The number of manual operations must be limited, so it is a system with a high degree of mechanisation.

For systems based on rotary tables Gilman's use a dial machine with a very original indexing mechanism of their own design.

2.1.2 *Benerson Corporation, Evansville, Indiana*

Benerson's also has long experience and many systems installed in many factories.

Its most widely used basic machine is an oval transfer of a modular construction. The pallets are connected by chain. This machine is intended for electropneumatic connection of the various stations, rather than mechanical. Consequently it has a cyclical distributor connected to the indexing mechanism and built into the chassis. The machine is very good for groups of many different components, has a high degree of mechanisation, but operates in cycles of more than 3–4 s.

2.3.1 *Bodine Corporation, Bridgeport, Connecticut*

Bodine Corporation is a firm of very old tradition in the field of rotary tables for different metalworking operations.

With particular reference to the requirements of automatic assembly it has developed new rotary tables, and of a linear transfer machine design quite different from that of others on the market. The transport element is a steel belt which goes round two big pulleys with vertical axes (Fig. 9). The belt section has its bigger side vertical. The belt carries pallets projecting to give free access to them both from above and below. The machine, again of modular construction, has ground plates for the fixing of the different stations, and two shafts which run all

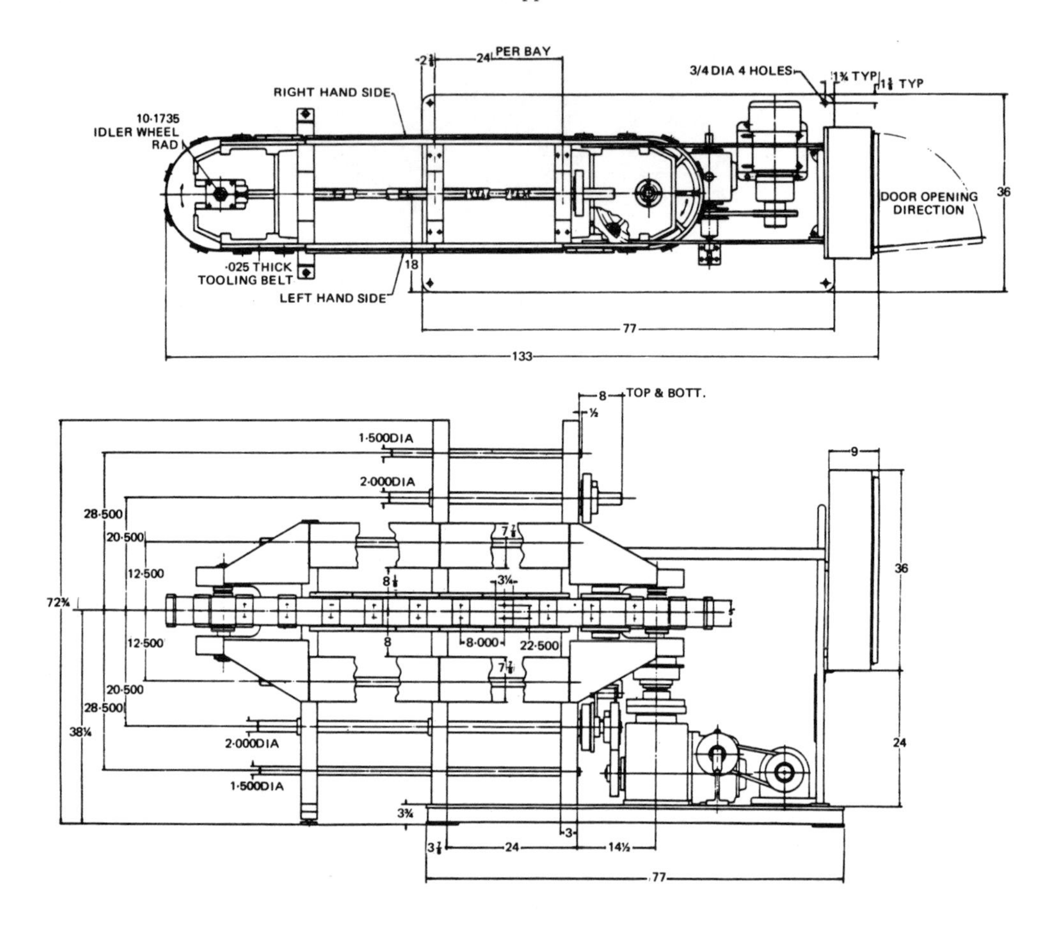

Fig. 9. Bodine Basic linear transport machine.

along the machine and which can drive, through cams, the various loading and operating stations, either above or below the pallets.

The machine is very useful for high productivity and has a high level of mechanisation.

2.1.4 *Swanson, Erie, Pa*

Before entering the field of automatic assembly for the metalworking industry, Swanson's gained long experience of a similar nature in the lampmaking industry.

The firm manufactures automatic systems of many kinds but is mostly specialised in rotary tables. It manufactures a large variety of these tables, which are quite popular on the American market. Some of them have a few coaxial rotary turrets.

One of the most famous machines manufactured by this firm is the one for the automatic assembly of Gillette razors.

2.1.5 *Dixon Automatic Tool, inc., Rockford, Illinois*

Dixon Automatic is very well known for its operating units and for its loading and positioning units. Its automatic screw-drivers, with automatic feeding of the screws, are used by many of the firms, which develop their own systems.

Dixon's also manufacture and sell assembly systems, usually fixed-position machines for the solution of special problems. Very good standardisation and care are shown in their modular electric and electronic controls.

2.2 *Metalworking Industries of Substantial Achievement*

The following list, like the previous one, gives a sort of ideal itinerary for anybody who intends to become familiar with the achievements in this field. The dominant sector is the automotive industry, or rather producers auxiliary to the car industry, where the volume of production justifies the investment required for intensive automation of assembly.

2.2.1 *Delco-Remy, Anderson, Indianapolis*

Delco-Remy is a division of General Motors that produces accessories for the car industry: starting motors, windscreen-wiper motors, alternators, horns, etc. There are 16 000 employees in nine plants, all in the area of Anderson. The output comprises a few hundred different products at very high volume. This is, to the best of the author's knowledge, the most automated metal working factory in the world. More than 200 linear transfer lines for automatic assembly are installed there, and dial machines number over a thousand.

The organisation has a mixed procurement policy, either making or purchasing equipment. Many assembly systems are bought from the market, others are designed and developed within the firm itself, sometimes using units or components from the market. The organisation has various kinds of machine, but the main orientation is towards linear transfer machines with fixed indexing, which is justified by the high degree of automation and by the volume of the production required. Many machines have been bought by Benerson's or tooled up on a Benerson chassis, and there are also a few very big Cargill power and free lines. Quite often the components of an assembly are adjusted automatically, as in the dynamic balancing of rotors and for the calibration of horn sound.

2.2.2 *Ford Saline, Saline, Michigan*

This is a Ford division that produces accessories for cars, principally dashboards and instrumentation. The most interesting system is the transfer line for automatically assembling speedometers. It has an irregular 'in-out' run because the rails can be adapted to any shape. Each of the pallets is driven by its own electric motor through a friction roller. The power supply is obtained by two brush contacts which run on two low-voltage rails. This line has been designed and developed by the firm itself.

2.2.3 *A. C. Spark Co., Flint, Michigan*

This is division of General Motors produces spark-plugs, fuel pumps, filters and other similar accessories. Spark-plugs are the main product, which is obviously made in very high quantity, and is run continuously both in the workshop and in the assembly shop, where many automatic lines are installed. Final assembly of the spark-plug is completely automatic. Also oil-filter production is highly automatic, but in this case the dimensions of the components and the very high volume of production were reasons for adopting very special solutions, which cannot be extended to other problems in different industries.

2.2.4 *Rochester Products, Rochester, New York*

Another division of General Motors, Rochester Products principally manufactures carburettors of different models – simple, double and quadruple – and also locks for car doors. The main lines for assembling carburettors are power and free lines made by Cargill. The loading and the positioning of big parts is usually by hand, while small ones are automatically fed, as are the parts for fastening operations. The final inspection and testing of the carburettors are very impressive—the operations are completely automatic.

Locks are automatically assembled on automatic machines with rotary tables, while the small covers for the locks are assembled on a fully automatic Gilman transferline.

2.2.5 *Eastman Kodak, Rochester, New York*

The Eastman-Kodak factory is one of the many which Kodak has in the area of Rochester. It produces the lowest-price camera on the company's catalogues, the camera manufactured in the greatest volume. The development of automatic assembly is not yet very high but is evidently increasing rapidly, following principles which are very original and interesting, and with the support of a very good team of full-time engineers. A few machines for assembling small groups have been installed. They have a standard line, home-designed and developed, which is a monorail on which motorised pallets run.

The firm has developed a very good unit for the picking-up and positioning of components. It is very versatile and the run can be easily varied. It is driven by a Slo-syn motor controlled by punched tape. When visiting Kodak's one realises that, for a firm which works on components smaller than those typical of the automative industry, it is not worth while to purchase automatic assembly equipment on a market which is standardised for bigger components.

2.2.6 *Westclox, La Salle, Illinois*

This firm also, like Kodak, found it inconvenient to rely very much on the market for automatic equipment, because its products, which are medium-sized clocks, have small parts. Its policy of self-sufficiency is practicable also because it has had very long experience in automatic assembling. It started many years ago, when commercially available automatic assembly equipment was not as good as it is now.

The most interesting basic machine developed by the firm is a power and free line with pallets standing on a couple of rubber belts, which run continually and drive the pallets. This is an extremely simple solution at a reasonable cost, and, if the author is not mistaken, Westclox was the first firm to adopt it. Now it is in use, with small changes, in many other firms, e.g. Bosch, Renault and Olivetti. With these power and free lines Westclox has taken the assembly of its products to a high degree of mechanisation.

Westclox achievement can easily be seen by anybody in the Glasgow area.

2.2.7 *Hoover Co., Northcanton, Ohio*

Hoover's have many automatic manufacturing operations, e.g. in the production of brushes, flexible tubes, etc. As far as automatic assembly is concerned, they have a few power and free lines made by Cargill, with automatic stations and manual operators mixed, for the final assembly of vacuum cleaners. They assemble different models of vacuum cleaner on the same line. The operators, who work standing, move from one station to another in such a way as naturally to balance their work load. These assembly lines also include semi-automatic final testing of the product.

2.2.8 *Bosch, Stuttgart, West Germany*

This firm has been engaged in the problems of automatic assembly for many years. It does not at all rely on commercial automatic assembly equipment but has developed a strong team of engineers specialised in the art.

Now Bosch is actually selling automatic equipment and modular elements for automatic assembly. The basic machine is the power and free line with pallets moved by a flat plastic belt.

The most impressive achievement is a very long and sophisticated line for assembling car alternators. This line is almost completely automatic, producing about 100 000 groups per month, in two shifts. Car lights are also assembled on lines of this kind, but at a lower degree of mechanisation.

3.0 SLOW ADOPTION OF AUTOMATIC ASSEMBLY

It is almost generally accepted that the present development of automatic assembly techniques is not satisfactory, even though there are places where, as has been described, very much benefit has been obtained. Many people are studying the reasons why a better average result has not been obtained. The author would like to contribute with an examination of the difficulties which one has to face when trying to introduce automatic assembly.

3.1 *Efficiency of an automatic assembly system*

Many are the complaints of users because machines are not very reliable. They claim that the overall efficiency of this equipment is low compared with values estimated beforehand. This is only partly true, since one can at least accept that this equipment calls for frequent skilled assistance. The efficiency of an assembly system, which is always a complex piece of equipment, is certainly well below 100%, but this has to be taken into account from the beginning.

The economic viability of a system is not at all jeopardised by low efficiency, if it has been considered while evaluating the economics of its introduction. The problem is to get a correct forecast of the final efficiency of the machine. A machine can be a good investment even if its efficiency is 50%, while another machine can be a bad investment even if its efficiency is 99%.

The efficiency that one can expect for an automatic system depends upon various factors. The first is the degree of mechanisation, which is the ratio of the total time of automatic operations and the total time of manual operations. The variation of efficiency with this factor is complex and cannot be expressed in a general formula for all groups to be assembled. If an operator is present for a manual operation on an automatic assembly system, this guarantees corrective intervention when simple faults occur on an automatic station within easy reach. The possibility of such intervention diminishes when the number of automatic stations to be assisted is increased. A completely automatic system could have zero efficiency if, the first time it stopped, nobody went to correct the faults. Obviously this is not a realistic case because at least a small fraction of a man is always available for assistance.

The second factor which influences the efficiency of the machine is the total number of automatic stations. The faults of one station seriously affect the functioning of the others, very much in the fixed indexing machines, a bit less in the power and free ones. In fact, the total efficiency of a system is equal to the product of the efficiencies of the single stations. That is why, particularly with the fixed indexing systems, one should not exaggerate by introducing too many automatic stations.

The third factor to be considered is the efficiency of single stations. The efficiency of a station is exceedingly variable, depending on the characteristics of the station and of the operations performed. For an operating station (for instance, riveting, projection welding etc.) efficiency can be easily forecast and can reach very high values. On the other hand, for stations at which parts are automatically positioned the forecast is much more difficult, and efficiency is generally lower. In this case the engineer has to rely on his whole past experience of such cases.

If one has to assemble components of particular difficulty it is always best to build an experimental station before starting design of the complete system, in order to be sure that the unknown efficiency of one station does not jeopardise the entire system.

3.2 *Quality of components*

Many people claim that the low quality of components is a big obstacle to the spread of mechanised assembly operations. This complaint comes from users of these machines, but also, and with greater strength, from their designers and manufacturers. It is true in the sense that good performance can be expected of an assembly machine only if the components are higher in quality than would be required if they were to be manually assembled.

This does not mean that closer tolerances must be imposed on the drawings of the components (the author has found very few cases where this was necessary), but rather demands of workshops more strict respect for the tolerances already on the drawings. A difficulty is that an assembly machine requires closer tolerances on components than are necessary for good functioning of the product.

In the author's opinion the point is that, when a certain characteristic or a certain dimension of a component is slightly out of tolerance an assembly machine will stop, while a manual operator may still be able to fit the component. In such a case nobody can evaluate the manual operator's loss of efficiency, which means loss of money for the firm.

It has still to be underlined that improvement in components, required in the sense described above, always results in improvement of finished products.

3.3 *Product design*

The complaint that product design does not facilitate assembly, which usually comes from the designer of automatic assembly systems, seems quite unreasonable. Whatever the aspect of production, the designer of the product is always blamed.

If it is a packaging problem the product designer has to contrive an easy way of packaging. If it is a service problem the product designer has to provide for easy serviceability. And if automatic assembly is being considered, the product designer has to make that easy too. But it should not be forgotten that the first objective of the product designer is the functioning of the product and its performances.

It is obvious that a good project engineer will design products bearing in mind the manufacturing techniques that are available. He knows how to design a component for manufacture on a lathe or on a milling machine because the workshop is full of lathes and milling machines. Let the assembly shops become full of automatic assembly machines and the project designer will design with the requirements of automatic assembly in mind from the start. Until this happens automatic machine designers must patiently ask product designers for small modifications which can help their work.

3.4 *Quality of labour*

This difficulty can be great. The assembly machine calls for technical knowledge which can tax the usual assembly technician.

The efficiency of the machines is substantially influenced by prompt and skilled attention to faults. This problem can be solved either by creating a new skill for the workers who operate the machine so that they may be able immediately to correct at least the most usual failures of the machine, or with the assistance of skilled maintenance workers on the spot. The training problems involved are not negligible and should be solved by means of an integrated scheme.

3.5 *Justification of investment*

The investments required for an automatic assembly programme can be very high. It is understandable that they perplex the people who are responsible for their authorisation.

As in any other such activity, it is necessary at the start of development to reserve a certain amount of money just for acquiring experience. A certain amount of money should also be annually set apart for research and development, but this will be easier if a certain number of good results is achieved in the meantime.

Apart from these 'start-up' investments and successive research investments, it is good practice to have all investments approved through very precise examination of their economic justification. The standard procedure for these calculations, as they are carried out at Olivetti's, is described in the fifth part of this paper.

Obviously mass production is the first condition for massive mechanisation of assembly. Olivetti's find that, in order to justify assembly systems with a high degree of mechanisation, taking into account the hourly cost of direct labour, the company has to consider only assemblies of above a thousand groups per hour. Since the maximum volume of production at Ivrea is about 300 machines per hour, fully automatic systems have been introduced only for groups which are assembled more than once on a single product. If a typewriter requires ten equal groups, the hourly consumption of that group will be thousand per hour if that typewriter is produced at a volume of a hundred per hour.

For lower hourly consumptions (below 500 groups per hour) semi-automatic procedures have been studied. Here the manual operator takes care of the more complicated operations, leaving the easier ones to an automatic device.

This recalls an important consideration. In a sequence of manual elementary operations one has always to try and mechanise those keeping the automatic station in operation for the longest times. They have the best chance of being economically justified. The volume of production may not justify a fully automatic station, with automatic feeding of screws if an operation involves fixing a screw. If the screw is manually fed to an automatic screw-driving unit, quite probably the equipment will be justified economically. The most tiring operations, and the slowest ones, are the ones to be mechanised. Those which require complex movements have to be mechanised more than others with simple movements. Obviously in the first case the automatic station will be more expensive and less reliable. Success in a project depends on the balancing of these different factors.

When volumes of production are still lower, the best way is merely to decide on a set of fixtures, more or less sophisticated, to facilitate assembly according to well-known techniques.

3.6 *Flexibility*

The greatest risk in a large investment on an automatic assembly line is that one may be mistaken in forecasting the product's life. In fact, the life of an assembly machine is more or less equal to the life of the product for which it has been built, even if a certain residual asset is considered.

Many initiatives are being taken in an endeavour to obtain standard machines or standard parts of them. The intention is to have systems which can be easily converted for the assembly of a second group when the life of the first one is finished. The poor flexibility of an automatic assembly line does not present itself only in relation to the life of the product to be assembled. It can happen that the product is to be modified in some of its parts. This also can result in substantial modifications to the assembly machine and in a big loss of money previously invested. When one evaluates the opportunity for an investment, it is necessary to forecast the volume of production in the following four or five years. If during one of these years, the actual volume of production is less than what has been forecast, the investment can become a bad one.

As a consequence of these considerations firms tend to be very conservative in evaluating the justification for such an investment. They are as much conservative as poor in their capability of long-range planning. What usually happens is that they mistake the opposite direction when they decide not to carry forward an investment which could have been fruitful.

In a few words one can say that many firms, and particularly the ones not very good at long-range planning, do not very much invest in automatic assembly because they feel that it is better to have manual operators instead, since the operators are easily convertible from one work to another.

3.7 *The trend of certain new industrial sectors*

The electronic industry has presented so far, as its particular characteristic, the very short life of its products and the very rapid introduction not only of new products but also of their basic components.

The switch from discrete components to integrated circuits, and now to the l.s.i. components, was a very rapid one and this is an obstacle to adequate development of mechanised operations in a field which is very suitable for the mechanisation from the technical point of view. At the same time, and in the author's opinion owing to the unreadiness of the automatic equipment market, there is now a new and unpredictable trend. This is a very anxious search for low-cost labour, and places to locate plants in order to find it. This new trend in American industrial policy, besides the fast turnover of new products, is in the author's opinion another very strong obstacle to the substantial development of automatic assembly in the near future.

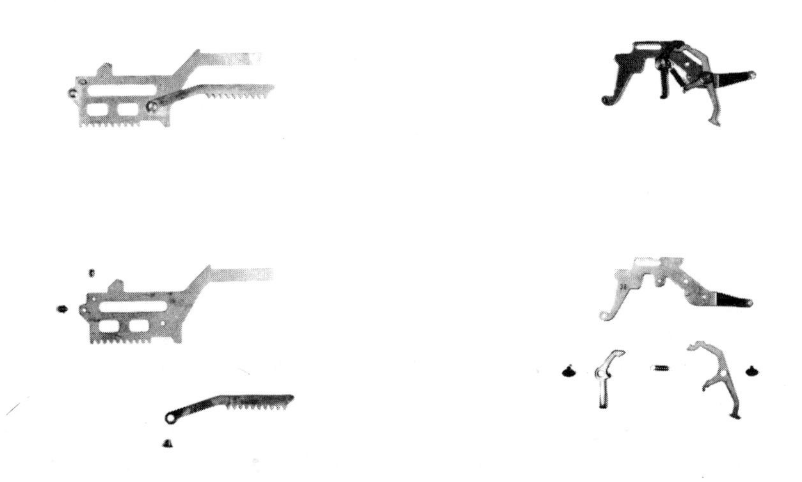

Fig. 10. Sheet metal parts assembled on rotary table.

Fig. 11. Parts assembled on rotary table.

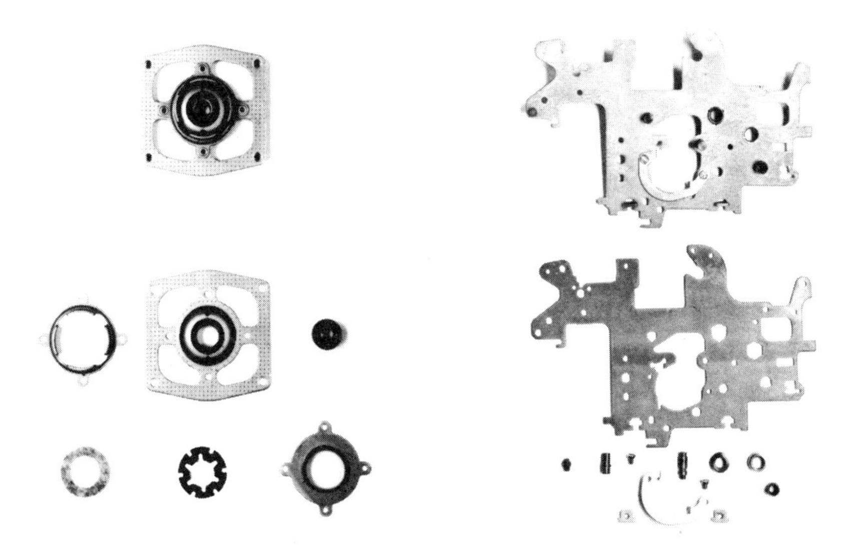

Fig. 12. Assembly from a linear transfer machine with fixed indexing.

Fig. 13. Assembly from a power and free line.

4.0 SOME GROUPS AUTOMATICALLY ASSEMBLED AT OLIVETTI'S

Figs 10, 11, 12 and 13 show typical examples of groups automatically assembled at Olivetti's. In each figure both the assembled group and its components are presented.

The group in Fig. 10 is assembled on a rotary ring table, with a cycle of 2·7 s. All components are automatically assembled. The sheet-metal parts are fed by a column magazine while the small rivets come from hopper feeders.

The group in Fig. 11 is also assembled on a rotary ring table with a cycle of 2·7 s. The main sheet-metal part is manually positioned on the fixture while all other parts come from hopper feeders, including the small spring.

The group in Fig. 12 is assembled on a linear transfer machine with fixed indexing. This machine is built on a Benerson chassis. The biggest sheet-metal part is manually located in the fixture while all other components are automatically fed and positioned. The cycle time is 6 s.

The group in Fig. 13 is assembled on a power and free line which has manual operations mixed with automatic stations.

The group in Fig. 14 is assembled on a rotary sector table (which is shown in Fig. 6). All components are manually positioned while the hot riveting operations take place one after another.

5.0 ECONOMIC JUSTIFICATION OF INVESTMENT

When the possibility of making an investment presents itself, the persons responsible for the capital to be invested must decide whether to invest or not. When the decision to invest could lead to the immobilisation of valuable capital for several years, or even to its total loss, and the decision not to invest could mean forfeiting a considerable profit, it is clear that 'hunch' decisions are insufficient. A study of accurate forecasts of future expenditures and incomes should give an indication of the economic convenience of a particular project.

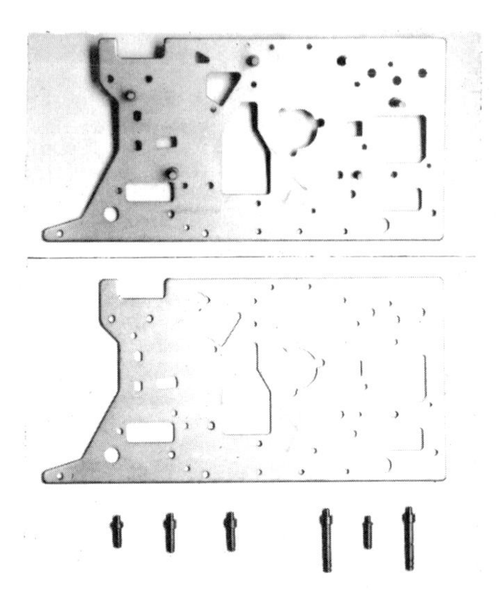

Fig. 14. Assembly from a rotary sector table.

5.1 *Discounted cash flow method*

A project is initiated by a firm to increase the firm's wealth.

There is a series of flows of money between the firm and the project, called *cash flows.* A negative cash flow is a flow from the project to the firm.

For a project life of k years there will be $(k + 1)$ cash flows. They are assumed to take place at the end of each year, and are denoted by $F_0, F_1, F_2 \ldots\ldots F_k$. Note that the end of year k is the beginning of year $(k + 1)$, so F_0 is usually the investment at the beginning of year 1 (i.e. time zero).

The project will have a particular value at any time, equal to the sum of the cash flows up to that time. However, since the cash flows take place at different moments in time, they cannot be summed directly. This is because money has a time value. Thus, to be compatible, cash flows must be referred to one point in time, usually time zero. This process, the opposite of compounding, is called *discounting.*

The value of the project after m years, the NET PRESENT VALUE after m years is PV_m and is a function of the discount rate i. Thus –

$$PV_m\,(i) = \sum_{k=0}^{m} F_k\,(1+i)^{-k}$$

and the value of the project at the end of its life is –

$$PV_k\,(i) = \sum_{k} F_k\,(1+i)^{-k}$$

These formulae can be used to give the required measure of the economic convenience of the project. One of the most commonly used methods is to find that value of i which makes –

$$PV_k(i) = 0$$

This value of i is called the *discounted-cash-flow* (d.c.f.) *rate of return.* It can be compared with standard criteria. For instance in many organisations the *minimum rate of return* is 10%. A project with a lower rate is discarded unless there are reasons why it will nevertheless prove advantageous to the organisation.

5.2 *Further evaluation*

The calculated rate of return does not make a clear-cut yes/no decision for the firm because it does not take into consideration such other factors as goodwill to customers and employees, risk, etc., which can influence the decision either way. It acts solely as a guide. There is also the problem that the calculations are based on forecasts, and are only as accurate as those forecasts.

These problems can be studied further in two ways.

5.2.1 *Sensitivity analysis*

Sensitivity analysis involves varying a forecast and noting the corresponding variations in the rate of return. The results are best displayed graphically. Initial project cost, labour costs, selling price, etc., are typical examples of factors examined. It is usual to deal with only one forecast at a time, the others retaining their original values.

5.2.2 *Risk analysis*

In risk analysis probabilities are assigned to variations in forecasts. Their combination gives the overall probability of any particular rate of return. More important, it gives the probability of earning at least any particular rate.

5.3 *Example – the deterministic rate of return*

The forms reproduced in the figures are an example of how d.c.f. rate-of-return analysis is applied in the Production Division at Olivetti's. The example is a special-purpose machine for assembling the printing-lever sub-group of an electric typewriter.

The names in the left-hand vertical column of each form are explained as follows.

In Fig. 15:

General	provides for a description of the project
Technico-economic characteristics	description of the initial expenditure
Production of interest	in 1969–1972 it is intended to manufacture every hour 38 typewriters requiring the printing-lever. Since each typewriter contains 46 of these sub-groups, the special machine must be capable of assembling 1748 sub-groups per hour.
Loads and returns	summaries from the following table

In Figs 16 and 17:

Utilisation forecasts:	times are divided into the following elements:–
T_M	machine time to produce one piece
t_u	measures the interventions of the operator before, during and after the machine operations Units: s/piece
t_{ciclo}	is the cycle time Units: s/piece
CO_t	hourly capacity of the man-machine system which equals $\frac{1}{t_{\text{ciclo}}} \times 3600$ Units: pieces/h
$\eta_M \eta_u$	$T_{M,}t_u$ are theoretical, $\eta_M \eta_u$ are percentages to allow for those factors that will eventually make T_M and t_u greater

OLIVETTI	GRUPPO PRODUZIONE					Page 1
Factory	Signed	Machine-shop or Service	Signed	Administative Office		Date

GENERAL

Description: Semi-automatic machine for assembling the printing lever of typewriter model MS. 48

TECHNICO-ECONOMIC CHARACTERISTICS

Unitary cost kL.	Basic machine	Accessories		Electrical plant	Transport and Taxes	Installation		TOTAL
	30,000					7,000		37,000

PRODUCTION OF INTEREST

HOURLY PRODUCTION				Years of Production						
PRODUCT	COMPONENT	OPERATION	PCS./MAC	69	70	71	72			
MS. 48	Printing lever	Assembly	46	38	38	38	38			
				1748	1748	1748	1748			

LOADS

	Years of Production						
	69	70	71	72			
EFFECTIVE MACHINE LOAD FORECAST	1·95	1·95	1·95	1·95			

RETURN

INVESTMENT FOR ONE MACHINE	37,000 kL.	YEAR OF EXPENDITURE	1968
RATE OF RETURN	21%	PAY-BACK PERIOD	3·2 years

Fig. 15. Form for description of project.

OLIVETTI	GRUPPO PRODUZIONE		Page 2

PRESENT SOLUTION

UTILIZATION FORECASTS

TIMES

PRODUCT	COMPONENT or OPERATION	T_M sec/piece	t_u sec/piece	t_{ciclo} sec/piece	CO_t pieces/h	γ_u %	γ_M %	CO_e pieces/h	C_t	t_{co} sec/piece	PO_t pieces/h	PO_e pieces/h	
MS. 48	Assembly		15·35	15·35		100			1	15·35	234	234	
	of												
	printing												
	lever												

LOADS

	Years of Production						
	69	70	71	72			
EFFECTIVE DIRECT LABOUR LOAD	7·5	7·5	7·5	7·5			
EFFECTIVE MACHINE-LOAD							

COST FORECASTS

COMPONENTS OF COST	COSTS	Years of Production						
		69	70	71	72			
DIRECT LABOUR	UNITARY ML/year	2·56	2·77	2·99	3·23			
	ANNUAL ML/year	19·2	20·8	22·4	24·2			
CONTROL	UNITARY ML/year							
	ANNUAL ML/year							
INDIRECT	UNITARY ML/year							
	ANNUAL ML/year							
CHARGE-HANDS	UNITARY ML/year							
	ANNUAL ML/year							
MAINTENANCE	ANNUAL ML/year							
REVISION	ANNUAL ML/year							
ELECTRICAL ENERGY	ANNUAL ML/year							
OTHERS	ANNUAL ML/year							
MATERIALS	ANNUAL ML/year							
TOTAL A	ANNUAL ML/year	19·2	20·8	22·4	24·2			

Fig. 16. Utilisation forecasts (1).

OLIVETTI	GRUPPO PRODUZIONE		Page 3

SPECIAL BRANCH

UTILIZATION FORECASTS

PRODUCT	COMPONENT or OPERATION	T_M sec/piece	t_u sec/piece	t_{ciclo} sec/piece	CO_t pieces/h	γ_u %	γ_M %	CO_e pieces/h	C_t	t_{co}	PO_t pieces/h	PO_e pieces/h	
MS. 48	Assembly	3	3	3	1200	95	78	900	1	3	1200	900	
	of												
	printing												
	lever												

LOADS

	Years of Production						
	69	70	71	72			
EFFECTIVE DIRECT LABOUR LOAD	1·95	1·95	1·95	1·95			
EFFECTIVE MACHINE LOAD	1·95	1·95	1·95	1·95			

COST FORECASTS

COMPONENTS OF COST	COSTS	Years of Production						
		69	70	71	72			
DIRECT LABOUR	UNITARY ML/year	2·56	2·77	2·99	3·23			
	ANNUAL ML/year	5·00	5·40	5·83	6·30			
CONTROL	UNITARY ML/year							
	ANNUAL ML/year							
INDIRECT	UNITARY ML/year							
	ANNUAL ML/year							
CHARGE-HANDS	UNITARY ML/year							
	ANNUAL ML/year							
MAINTENANCE	ANNUAL ML/year	1·20	1·20	1·20	1·20			
REVISION	ANNUAL ML/year							
ELECTRICAL ENERGY	ANNUAL ML/year							
OTHERS	ANNUAL ML/year							
MATERIALS	ANNUAL ML/year							
TOTAL B	ANNUAL ML/year	6·20	6·60	7·03	7·50			

Fig. 17. Utilisation forecasts (2).

OLIVETTI	GRUPPO PRODUZIONE		Page 4

Description: Comparison between the reference solution (manual assembly) and the suggested solution (automatic assembly)

CALCULATION OF RATE OF RETURN

			YEARS OF PRODUCTION							
			68	69	70	71	72			
PREVIOUS SOLUTION	INVESTMENTS	ML								
	VARIABLE COSTS	ML/year								
	TOTAL A	ML/year		19·20	20·80	22·40	24·20			
INVESTMENT	INVESTMENTS	ML	37·00							
	VARIABLE COSTS	ML/year		6·20	6·60	7·03	7·50			
	TOTAL B	ML/year	37·00	6·20	6·60	7·03	7·50			
CASH-FLOWS	REAL VALUES = A - B	ML/year	-37·00	13·00	14·20	15·37	16·70			
	DISCOUNTED VALUES	ML/year								
		i =								
		i =								
		i =								
		i =								

RATE OF RETURN 21%

CALCULATION OF PAY-BACK PERIOD

YEAR	K	F_k	i^{-1}	$(1+i)^{-k}$	$F_k(1+i)^{-k}$	$F_k(1+i)^{-k}$
	0		10	1		
	1		10	0·909		
	2		10	0·825		
	3		10	0·751		
	4		10	0·683		
	5		10	0·620		
	6		10	0·564		
	7		10	0·513		

PAY-BACK PERIOD 3·2 years

Fig. 18. Summary of totals.

CO_e	effective hourly capacity = $\eta M \times \eta u \times CO_t$ Units: pieces/h
C_t	theoretical coefficient; takes account of cases where the number of men to one machine is not one, e.g. one man to two machines $C_t = 0\ 5$ Units: men/machine
t_{co}	$t_{co} = C_t \times t_{ciclo}$ Units: s/piece
PO_t	$= \frac{1}{t_{co}} \times 3600$ Units: pieces/h
PO_e	$PO_e = C_t \times CO_e$ Units: pieces/h

From these data are calculated:

Effective direct labour load labour load	Hourly production PO_e which is used to calculate the cost of direct labour = load × unit annual cost
Effective machine load	equal to Hourly production CO_e
—	indicates the degree of utilisation of the machine. If it exceeds 1, it becomes necessary to consider the possibility of either working a double shift or buying another machine.
Cost forecasts	give a summary of the annual costs of each production method.

Fig. 16 deals with the old method, and Fig. 17 deals with the suggested solution. Notes: (a) there is no machine load for the old method – it is manual, and (b) the machine load in the suggested solution is 1·95, so two shifts will be necessary.

Fig. 18 gives a summary of the totals. The difference between the costs of the two methods gives the saving, which is the income on the project. Space is provided for calculating manually the d.c.f. rate of return and the pay-back period. The calculations are usually made using the Olivetti Programma 101 desk-top computer.

5.4 *Example – further evaluation*

When the above technique has been applied, the deterministic result (21%) is further evaluated using sensitivity analysis. The example in Fig. 19 shows the sensitivity of the rate of return to the initial project cost. The range investigated is from 50–150% of the original estimate of lire 37 million (£24 700). The graph shows that there is a zero rate of return if the initial expenditure reaches 160% of the original estimate, i.e. lire 59 million. In fact if the minimum rate is 10%, the project will need careful reconsideration if the cost rises by 25% to lire 47 million. To the right the graph is asymptotic where zero project cost gives an infinite positive rate of return.

There are many other parameters that can be examined. Note that it is important to ensure that only one is varied at a time, and that the same conditions are applied to both systems being compared. For example, while investigating the effect of variations in the rate of assembly by the special machine, the cost must be compared with the cost of assembling at the same rate manually.

A	a	B				C
50	-18·50	13·00	14·20	15·37	16·70	67
80	-29·60					34
95	-35·15					24
100	-37·00					21
105	-38·85					19
120	-44·40					13
150	-55·50	▼	▼	▼	▼	3

A – Percentage of original value

a – Value in Lire

B – Cash flows

C – Rate of return

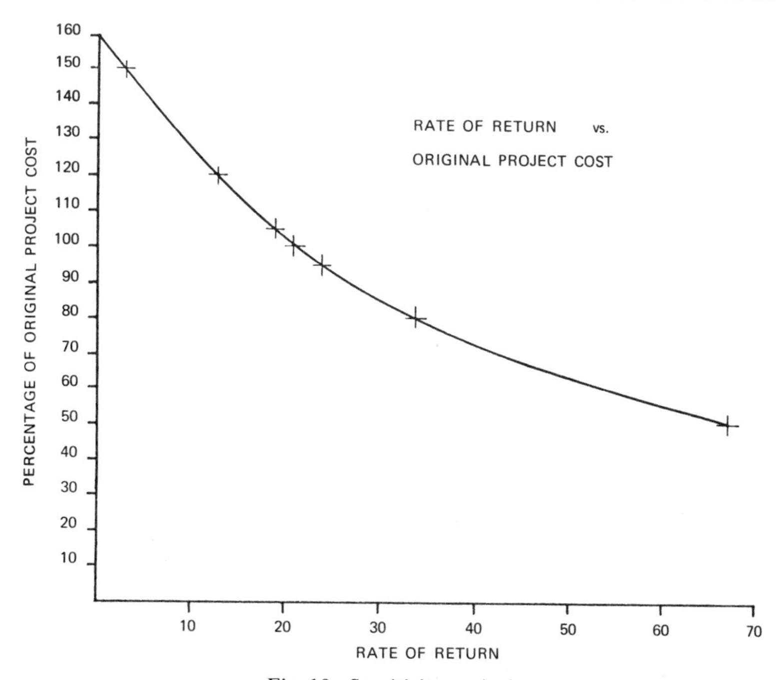

Fig. 19. Sensitivity analysis.

DEVELOPMENT AND APPLICATIONS OF A NEW PNEUMATIC *NOR* DEVICE

A. R. Baumann,
Industrial Liaison Department, T.N.O., Delft

SUMMARY

The development of an inexpensive pneumatic logic device (*nor*), capable of operating from a normal compressed-air system in the range 2·5 to 100 lbf/in^2, is described. A manifold interconnection system of simple design has been developed to permit assembly of *nor* devices in multiple form. Four typical industrial applications are described.

1.0 NEED FOR A LOW-COST PNEUMATIC SWITCH

In all types of industry pneumatic equipment has during the last three decades developed into a basic tool for higher productivity.

In automation compressed air is largely used as a driving medium for different types of output device or actuator, e.g. cylinders, motors, machining units, valves, etc. Actuators have to be controlled according to a program to suit the process.

Only in simple cases, and for a limited number of actuators, can control be implemented completely with traditional air valves, which need lubrication and have only a single input and two alternative output connections. In more sophisticated control circuits programming often has to be done electronically, at least for circuits of fairly high complexity. Electromagnetic relays may suffice for less involved circuits.

Mixing two media, air for power and electricity for control, has several disadvantages. The most severe are:

- Electric components need an enclosure, and, because of safety requirements, their connection calls for a qualified technician.
- The machine needs two connections to different power sources, as well as two different skills for maintenance. This is a point of great importance, and each technician, a member of a union, tends to be sure that the failure is to be found in the part that he is not allowed to touch.
- Each translation from one medium to the other costs money.
- Each translation raises an additional risk of break-down.
- Electric supply may suddenly fail while pneumatic power remains fully available. These risks call for special switching arrangements, and they raise the costs of control too.

Fluidic devices, originally developed for space applications, are pneumatic devices which apparently solve these problems. Some have no moving parts and operate at a very low power level. Though they were developed some ten years ago, industry does not use them yet on a considerable scale. The differences between existing fluidic devices and the *nor* devices discussed here boil down to:

- The power level on which existing fluidic devices work is low, so amplification is needed on each output. The new *nor* device has sufficient power to actuate directly even big valves and small air cylinders.

- Fluidic devices with no moving parts, and therefore no wear, are presumed to have infinite service life. The new *nor* valves have moving, but not sliding, parts.
- For fluidic devices absolutely clean and dry air of a constant low pressure is needed. For the new *nor* valves, compressed air between about 5 and 100 lbf/in^2 needs no special treatment.
- Fluidic devices operate on a constant flow of air, so continuous power is needed for each element, whether actuated or not. The new *nor* device operates on a certain amount of air per switching cycle. It is a 'closed' system, with no air consumption beyond the amount needed for pressurising its pilot chambers plus connections for each actuation.

These four points show that, in a general sense, established fluidic devices may be the more suitable for high switching frequencies, technically in view of the absence of moving parts and economically because no extra power is needed for each actuation. Fluidic devices will also be the answer for applications with a high degree of logic and relatively few outputs.

Actually, the same considerations lead to the choice of electronic systems, which are still considerably cheaper. The new *nor* device is intended for industrial applications within the scope of 'low-cost automation'. The aim is to eliminate relays in control units for air-operated actuators. The device is suitable for circuits of medium complexity, for operations of medium or low frequency and for circuits with relatively many outputs.

2.0 DEVELOPMENT OF NEW *NOR* DEVICE

For years we had dealt with pneumatic as well as with electric and electronic systems. One day, when drawing a circuit with Norbits (proprietary transistorised switching units) for a finally air-driven system, we came to think of a pneumatic valve that might perform the same function. We simply had to find a way to make such a rather inexpensive valve. With it, as with electronic (or fluidic) *nor* devices, all logic switching problems could be soluble. Each circuit-stage should get the full power level out of the main supply.

The next step was to find a manufacturer sufficiently interested in the idea to supply funds. A Dutch pneumatic and hydraulic component firm – Sempress Rotterdam – sponsored the project.

2.1 *Search for a specification*

Intended for industrial applications, the design of the *nor* device had by definition to meet industrial requirements. Advantages and disadvantages of existing pneumatic control equipment were listed. The experience of the sponsor and ourselves was pooled.

The component had to fit into the production facilities of Sempress and its ultimate cost had to be, at worst, equal to that of any alternative system. Accordingly, it had to be suitable for mass-production and automatic assembly.

For maintenance and control a manual override and an indication of actuation were desirable. The connections had to be such that the quantity of fittings and tubing, one of the major items of additional cost in any pneumatic system, would be an absolute minimum.

Life expectancy, reliability, and insensitivity to impure and wet air, as well as to dusty and corrosive atmospheres, had to be high.

The working pressure had to be high enough to operate traditional power valves, if possible up to 100 lbf/in^2.

There were, of course, other details, but this list of partly conflicting requirements was itself long enough to drive the designer to despair.

2.2 *Search for a system*

Nor function means that an output signal appears if no input is energised. Pressure on any input drives the output to exhaust. In principle, any traditional air-operated, normally open, three-way valve, whose input is extended by a number of shuttle-valves, performs this logic function.

Our first experiment was based on the use of a fully enclosed liquid as the transmission medium, displaced by inflating dead-ended rubber tubes connected to each individual input (Fig. 1). This system has absolutely equivalent inputs and is simple to make, but it does not easily permit manual override and fails completely if the liquid leaks.

The next step was really new, and decisive: no liquid, only air and mechanical transmission.

Fig. 1. First hand-made Perspex model with liquid transmission medium.

The first, hand-made, prototype was cut from Perspex sheet by means of a fretsaw, and it had no fewer than eight inputs (Fig. 2). The inner valve consisted of a thick rubber disc actuated by a rivet. Signal input ended in chambers separated by diaphragms and containing Perspex discs (the cut-outs) as spacers. Each chamber, when pressurised, expands vertically, and the upper pile of spacers is stopped against the top cover. The lower pile of spacers is forced down against the inner valve, which then closes the inlet and connects the output to the exhaust. This became the final principle.

2.3 *Improving some characteristics*

Though the prototype was able to perform the desired function satisfactorily, the chief development began after this was demonstrated.

First, a more robust prototype had to be made, without the leakage between layers which high pressure caused in the Perspex model. As we had expected, the very elimination of leakage between parts, and, at a later stage, between elements and sub-base, was crucial.

Fig. 2. First prototype of final system (again hand-made), with eight inputs and manual override.

This problem solved, the best material and manufacturing method had to be determined, these factors being decisive for the final design. Though metal in a cylindrical shape was the most obvious choice, in view of the workshop facilities at Sempress, e.g. automated lathes, there was no hope of getting a reasonable cost price that way (Fig. 3).

By every known criterion the first all-plastics model (Fig. 4) was a considerable improvement (for instance in response time, owing to its lower mass). This approach opened prospects of moulding. However, at the time only thermosetting types of plastic were able to stand the

Fig. 3. First set of *nor* valves able to hold more than 100 lbf/in^2, interconnected by a manifold for long-term oscillatory test.

Fig. 4. First production prototype, in thermosetting plastic.

mechanical pressure needed for a leakage-free assembly at 100 lbf/in^2: thermoplastics would creep. Thermosetters, unfortunately, could not allow a sufficient decrease of production cost through increased quantity, but at the time there was no alternative. After some months the Plastics and Rubber Research Institute, T.N.O., advised that a new technology, and material, was available to meet the requirements; it allowed injection moulding. Meanwhile time was spent on improving speed, performance, and life expectancy (by reducing the stroke of diaphragms, and streamlining the shape of spacers and bodyparts), and on studying the system of interconnection. Speed, performance and life expectancy are interrelated in a very intricate way. To improve speed and life expectancy one can reduce the movement of the diaphragms, but this reduces performance.

Low performance, in turn, reduces speed. Then one can miniaturise, to get less volume in the chambers between the diaphragms. Then performance becomes less important. This has two main consequences: reduction of life expectancy owing to relatively higher deformation of the diaphragms, and, at the bottom, shortage of space for the interconnections. This shortage of space particularly leads to leakage problems in the programming layer.

All in all, we had to find the best ratio between stroke, size, speed, performance, life-expectancy and, last but not least, cost price. This meant doing hundreds of experiments.

Next, the final shape had to be adapted to the production technique developed. A set of first experimental models underwent a long test for durability. Three units were connected in series to form an oscillator. At two points the output and an input of one device were simultaneously inspected electronically; the rise and fall of pressure was displayed on an oscilloscope. The oscillator was fed with air direct from the compressor accumulator without filtering or reducing pressure, at between 90 and 120 lbf/in^2. The frequency was 39 Hz (later improved to about 50).

After a week there was no difference in display on the oscilloscope, the photographs showing slopes covering each other perfectly. We were forced to round-the-clock operation; with automatic control to stop the air supply in case of any predictable failure. After four weeks the tests were stopped. There was still no change in characteristics. Mechanical inspection showed no wear that would indicate any considerably decreased service life.

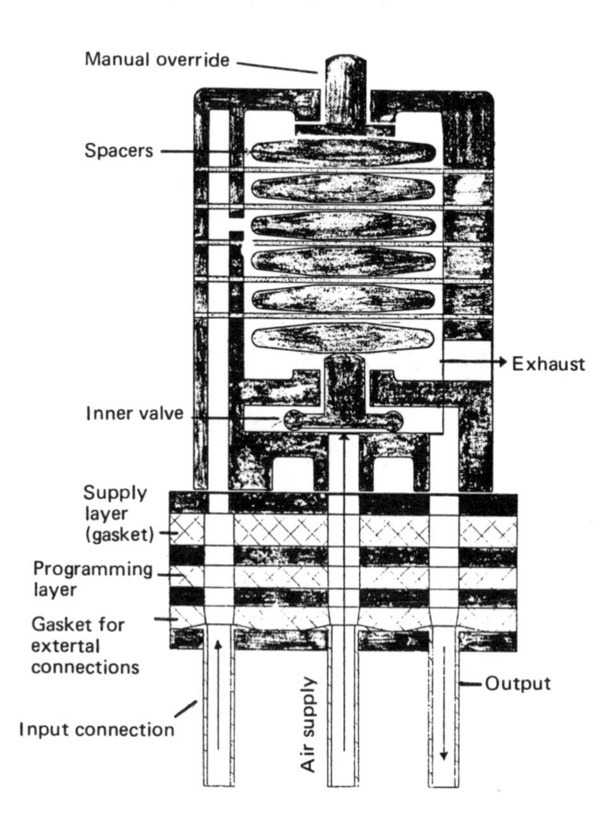

Fig. 5. Cross-section of commercial element, showing also the system of connection.

Further long-run tests, for instance under caustic water, did not lead to either destruction or failure. The element had been developed. Parallel to the *nor* device, a technique of interconnection was developed. Again this meant an extensive search for adequate materials. The final system is shown in Figs 5 and 6.

3.0 APPLICATIONS

3.1 *Two-hand safety device for presses*

Connecting two hand-operated three-way valves in series is a simple method to allow the operation of a press only by actuating both valves, but when the operator 'illegally' ties one of the valves down, he can work with only one hand and is no longer protected. A real safety device allows the operation of the press only after *release* of both valves, and their subsequent simultaneous actuation. The circuitry for traditional valves is shown in Fig. 7.

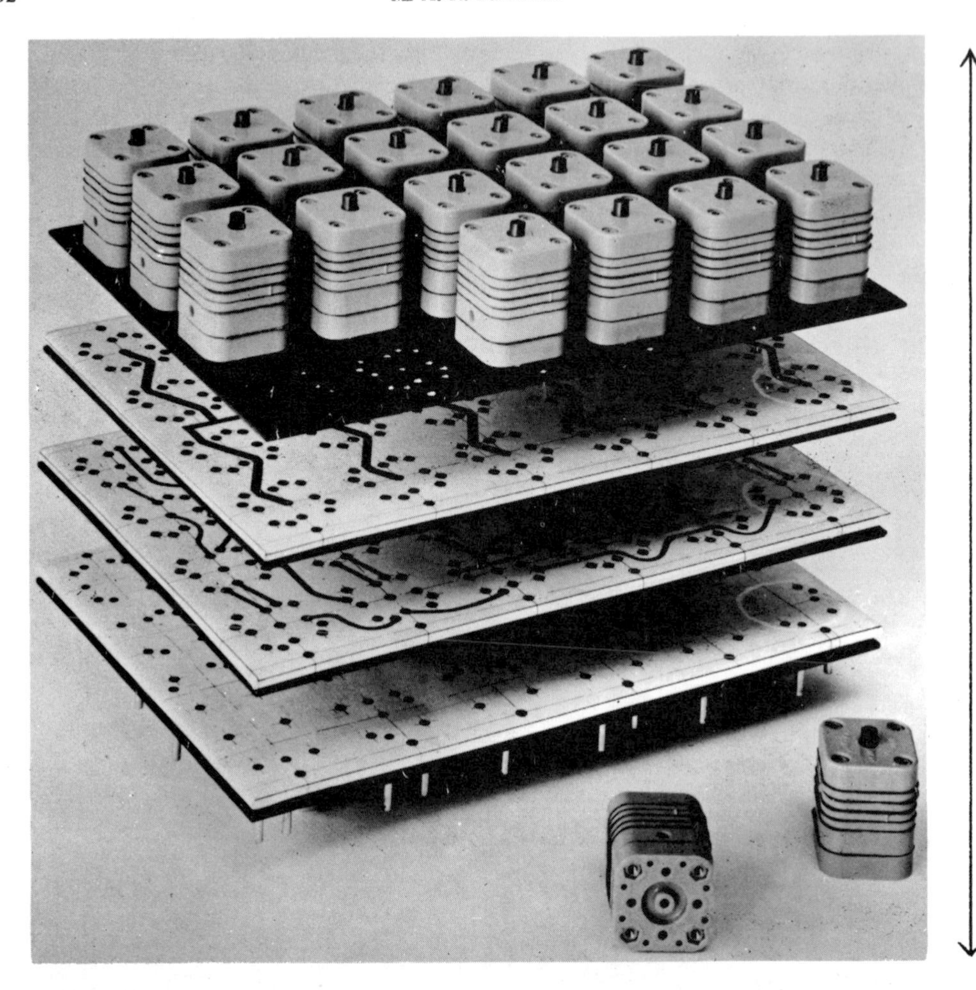

Fig. 6. Exploded view of standard 24-element unit. Sandwich sub-base consists of four identical metal plates and three gaskets, respectively for supplying power to each element, programming, and (at the bottom) external connection. Arrowed dimension represents 15 cm.

As a standard unit, Sempress market a special assembly, which is ready for connection to a press. It is equipped with three *nor* valves (Fig. 8).

3.2 *Control of liquid pumping system*

The flow sheet of a pumping system for liquids is shown in Fig. 9. The liquid has to be pumped from a reservoir *via* a buffer (vat) to a processing unit. Along the same route the liquid is simultaneously filtered. The installation proper is shown in Fig. 10.

The offtake of liquid during the process varies in a wide range. Two pumps maintain the level in the buffer between 'DL max.' and 'DL min.'. If the level falls below 'DL max.', one pump starts. As soon as the 'DL min.' level is reached, the second (stand-by) pump also starts. Then both keep on working until the 'DL max.' level is reached again. Each pump is connected in the circuit by means of two air-operated shut-off valves. Three filters are mounted between two valves each. The pressure drop across the filter is measured to indicate degree of fouling.

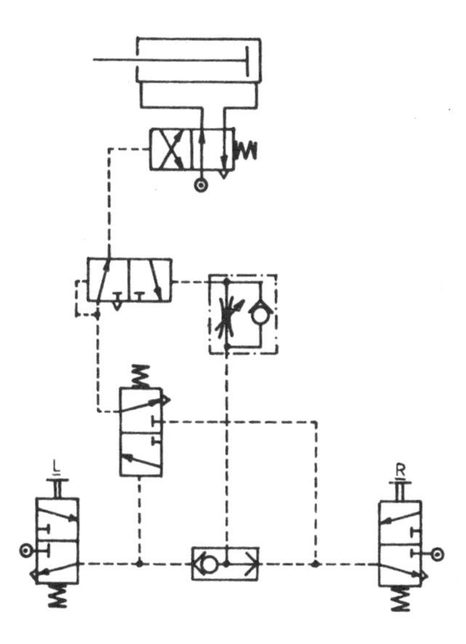

Fig. 7. Two-hand safety circuit using conventional valves.

When the pressure drop across one filter becomes too large, the next filter is automatically connected to the system by opening the two adjacent valves, and the 'dirty' filter is completely isolated by its two valves. An indicator in the control panel shows at a glance that filter x has to be cleaned. When this large pressure drop occurs during a period in which both pumps are delivering through one filter, a second filter is connected as a stand-by, but the first keeps its own turn in the queue. After a filter has been cleared a specific pushbutton has to be pressed to put the filter in question back in the queue. The indicator then shows *'Ready for service'*.

This system needs a rather complicated circuit to guarantee foolproof and fail-safe control. The circuit has two fully equipped manifolds of 24 elements each. Sensing and control are effected pneumatically; the motors of the pumps are directly controlled by pressure-switches. All in all thirty incoming pneumatic signals are concerned in the selection pattern for sixteen output commands.

3.3 *Sequence control of automatic machines*

Two examples of special-purpose machine are shown in Figs 11 and 12. Built up from existing machines, they were automated by adding feed-tables, drillpress feed units, clamps and

Fig. 8. Standard two-hand safety unit equipped with *nor* valves.

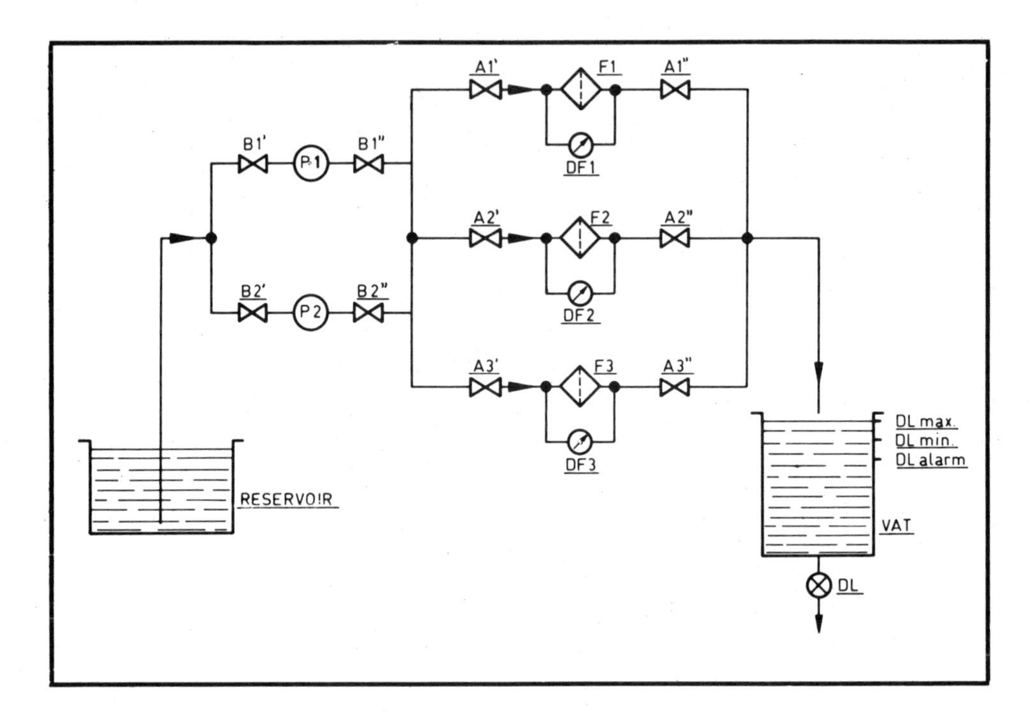

Fig. 9. Flow sheet for typical liquid pumping and filtering system.

cylinders, all powered pneumatically. Sequence control of these machines, each with a very-high-production output, is by pneumatic *nor* devices. Continuous production of an item in one or a few seconds, depending on the inherent machining operations, leads to an average of about 100 000 cycles a week.

This means a maximum life expectancy for electromechanical relays of two years. With plug-in relays, and one set in stock for quick replacement in case of a break-down, this may be considered a reasonable solution. But comparison of costs for relay control and fully pneumatic *nor*-control yielded points in favour of the latter. For very simple sequence control there was no difference either way. With *nors*, however, taking full advantage of the inputs which are available anyway, a higher degree of control was achieved without more elements.

For this kind of application, where electric-motor drive is used for rotation of tools and pneumatic power for ancillary motions, a standard assembly of *nors*, called a 'safety unit', has been developed by the manufacturer. This provides for interlocking of the two power sources. In case of a break-down of the electric power the compressed air is shut off. The electric power, in turn, can be switched on only after a preset pressure is reached; it is automatically shut off if the pressure drops to an inadmissibly low level. To avoid inaccurate stepping of the pneumatically turned table, the amount of compressed air needed for the feeding operation is stored in an accumulator. In any emergency this 'safety unit' also provides for safe positioning of all moving parts of the machine.

Such a unit occupies the middle of the control desk of the automatic milling machine shown in Fig. 11. The *nors* can be seen at the extreme left. All pushbuttons and indicators in the left half of the steering panel, on top of the desk, are pneumatic components.

Fig. 10. Full-scale exhibition model of system shown in Fig. 9, as installed at Cockburns Ltd. Control desk in foreground mounts fully pneumatic control unit.

A drilling and tapping machine is shown in Fig. 12. The auxiliary valves and other pneumatic equipment, as well as the index table and the drill press-feed units used here, are all made by Sempress, the manufacturer of the *nor* devices. This machine is controlled by the set of *nors* visible on the cover of the control box at the left of the base. The clean look of this fully pneumatically controlled machine is noteworthy. There are absolutely no floating tubes because with *nor* elements pilot valves are connected directly to the control unit, without any series or parallel connections of valves across the machine.

3.4 *Control of mixing process*

Last but not least, we take a look at a distillery. Brandy, malt wine, alcohol, etc. are very expensive. Every chance of wrong blending, by human error for instance, carries great financial risk with it. The primary equipment of the process consists of vessels, flowmeters, pumps, tubes and pneumatically actuated shut-off valves.

A picture (Fig. 13) taken during the installation of the control unit gives an impression of part of the blending department. Behind the panel, temporarily mounted on a Dexion frame, about a hundred *nor* valves provide fail-safe and foolproof control of blending and storing. There is, for instance, no possibility of transfering any liquid to a tank which has not previously been completely emptied by the bottling department. Level control in the tanks is fully pneumatic. Consequently the only control medium used is compressed air, without any lubri-

Fig. 11. Automatic milling machine for four simultaneous operations and automatic parts-handling and clamping, fully pneumatically controlled. Safety unit provides for automatic withdrawal of tools in case of electrical break-down.

Fig. 12. Automatic drilling and tapping machine. All motions controlled by pneumatic *nor* units. Note that no tubes are visible.

Fig. 13. Part of blending department in Dutch distillery. Human errors in blending are prevented by pneumatic *nor* devices.

cation. This latter point is, of course, important where goods are made for consumption, as in the example.

4.0 CONCLUSION

The *nor* device described is a reliable, low-cost unit suitable for use in pneumatic circuits of medium complexity for controlling operations of medium or low frequency. It has the advantages of utilising normal factory air supplies, not specially dried or filtered. Its output is capable of directly actuating large valves and small air cylinders. Industrial applications have proved the device to be entirely satisfactory.

FASTENING TECHNIQUES AND FUTURE DEVELOPMENTS IN THE INDUSTRY

P. J. Gill and
J. H. Turnbull

G.K.N. Screws & Fasteners Ltd

SUMMARY

The continuing trend towards more economic fastening techniques is stressed, and the system approach is illustrated. Developments in fastener system design and fastener manufacturing are described. The influence of automatic feeding, newer materials such as plastics, and metrication are discussed. Future trends in the industry are covered, together with problems of metric thread pitch selection. Data are now available on which more logical selection of the optimum thread system can be made.

1.0 INTRODUCTION

The demand for improved fastening techniques arises out of two main factors:

(i) The straightforward requirement for a cheaper method of fastening than that used at present, in order to increase the competitiveness of the end product.

(ii) The development of new applications, generally of more sophisticated nature and utilising new materials.

There is no doubt that scope for more economic fastening techniques exists. Some figures recently published by the Industrial Fasteners Institute in the U.S.A. highlight the potential. They show that, in assembly alone, one automotive manufacturer has found that over twelve billion individual fasteners are required annually. Several years ago almost all these twelve billion items were handled and assembled one at a time! Over 30 000 people, using some 40 000 power tools, were involved in these operations.

The U.S. Government Census of Manufacturers' Statistics also showed that 53% of the total production man-hours in thirteen manufacturing industries were devoted to the assembly function alone. In the U.K. the quantities of fastenings used are far smaller and only in the order of one tenth of an equivalent industry in the U.S.A. The proportion of time spent in assembly is, of course, roughly equivalent.

A final point to bear in mind is that the cost of the fastening itself rarely exceeds 5% of the total 'in-place' cost.

The break-down of these in-place costs becomes more and more important when more economic ways of assembling products are being assessed, since many of the newer fastenings and techniques rely on savings other than those of just cheapening the product.

Functional, environmental and service life considerations are usually covered thoroughly by the engineer in choosing a fastener, but the *total* economics of fastener selection are sometimes minimised, overlooked, or even misinterpreted. Company cost accounting systems are not always geared to providing the required data in sufficient detail for a true comparison to be made.

2.0 DEVELOPMENT OF CHEAPER FASTENING TECHNIQUES

There are many ways of reducing the assembly cost of a fastening, for example captive washers or 'Sems' assemblies which eliminate the risk of lost washers on assembly in production. Double ordering, stocking and invoicing are also reduced. Stiff-nuts are available which eliminate tab washers and expensive wiring operations. Self-tapping screws have often been used to eliminate tapping operations on the production line. These can now be supplied in normal thread forms (Taptite). The list of such items is long and all-embracing, and most have features which either simplify the product or eliminate the need for certain components or operations.

Most of these fastenings have been developed during and since the last war. Whilst there are still areas where improvement is possible and desirable (e.g. an all-metal stiff-bolt), it is fair to say that the variety of fasteners appears to have nearly saturated the need.

2.1 *The system approach*

A new approach has been adopted by many fastener suppliers, as a result of the limitations of attempting to improve the fastening itself. The success of each products as the 'pop' rivet showed the possible avenue to be explored, and the 'system' approach was born. By broadening the scope of thinking to include the process of installing the fastener one brings all sorts of new possibilities to light. Whilst not a new observation it is nonetheless a true one that since the invention of screw and screw-driver the development of both has not been intimately linked.

There are obvious reasons for this. The screw trade has dealt exclusively with mass production techniques and a relatively cheap end-product. On the other hand the application tool, whether a simple hand screw-driver or a sophisticated power tool, poses other problems of relatively small production quantities, ergonomics, weight reduction etc.

The two can, however, be married up. It is still essential that the fastener manufacturer regard the fastening itself as the means of making his profit, but providing the 'system' reduces the in-place costs, the product becomes more competitive, more fasteners are sold and the cost of the power tool can be subsidised out of the increased profits made. This cost is low even with a tool costing say £100, when spread over several years and possibly millions of fasteners.

Of course there are parallels. The razor is sold cheaply and paid for by the blades. A paper stapling machine is often given away when the staples are purchased. Riveting has already undergone this change to a large extent since it has been difficult to sophisticate the rivet without the accompanying machinery.

In all areas of fastening this approach may be taken to its logical conclusion. A system can be provided which will eliminate preparative operations or allow features to be designed into the assembly which were previously not possible or which were uneconomic. In addition this approach will require automatic feeding devices to be designed. These may require modifications of the fastener for orientation on a continuous belt. By such means it is possible to solve many of the problems associated with automatic feeding.

Further developments in the system approach to fastening are also evident in the following product lines:

1 Riveting, which has moved from the aerospace market to the automotive and commercial vehicle/container markets.
2 Nut-running using N-Driv, Brooklok, Hi-Shear and Huckbolts.
3 Welded studs and nuts.
4 Self-piercing Hank rivet bushes and inserts which eliminate predrilled or pierced holes.

The implication of the system approach is that a special-purpose tool will inevitably be required. In some cases this may be little more than an attachment for a conventional power tool. The Brooklok fastening is an example; the principles of this fastening system are shown in Fig. 1. The self-drilling screw is another example: here the driver requires only higher speeds than those normally used.

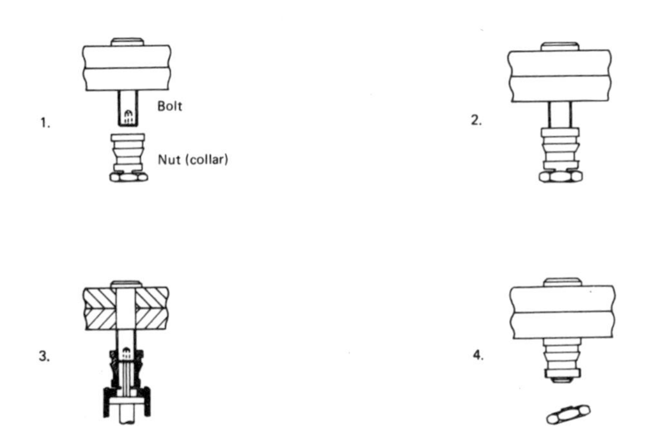

Fig. 1. BrookLok fastener system. The method of installation is as follows. At 2, hand engagement of collar on bolt. At 3, insertion of hexagonal wrench tip of power driver into bolt recess to resist rotation, pressing of wrench onto hexagonal nut. At 4, operation of gun to 'torque off' wrenching device, leaving fastening installed.

2.1.1 *The Spat system*

The Spat system requires a more specialised tool and is, in effect, two tools in one. A normal air-turbine motor is used but in addition an impact is provided which punches the screw into the sheet metal. The system is integrated, i.e. the gun is tailored to the range of screws produced and one used without the other does not provide the full benefits of the fastening.

The important points here are that time is saved by eliminating drilled or punched holes, the fastening itself is improved by virtue of the plunged hole, giving improved vibration resistance and pull-out loads, and normal tapping speeds are used to drive the screw home. The screw is inexpensive and the guns can be rented with full service and replacement facilities.

The system is widely accepted in the motor trade at home and abroad for fixing trim into single thicknesses of car body material. It is also well received for many applications in other trades, in particular those using combinations of sheet metal, wood, plasterboard and plastics.

Developments are in hand to widen the capabilities of the system for heavier applications or where multiple thicknesses of metal are encountered. Other features have been incorporated in the basic system to aid quick assembly, e.g. automatic depth cut-outs, counterbalances and magnetic bits.

3.0 NEWER MATERIALS AND THEIR INFLUENCE

The second major factor influencing future fastening techniques is more obvious. The development of plastics, alloys and other new materials has inevitably led to a demand for fasteners which suit the new environments created. In some cases the new materials have been found suitable for the fastener itself. For example, a new generation of plastic fasteners has resulted.

There is, of course, a tendency for such families of fasteners to become highly specialised. For example, in the aircraft industry the requirements justify the economic penalties of using the more exotic materials. An automotive manufacturer is not likely to specify a titanium bolt at say 7s 6d each even though a weight reduction may be desirable, but the aircraft manufacturer can show that a pound of weight saved is worth £15 to £25, depending on the aircraft's role. Naturally the picture is ever-changing. Possibly the electric town-car of the future, having a less favourable performance/weight ratio, will favour the use of exotic steels and alloys. In that case, as the requirements grow, manufacturing costs will fall. Improved manufacturing methods will follow and the fastener may become economically viable.

Looking at the newer materials being joined one finds it interesting to note some examples and the trends that they illustrate.

– The general heading of *Plastics* covers a wide range of materials. Many of the problems generated by the use of plastic materials have been overcome by conventional fastening techniques, bearing in mind the strengths and properties of joints required.

Apart from plastic fasteners, which will be dealt with later, perhaps the most significant techniques evolved for plastic materials have been in the insert bush category. Owing to the inherent weakness of plastic threads, particularly on assemblies frequently loosened and tightened, such inserts are desirable. They can be moulded in, which slows down moulding rates, or alternatively placed after moulding in a cored hole. Various such fastenings are available, generally relying on the expansion of a brass bush by mechanical means for an interference fit. In some materials advantage can be taken of thermoplasticity and the bush can be spun into friction-welded position. Again this may be considered as a 'system approach'. Obviously both the interference-fit and the friction-welded types are suitable only for certain plastics and configurations. Undoubtedly new developments of this type are likely, possibly using techniques such as ultrasonic welding.

Building techniques have undergone drastic changes in the last decade. Pre-assembled and modular systems, using combinations of plasterboard, asbestos and metal in most cases, have led to requirements for new fasteners. For example the Panel-Spat screw has been specially developed for fastening plasterboard to metal purlins (Fig. 2).

The constructional methods used also show the need for blind-side fastenings for fixing to walling with little or no inherent strength. Expanding rubber bushes have been devised together with collapsible-leg varieties which operate when the male fastening is installed.

Cartridge-powered impact tools for threaded and plain studs are now commonly accepted in

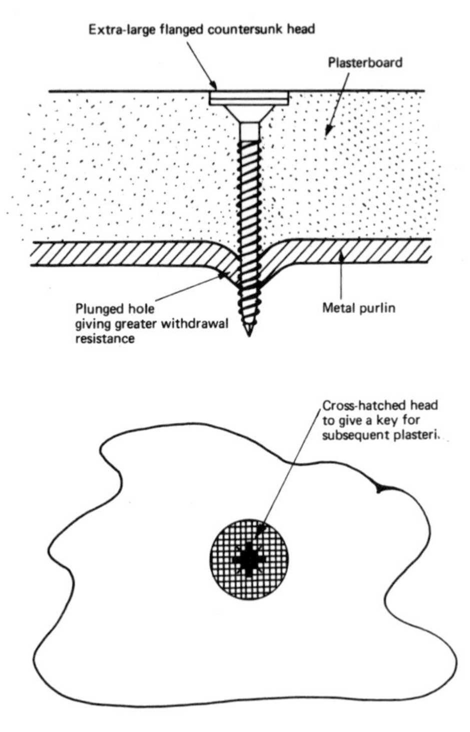

Fig. 2. Panel-Spat screw.

the building trade where fixing to heavier beams is required. Developments on this 'system' are continually being made both to the speed of the operation and the type of charge.

Fastener suppliers have been very quick to appreciate the potential for fasteners made wholly or partly in plastics. On the one hand we now have high-strength products such as hexagon-socket devices using plastic 'muscles' in the form of inserts to provide stiff features, whilst at the other extreme we have relatively low-strength grommets and studs made wholly of plastic and taking advantage of the cheapness of injection-moulded materials.

The range of these fastenings is wide and by now familiar. They score heavily over conventional fastenings on a number of points. They are generally cheaper, simpler, quicker to install, have improved corrosion resistance and may be moulded easily to any desired head form.

A more recent application of plastics has been made in quick-release fastening. As an example, Rotolok has reduced assembly times by eliminating staking and riveting. The three parts – cam, grommet and rotor – clip in, and on a quarter-turn of the rotor the cams engage and the fastening 'clicks' into the locked position. The joint is held together by a sprung diaphragm built into the rotor. This also seals the joint against fumes and dust – an important point on a van engine cover for example.

A single $\frac{5}{16}$ in Rotolok will withstand a 180 lbf tensile load – the weight of a full-grown man. The strength, coupled with spring characteristics, is achieved by using an acetal homopolymer, whilst the wear resistance of the cams is obtained from nylon. The development of this product highlighted the need for careful material selection, bearing in mind the likely operating temperatures and resistance to oils and the like.

A further advantage of plastics in the availability of various colours, which for automotive trim and furnishing applications makes the product far more attractive (e.g. Plastidome mirror screws).

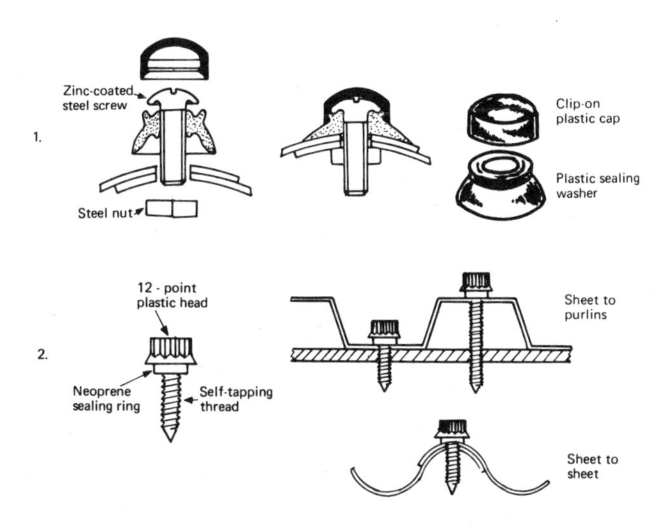

Fig. 3. Examples of plastics in building fasteners. 1 – Sealawashers. (a) For securing roof and wall-cladding sheets to purlins of any normal metal section. Applicable in valley or ridge of corrugation. (b) For 'stitching' sheets along laps or seams. NOT suitable for asbestos/cement sheets because very rigid. 2 – Sealascrews for securing roofing and wall cladding.

A further plastics development over recent years has been in roofing fasteners (Fig. 3). They supersede lead washers, which are very expensive, and with which the nut and bolt are liable to corrosion.

Of course not all the new materials have been plastic. In some cases improved manufacturing techniques have gone hand in glove with the newer materials, resulting in improved performance without change in appearance (e.g. stainless steel socket products).

Developments have continued even to the extent of plating finishes. Chromed plastic (ABS) fasteners are possible and improved 'duplex' plating processes are available.

Future materials, such as oriented-fibre composites, will undoubtedly provide new problems for fasteners and fastening techniques, and may help in solving old problems with greater economy.

4.0 IMPROVED MANUFACTURING TECHNIQUES

As with any other manufacturing industry there is always scope for improvement. Sometimes this is slow and creeping, with rates of production increased over the years as automation reduces the labour content. Occasionally a more revolutionary breakthrough occurs and a totally new conception of manufacture results.

The basic problem of the fastener manufacturer is how to utilise material with as little wastage as possible and produce parts quickly, bearing in mind the economics of the process and the quality required.

We have seen cold forging replace slow and wasteful metal-removal techniques. Rolled threads have become accepted as the logical method for speeding up manufacture, again saving material and indeed enhancing the properties of the fastening by improving grain flow. These processes are being developed so that stainless steel and other difficult materials can be formed in the same way.

4.1 *Dynaflow forging*

One of the more sophisticated forging techniques to have evolved has been the Dynaflow process. It couples cold extrusion with cold heading. The parent wire is both extruded down and forged up, permitting production of parts containing very large unit shank volumes in the upset portion (usually about 21 volumes but possibly up to 35). The stages of this process are shown in Fig. 4. An additional bonus from this method is that, owing to the cold work done

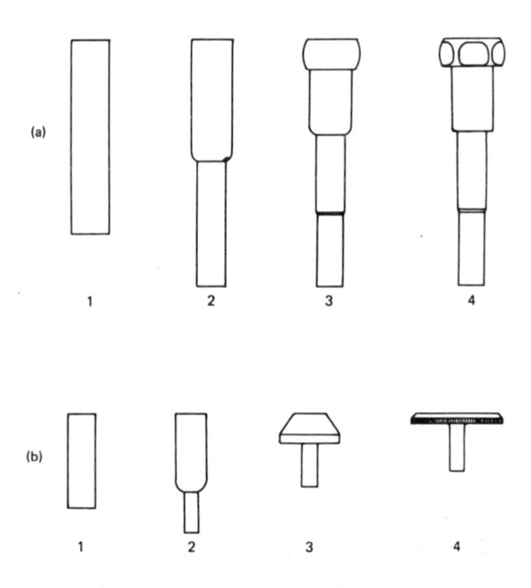

Fig. 4. Examples of Dynaflow process products. (a) Shouldered part: 1 – cut off, 2 – extrude, 3 – forge first blow, 4 – forge second blow. (b) Large-headed part.

during extrusion, the tensile and yield strengths of the component are increased. This allows cheaper materials to be used, or the elimination of subsequent heat treatment with its attendant distortion problems.

Heads may be circular, rectangular, square or hexagonal, and may be off-centre if required. One or more shoulders can be produced under the head. These again may be of any section, and in some instances can be eccentric to each other or to the head or shank. Consequently many parts may be produced by this process which are currently manufactured from bar or by other expensive methods. Outputs of 100 to 150 pieces per minute are normal.

The full benefits of the process are obtained with quantities in the region of 50 000 pieces or more, and the biggest savings are made with parts previously machined. The savings are most apparent in expensive materials such as stainless steel, aluminium and copper.

For example, a stainless steel bolt for washing machines is now being made at a rate of 20 000 a week, saving about £110 000 a year. In another case a bolt produced from 45 tonf tensile steel for the motor industry is now being made from 30 tonf tensile steel. If conventionally heat-treated it would be deformed, but the Dynaflow process keeps it within 0·005 in of straightness.

Altogether some 250 different small components have been made, ranging from $\frac{1}{4}$ in long and $\frac{1}{8}$ in diameter to 4 in long and $\frac{1}{2}$ in diameter, in a full range of materials.

We see this process as an addition to the basic fastener manufacturing techniques, applicable to special-purpose fasteners as well as 'standards'.

4.2 *Other techniques*

The dual cold-extrusion and forging technique is likely to grow. Large cap screws have already been produced by a similar process involving die pressures as high as 175 tonf/in^2.

Investigations continue into hydrostatic forming, explosive forming and high-energy-output (Petroforge) forming. Friction welding could also be beneficial if used to increase shank length with least wastage.

The reduction of machining operations on the preforging billet will become of increasing significance and lossless plane cropping machines will be developed. Gradually all these processes will be integrated to form balanced production lines of fully mechanised or automated machines. This phase has already occurred on woodscrews, where wire is fed in at one end and the finished screws come out, at very high rates, at the other end, with minimal manning on the line of manufacturing machines.

5.0 METRICATION: IMPLICATIONS OF THE CHANGE-OVER

In many ways the change to the use of metric bolts and nuts may be considered one of the least difficult aspects of engineering metrication. For example, in light engineering there has never been any great difficulty among 'inch designers' in working with fasteners having nominal diameters which do not measure in round numbers of fractions of an inch, i.e. B.A. screws and nuts. The B.A. system is metric-based.

Metric nuts and bolts have been standardised internationally and the basic geometry of their threads is exactly the same as that of Unified inch threads. Unified and metric thread systems have different formulae for the calculation of manufacturing tolerances, but, as shown in Fig. 5, the differences between the tolerances themselves are not significant.

Fig. 6 shows the standard combinations of pitch and diameter for Whitworth, Unified and metric threads, and this highlights the matter which is causing most concern regarding the future use of metric threads in the U.K. It is simply that many engineers consider the threads in the metric fine-thread series too fine.

Quite apart from the practical shop-floor pros and cons of fine and coarse threads, the resulting controversy emphasises the need for design data which would allow fine or coarse threads to be judged from a strength point of view. It has been realised that there is a basic need for a procedure which would enable a designer to calculate the strength and determine the mode of failure of a threaded connection with any diameter-pitch combination, any length of thread engagement, and any combination of materials of internally and externally threaded members, etc. Practical work to achieve this objective is one activity in the industry.

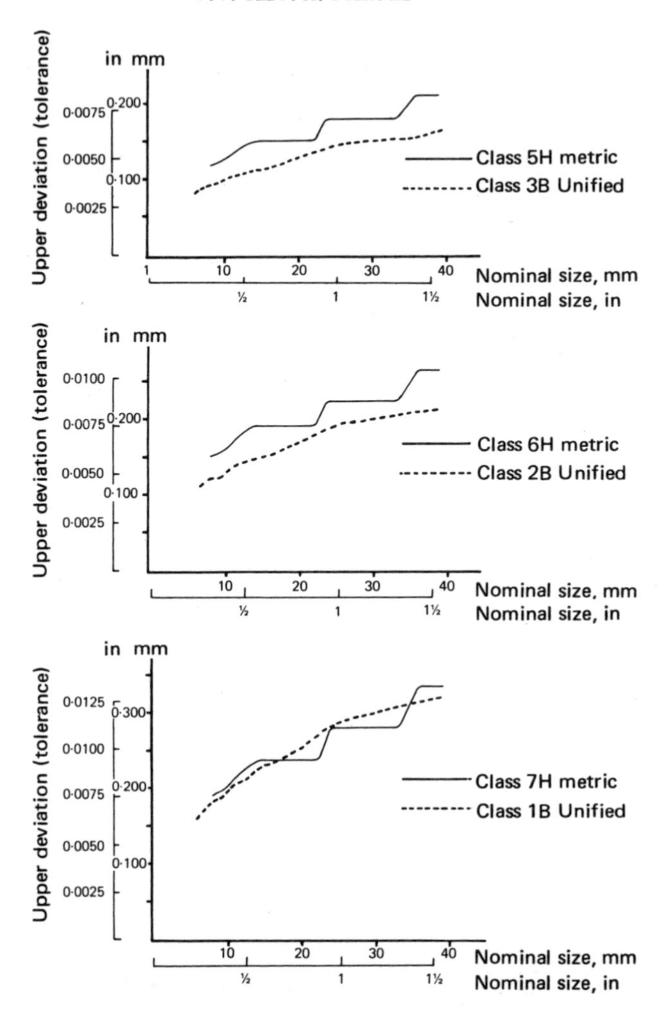

Fig. 5. Comparison of upper deviations (tolerances) of effective diameter for internal metric and Unified Fine Series threads.

One method of presenting the results of such development work is shown in Fig. 7. This diagram relates to ¾ in bolts and nuts with Unified threads over a wide variation in pitch. The work was confined to test specimens in the form of standard bolts and nuts because they are the most common threaded components and it was necessary to get indications regarding the strength of metric fine threads as soon as possible. As already stated, the basic geometry is the same for metric and Unified threads and the tolerance bands are similar. Thus, in view of the very wide experimental variation in pitch, the results are applicable to threads in the metric series. Threads of ¾ in diameter were chosen for manufacturing convenience at the time.

Fig. 7 is useful in showing how variations in nut strength/bolt strength ratio and pitch/diameter ratio affect the mode of failure in a threaded connection which is loaded axially in tension, but the most useful results are the measured failure loads at each of the plotted points. These will permit strength formulae to be derived for design purposes.

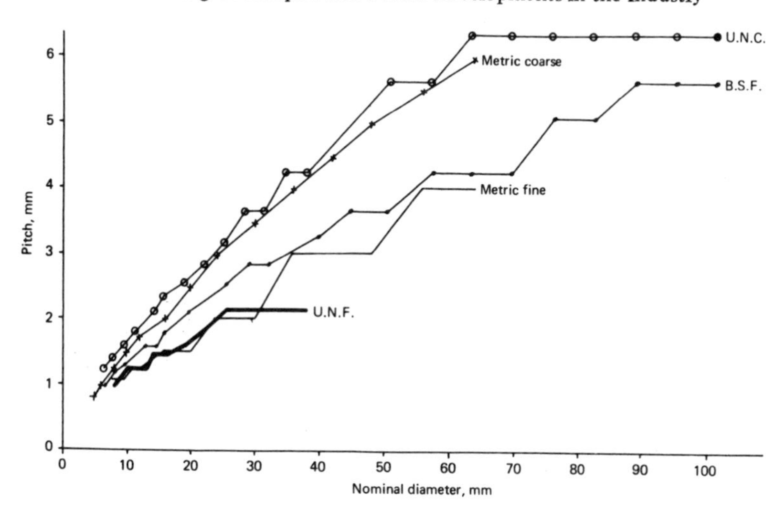

Fig. 6. Standard combinations of pitch and diameter of screw threads.

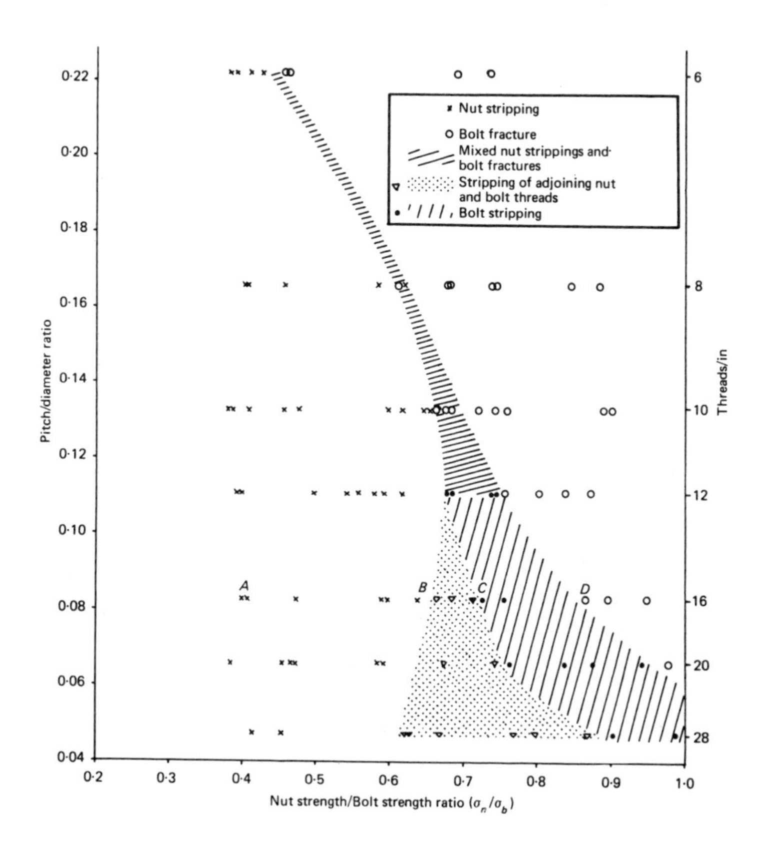

Fig. 7. Mode of failure of ¾ in diameter nuts and bolts with Class 2 Unified threads, having minimum metal thread overlap, and loaded axially under static tension.

So far the results obtained with the bolt fracture mode of failure have shown that, when the length of thread under load is equal to at least one diameter, the effective breaking area is the area of a circle having a diameter equal to the mean of the thread core diameter and the effective diameter, that is:

$$\text{tensile fracture load} = \text{U.T.A.} \times \frac{\pi}{4}\left\{\frac{\text{core dia.} + \text{eff. dia.}}{2}\right\}^2 \tag{1}$$

With measured values of core diameter and effective diameter the formula was found to be accurate within +5% and −3%. Moreover, the results were found to apply to bolts with material strengths up to 80 tonf/in^2. Previously the formula had been verified up to bolt material strengths of only 50 tonf/in^2.

For the calculation of the stripping strength of internally threaded members a basic formula can be derived on the assumption that the internal threads fail by shearing on a cylindrical surface having a diameter equal to the outside diameter of the external thread. This gives the following formula for the area under shear:

$$A_{gn} = \pi L_e D_s \left[0{\cdot}5 + \frac{0{\cdot}577}{p}(D_s - E_n)\right] \tag{2}$$

where p = thread pitch, L_e = length of thread engagement, D_s = bolt thread major diameter, $\bar{E}_n$ = nut thread effective diameter.

Multiplication of this area by the shear strength of the nut material would give, in most cases, a calculated strength much higher than the actual one because no account is taken of nut dilatation and thread bending. Consequently, the formula is usually used in the form:

$$\text{stripping strength} = 0{\cdot}5\, A_{gn} \times \text{ultimate tensile strength} \tag{3}$$

Here 0 5 is the median value of a quantity C_n which includes the ratio between shear strength and tensile strength of the nut material and makes an allowance for dilatation and thread bending. The value 0·5 has been found to be reliable on standard nuts. For increased accuracy in general design it is necessary to determine how C_n is affected by design variables. Fig. 8 shows the general trend of its variation with the ratio nut material strength/bolt material

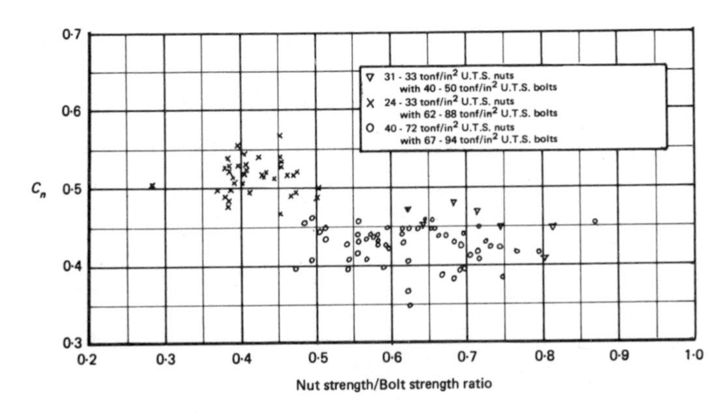

Fig. 8. Variation of C_n with nut strength/bolt strength ratio for ¾ in nuts and bolts with Class 2 Unified threads with various pitches and maximum and minimum thread overlap.

strength. When the internally threaded member is massive enough to prevent dilatation, the value of C_n is about 0·7. There is evidence that C_n also varies according to the absolute size of the fastening and the clearance between the threads.

Assignment of accurate values to C_n for various design conditions is the main objective of future development work in this field.

Returning to the problem of the alleged 'over-fineness' of the metric fine-thread series, we should be clear that from the point of view of static strength no standard thread series can be judged as generally inferior to another. For a given application there will be a certain optimum fineness or coarseness of pitch which will fall near to one or other of the standard values and which will give maximum axial strength. In many instances this optimum pitch can be determined as the value which equates nut stripping strength to bolt fracture strength, that is:

$$\sigma_b \times A_s = \sigma_n \times \overline{A_{gn}} \times C_n \times L_{e/d}$$

$$A_s = \overline{A_{gn}} \times C_n \times \frac{\sigma_n L_e}{\sigma_b d} \qquad (4)$$

where σ_b = u.t.s. of bolt material, σ_n = u.t.s. of nut material, $\overline{A_{gn}}$ = basic nut stripping area for length of engagement equal to one nominal diameter, A_s = effective breaking area of bolt, L_e = length of thread engagement and d = nominal diameter.

For a given value of:

$$C = C_n \times \frac{\sigma_n L_e}{\sigma_b d}$$

there will be for any nominal diameter a value of pitch which will satisfy the equation $A_s = C\overline{A_{gn}}$ and this is the optimum value. Thus by giving C some value which may be appropriate to a certain design case, the corresponding optimum relationship between pitch and diameter can be calculated. For example, for ordinary nuts and bolts:

$$\frac{\sigma_n}{\sigma_b} \simeq 0{\cdot}6 \text{ to } 0{\cdot}7, \quad \frac{L_e}{d} \simeq 0{\cdot}7 \text{ to } 0{\cdot}8$$

and as a starting point C_n may be taken as 0·5. Thus a useful indication of probable optimum pitches might be obtained by making $C = 0{\cdot}25$. Accordingly, the optimum relationship between pitch and diameter for nuts and bolts given by $A_s = 0{\cdot}25\overline{A_{gn}}$ is shown in Fig. 9. This diagram also shows the standard thread series. Some indication of comparative strengths for any combination of pitch and diameter is given by the narrow lines, which represent fixed values of the ratio:

$$r = \frac{\text{axial strength of fastening}}{\text{tensile fracture strength of unthreaded shank of nominal diameter}} \qquad (5)$$

For the assumed conditions applied to components with proportions near those of standard bolts and nuts, Fig. 9 suggests that metric coarse threads are better than metric fine ones, but that fairly wide variations in pitch can be made about the optimum line (particularly below) without causing great losses in axial strength.

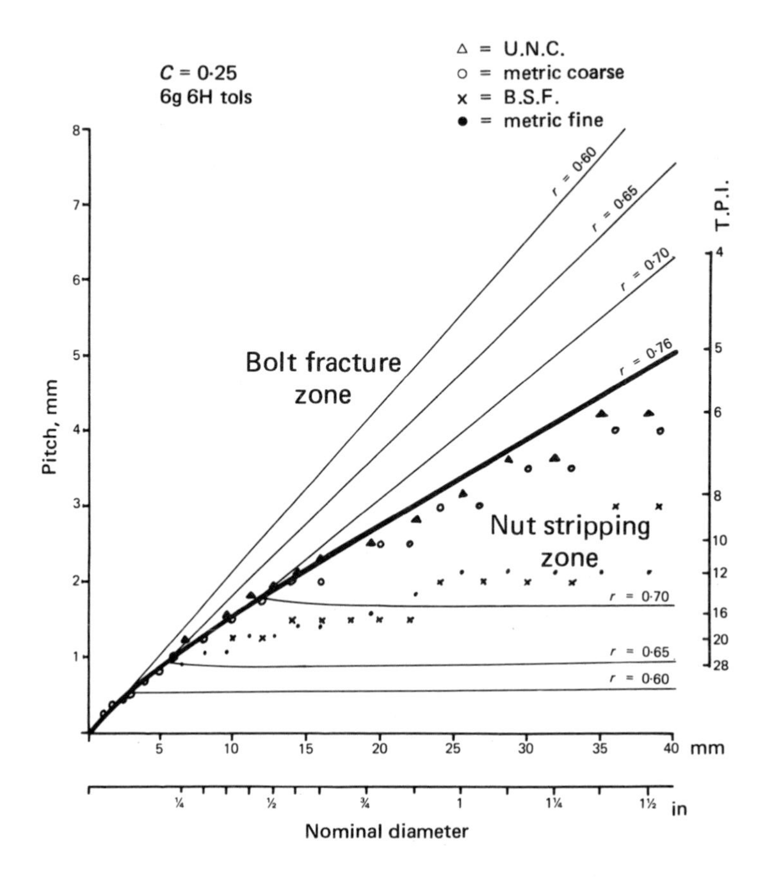

Fig. 9. Pitch and diameter relationship for nuts and bolts.

Unfortunately the value of C_n may vary with nominal diameter and hence a chart as Fig. 9, based on a fixed value of C, may not give an altogether true indication of optimum pitches over a wide range of diameters when the ratios σ_n/σ_b and L_e/d are kept constant. In fact, tests conducted so far on $\frac{3}{8}$ in and $\frac{3}{4}$ in bolts and nuts suggest that Fig. 9 indicates too coarse an optimum pitch for $\frac{3}{8}$ in diameter and is approximately correct for $\frac{3}{4}$ in diameter.

The manner in which optimum pitches are affected by various choices of C value and by variations in thread accuracy is shown in Fig. 10.

The indication obtained so far is that the metric coarse-thread series should be suitable for general use in applications where previously BSW, BSF and UNC would have been used. The use of finer threads, or even non-standard pitches, may be considered for special applications where design for maximum strength is necessary. For this to be possible, more accurate basic design information is wanted, and, as already stated, its acquisition is the main objective of future development work in this field.

The opportunity for greater variety reduction by standardisation on the metric coarse thread is presented by the need to go metric. The metric fine thread can be retained as a 'special' standard applicable to fasteners of smaller diameters.

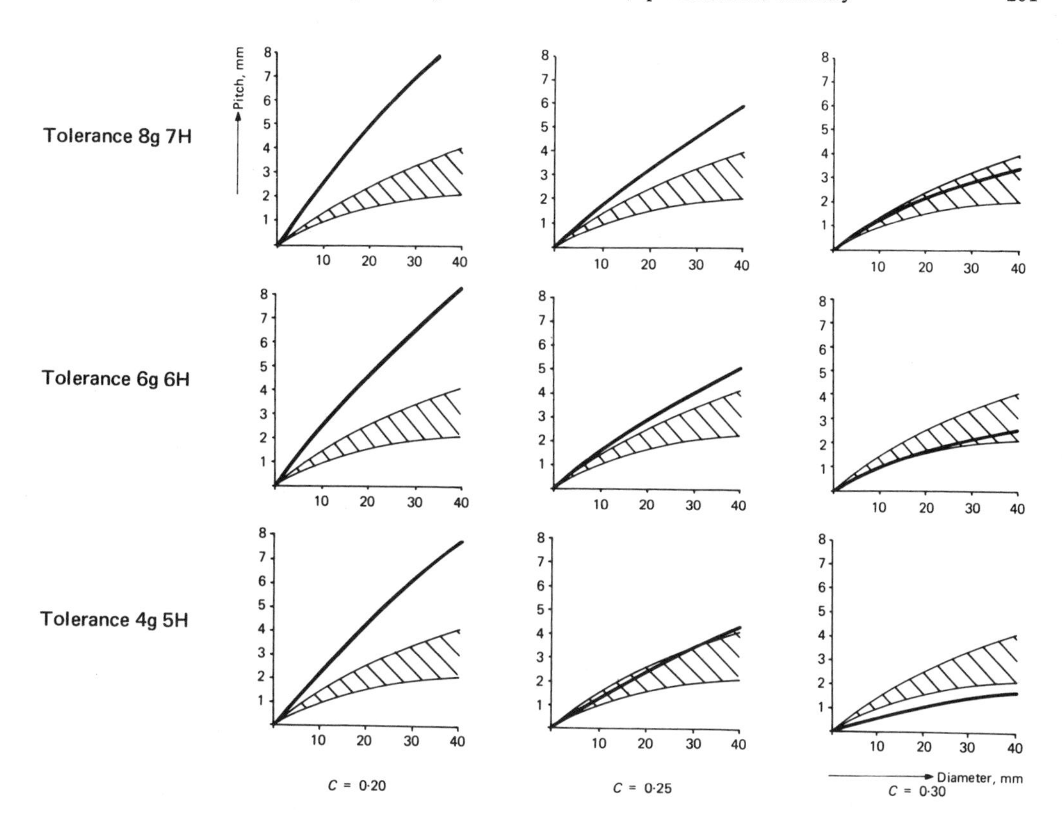

Fig. 10. Pitch and diameter relationships for varying *C*. Shaded areas represent range covered by standard thread series.

6.0 CONCLUSIONS

The mechanical fastening field will continue to move with the rest of industry. It is recognised that cheaper and better fastenings will always be required and to this end the system approach is typical of the movements afoot. The accent of course is on reducing 'in-place' costs.

New materials will give birth to new fastening techniques in both the product and application sense. These improvements will go hand in hand with new manufacturing methods so that speeds of production will increase with less waste of material.

One facet of fastener development – metrication – need not worry the user. Indeed the opportunity exists to rationalise future fastener usage with confidence in the proposed changes, since many more scientific data exist today, on which a logical choice can be made, than existed when the large variety of thread systems was created.

PLASTICS IN INDUSTRY

F. I. Simpson
University of Strathclyde, Glasgow

SUMMARY

Thermoplastic and thermosetting resins are briefly reviewed. Questions of material selection and product design are discussed. The paper concludes with a summary account of reinforced plastics.

1.0 INTRODUCTION

A *plastic* material is one which under pressure will change its shape and on release of that pressure retain its new shape. This definition is obviously too wide for industrial consideration as it includes clay, steel and most metals.

The important point is that the plastics industry's manufactures, which are rigid or semi-rigid items of considerable mechanical strength, are made from plastic organic materials exclusively, and not metallic or mineral compounds. Where a metallic or mineral compound does become an ingredient it is merely as a filler for the main organic binder, to give the latter special properties.

Celluloid, the first synthetic plastic, introduced about 1875, was used to replace many materials because it stayed white, was in good supply, retained its original shiny, white surface and was less costly than ivory. Celluloid has, however, been replaced by plastics with even better appearance and scratch resistance. Today almost every manufacture involves some form of plastics in the end product or the manufacturing process.

Plastics include paints, fabrics, rubbers, insulations, foams, greases, oils and basic moulding and fabricating materials.

2.0 THERMOPLASTIC AND THERMOSETTING RESINS

Plastics are so varied in composition that it is necessary to classify them as *thermoplastic* synthetics which can be remoulded when heated and *thermosetting* materials and *cold-moulded* plastics which flow and can be moulded by heat and pressure, but in their finished shape or curved condition cannot be resoftened or remoulded. The final moulded shape remains rigid and hard when reheated.

Fillers play an important part in the manufacture of plastic compounds. They reduce cost, provide 'body', speed the cure or hardening, minimise shrinkage, reduce crazing, improve thermal endurance, add strength and provide special electrical and mechanical properties.

2.1 *Thermosetting plastics*

2.1.1 *Phenolic plastics*

The development in 1907 of phenolic plastics by Dr Baekeland gave industry a plastic which had very wide uses, both for the non-metallic market and in substitution of plastics for metals.

Raw material manufacturers offer a wide selection of standard materials with varying characteristics. As each material is designed for specific applications, users must select the compound that is best suited for a particular application, bearing in mind that fillers and resins play an important part in determining the properties of the materials available.

Design considerations. When designing parts to be made from phenolics and other thermosetting compounds one must give careful consideration to their various mechanical strengths. Phenolics do not have so great a tensile yield or ultimate strength as metals such as steel. However, phenolic material has great tensile strength when compared with wood or a thermoplastic such as polyethylene, and, because of the lower specific gravity of phenolics, weight relationship with metals is favourable. Steel, the hardest of the above materials, is followed by the melamines and phenolics. Thus phenolics are scratch-resistant, and they are widely used where there may be abrasion. Phenolics are good heat insulators compared with steel and aluminium. While metals are good conductors of electricity, phenolics are good insulators, and they are self-extinguishing after exposure to fire.

Phenolic resin. Mouldings and laminated sheet materials were the principal original products in phenolics. The versatility and low cost of phenolic resins have led to use in numerous ways. Examples are:

- Thermal and acoustical insulation. Products consist of various mineral fibres, e.g. glass bonded with phenolic resin for strength, resilience and 'self-support'.
- Plywood bonding.
- Foundry applications. Phenolics are used for bonding sand to form accurate moulds and cones for metal casting.
- Other large-quantity markets. Adhesives, coating, bonded brake linings, etc.

Summary of phenolic materials. Phenolic materials form a general-purpose group of plastics. They are widely used for industrial products. Many are relatively easy to mould, have an excellent finish, good electrical and mechanical properties and low cost. Fillers play an important part in determining the physical properties, and users will find the best guide to the value of any given material by making a study of the filler used. Future growth of phenolic plastics will depend to a large degree on the development of the faster, fully automatic moulding machines that will facilitate competition with thermoplastics.

2.1.2 *Amino-plastics*

Melamine formaldehyde and urea formaldehyde plastics are the most important aminoplastics. Both are widely used as basic materials. Amino-resins are water-clear. Amongst thermosetting materials they offer the best colour potential. Melamine dinnerware materials and many of the urea compounds use purified wood cellulose as a filler. Other fillers include cotton fabric, asbestos, minerals, wood flour, glass fibres and paper.

Melamine applications. Large quantities of melamine plastics are used for dinnerware because of their hardness, attractive colours, thermal endurance, scratch resistance, stain resistance and mouldability. Melamine and urea compounds offer better arc resistance than do phenolics, and are commonly used (with mineral or wood flour fillers) in circuit-breaker applications. Glass-fibre-filled melamines are used for high-shock electric-arc applications. Better dimensional stability is gained from these mineral-filled products.

Urea compounds are primarily selected when the product is of a kind demanding a colourful thermosetting compound with heat resistance or without cold flow. Urea compounds have good resistance to heat and boiling distortion and are available in an unlimited colour range. In addition to thermal and cold flow stability, ureas provide good dielectric properties and resistance to solvents, oils, greases, scratches and flames. Ureas do not attract dust from static. They are low in cost. The compounds are used extensively for lighting fixtures because of their heat and static resistance.

2.1.3 *Allyl plastics*

Di-allyl pthalate ('d.a.p.') thermosetting resins will harden or cure with peroxide catalysts to form heat- and chemical-resistant products having superior electrical and dimensional control properties. Fillers used with di-allyl pthalate resins include Orlon, Terylene, minerals and glass. The mineral fillers most commonly used are calcium silicate, silica and treated clays.

D.A.P. compounds are characterised by their excellent chemical resistance to all reactants except the strongest oxidisers, low electrical loss, excellent weathering, very low mould shrinkage, and the best stability among organic plastics.

The compounds are very inert and stable, releasing no metal-corroding vapours to attack inserts, and will not support galvanic corrosion in the presence of moisture.

2.1.4 *Alkyd plastics*

The name *alkyd* derives from the words *alc*ohol and ac*id*. Mineral and modified mineral fillers are used for the basic alkyd compounds. They are characterised by their ability to flow freely under very low moulding pressures. Colours are readily available.

Typical volume applications include valve bases, car distributor caps, television receiver components, switches, etc.

Because of their low-pressure moulding characteristics alkyds are chosen for use as an encapsulation compound for resistors, capacitors, transformers, etc.

Other moulding advantages are: short cures, freedom from volatiles and the ability to mould by compression and transfer automatically. Alkyd compounds with glass fillers exhibit very high shock resistance, leading to their use in switchgear and computer components in aircraft and warships. The term *alkyd moulding compound* refers specifically to unsaturated polyester compounds having a low-volatile-content monomer and the appropriate fillers. *Alkyd* is also commonly used to refer to the vegetable-oil-modified polyesters widely used for coatings and paints.

2.1.5 *Unsaturated polyester plastics*

The unsaturated polyesters are hardened or cured by catalysts, added in most cases at the time of moulding. They are best known for their use in reinforced plastics. For example, they are employed in combination with glass fibre for the moulding of car bodies, machine covers, boat hulls, etc.

For the conventional compression and transfer moulding process, premixed compounds are made up of chopped glass fibre mixed with polyester resin, pigment and catalyst. These materials must be kept at a low temperature or used quickly after the catalyst or hardener has been added. Typical products include switchgear, trays, housings, containers etc.

2.2 *Thermoplastic materials*

Thermoplastics are usually moulded by the injection moulding process (thermosetting plastics are moulded by the compression or transfer process). Fillers, as for thermoplastics, are often added to confer stiffness, dimensional stability, thermal endurance, heat conductivity, magnetic properties, etc.

Plasticisers are added to thermoplastics to improve their processability, flexibility and other desirable properties. As a class, thermoplastics are attractive, colourful materials that may be produced as fabrics, moulded products, films, bottles, adhesives and coatings by many varied methods. The following are the more important thermoplastics and their uses.

3.2.1 *Cellulosic and other plastics*

Cellulose nitrate. Celluloid was the first of the synthetic plastics. It was mainly a fabrication material and was used for collars, minor coverings, combs etc. Later, as cellulose nitrate sheet, it became the first bonding material for car safety glass. Photographic films, spectacle frames etc. were all made of it before slow-burning materials were developed. The physical properties of cellulose nitrate plastics are: easy workability, excellent colours, water resistance and toughness. Cellulose nitrate plastics are little used today because of the ease with which they burn and because of the availability of other low-cost materials which are better for the various applications.

Cellulose acetate. Cellulose acetate is mouldable, whereas cellulose nitrate is not. Real volume use started in 1934 with the introduction of the injection moulding machine. Self-extinguishing variations are available to permit use in household appliances. Other uses include toys, beads, disposable tubes, syringes and packing materials.

Cellulose acetate butyrate. The moisture resistance of acetate materials was originally poor. Consequently cellulose acetate butyrate material was developed. Similar to cellulose acetate, it can be used for the same applications when improved resistance to moisture as well as improved dimensional stability are required. Cellulose acetate butyrate plastics may be compounded with fire-retardent additives. They weather well. All fabricating and moulding processes may be used. Major applications today are car fittings, outdoor signs, tool handles, packaging blisters, metallised sheet and film.

Cellulose propionate is noteworthy for its short moulding cycles and its freedom from lamination during moulding. Propionate compounds require less plasticiser than do other cellulosics. They have better weathering properties and colour retention than has acetate. Important features are high impact resistance and toughness. Propionate is most often used for extrusion and injection-moulded products such as magnetic tape containers, small radio cases, toothbrushes and fancy goods.

Acrylic plastics possess great clarity, excellent colourability and very valuable optical properties (including a low refractive index). Other valuable properties of acrylics are their weatherability, high degree of uniformity and high resistence to scratching and abrasion. Acrylics withstand food oils, non-oxidising acids, petroleum lubricants and household alkalis. They do not react with photographic solutions. Acrylics may not be used freely with alcohols, esters, ketones, hydrocarbons, phenols and fluorocarbons. They are slow-burning, and with certain additives may be classed as self-extinguishing. Acrylic plastics may be injection- or compression-moulded, extruded and blow-moulded. Acrylic sheets are cast and extruded. The materials are readily welded, machined and thermo-formed. Acrylic plastics have good dielectric strength and are non-tracking. The combination of weatherability, high dielectric strength and low moisture absorption results in wide use for high-voltage line spacers and cable clamps. Acrylics find many uses in the car industry, e.g. for tail-lamp clusters. Acrylic and p.v.c. alloys make an excellent thermo-forming sheet that is tough and has a high tear strength. Popular applications for acrylic plastics include lenses, aircraft, building and lighting fixtures, dishes, knobs, dials, nameplates, telephone dials, fountain pens, signs, packaging and textile fibres.

Styrene plastics. Polystyrene materials are prepared in all transparent and opaque colours and are easily distinguished from any other plastic material by the distinct metallic sound they produce when they are dropped. The plastic is generally used in pure resin form, but can be used with glass and other fillers up to 40% by volume. Excellent mouldability is an important property of styrene. It is one of the very-low-cost, rigid and colourful materials, and is extensively used where price alone is the consideration. Styrene has excellent resistance to organic acid, alkali salts and lower alcohol. It softens when used with hydrocarbons, ketones, esters and essential oils. Styrene stress-cracks easily and must be annealed for many applications. The electrical properties of polystyrene are admirable within its temperature range, but since styrene is not self-extinguishing it is unsuitable for exposure to arc. Impact-resistant styrene materials are produced by including rubber modifiers, which give toughness and resilience at the expense of clarity. Typical styrene applications include jewellery, light fixtures, packages, toys, housewares, medical syringes, etc. Expanded styrene products make ideal packaging and insulating materials, and can be as light as 2 lb/ft^3, have very low thermal conductivity, and be very well able to cushion shock. These materials are good for packaging material, ceiling and wall tiles, and thermal or acoustic insulation.

A.B.S. plastics. Three chemicals, acrylonitrite, butadiene and styrene, are combined to make the a.b.s. plastics. Acrylic and styrene polymers are resinous and butadienes are rubber-like materials. These plastics can be compounded with a high degree of hardness or with great flexibility and toughness. Stiffness and dimensional stability are greatly improved by the addition of glass fillers. A.B.S. materials can be processed by thermo-forming injection, blow-moulding, rotational moulding, and extrusion. A.B.S. plastics are mainly used where resistance to abuse is necessary and where colourability, hardness and moisture stability are important. Typical applications for a.b.s. compounds are camera housings, telephone handsets, drill housings, knobs, handles, pump impellers, etc. A.B.S. plastics may be metal-plated, and such pieces have a good future as replacements for die castings, metal pressings and light fabrications.

Vinyl plastics. Perhaps polyvinyl chloride ('p.v.c.') is one of the largest-, if not the largest-volume, plastics materials in the world, and is potentially one of the lowest-cost materials. P.V.C. has achieved this market leadership because of its good physical properties, low cost and ease of processing. Its properties include self-extinguishing characteristics, water-, chemical- and abrasion-resistance, good strength and a complete range of colours. Its compounds range from soft, flexible films to rigid, high-strength materials. Plasticisers, lubricants, fillers and stabilisers confer this versatility. Products are usually made by injection-, transfer-, rotational or compression-blow-moulding, calendering, or extrusion. Main uses for rigid p.v.c. are pipes, conduits, core and cable insulation. Flexible p.v.c. is used for raincoats, dolls, bottles, garden hose, gaskets, etc. p.v.c. is a suitable blow-moulding material. It combines a clarity approaching that of glass with a break resistance as good as that of polythene. Polyvinylacetate resins are used as adhesives for glass, paper, metal, wood and porcelain. Photographic flash bulbs may have a coating of polyvinyl acetate to eliminate danger from glass particles if broken. Polyvinyl aldehyde plastics are made from vinyl acetate and formaldehyde, producing a resin which is very strong, tough and flexible. It can be used to coat the wire employed in coil winding and will withstand the abuse of modern high-speed winding and assembly operations.

Polyolefin plastics. Polyethylene is a wax-like polymer which has a use in every field. It has most desirable electrical and chemical properties and can be processed by all methods. It is perhaps best known for its wide use in plastic films and squeeze bottles. Polyethylene is composed of ethylene molecules joined together in long chains. The basic characteristics of a particular formulation depend on the number of units making up a chain and the method by which they are combined. Short, simple chains make a brittle, waxy polymer. Large molecules forming long chains produce a very tough, difficult-to-process polymer. In between are formulations with different properties. The density of a given material depends on the shape of the molecules. Closely fitting chains produce high-density materials. Other chains are widely spaced and so are of lower density. Density is the clue to properties.

AS DENSITY INCREASES
Stiffness increases
Yield strength increases
Hardness increases
Creep resistance increases
Toughness decreases
Softening temperature increases
Stress crack resistance decreases
Permeability decreases
Gloss increases
Grease resistance increases

A widely used criterion is the melt index, which is a measure of the viscosity of a polymer at a specified temperature and pressure. The melt index indicates the performance of a given formulation when properly processed.

AS MELT INDEX DECREASES
Stiffness increases
Tensile strength increases
Yield strength increases
Hardness increases
Creep resistance increases
Toughness increases
Softening temperature increases
Stress crack resistance increases
Permeability decreases
Gloss decreases
Grease resistance increases

The consistency of polythene formation also affects properties.

AS MOLECULAR STRUCTURE BECOMES MORE HOMOGENEOUS
Tensile strength increases
Creep resistance increases
Toughness increases
Softening temperature increases
Stress crack resistance increases

Uncoloured polyethylene has poor weathering power and becomes embrittled in the presence of oxygen and sunlight. Carbon black added to natural polyethylene greatly increases its weatherability. Polyethylene products are made by injection-, blow-, and rotational moulding and extrusion. Sheets and films are easily vacuum-formed to make blister packages and functional products. Blow-moulded bottles provide a major market for polythene.

Polypropylene plastics are produced by polymerising polypropylene gas at low temperatures and pressures. Polypropylene does not present stress-cracking problems and offers excellent chemical resistance at higher temperatures. The main uses of polypropylene occur where advantage can be taken of its quality at higher temperatures. Typical applications include consumer-good parts, e.g. washing machine impellers, car trim hinges, bottles, packaging, etc. Products are made from polypropylene by all the conventional processes of thermoplastics.

Nylon is classed chemically as a polyamide. It is made by a complex chemical process, and is similar to the protein products created naturally in the human body. In one manufacturing process, nylon material is heated to 450°F and forced through small holes to form continuous filaments. The filaments may be stretched to from four to seven times their original length, causing molecular rearrangement which adds great tensile strength and elasticity. Hence the use of nylon as a tough hosiery material and synthetic 'silk'. Moulded nylon materials are noteworthy for their toughness, abrasion resistance, strength, low friction and heat resistance (250°F). Many special types are made to facilitate injection moulding, blow moulding and extrusion. Asbestos, glass and other fillers improve dimensional stability, minimise shrinkage and increase stiffness in nylon compounds. Typical applications include mechanical components, gears, cams, bearings, fabrics, bristles, etc.

Acetal resins are a highly crystalline, stable form of polymerised formaldehyde. They were originally designed because of the shortcomings of other thermoplastics intended to replace die-castings and other components in 1960. The special properties are rigidity, resilience, toughness, high strength, and resistance to common solvents such as petrol, paraffin, carbon tetrachloride, etc. Better-than-nylon dimensional stability is achieved by acetal products because of their low moisture absorption under varying conditions of humidity. Rigidity and dimensional stability are greatly improved by glass fillers. Creep resistance of acetal resin is good. Good holding power for self-tapping screws is an assembly asset. Acetal resin is best for precision small gears, whereas nylon is best for impact gears. Acetal resin can be injection- or blow-moulded or extruded. It can be heat-formed, machined, painted or plated. Typical applications include pump impellers, valves, gears, cams, hardware, screws, etc.

Polycarbonate plastics. Polycarbonate is important because of its excellent heat resistance, outstanding impact strength and good dimensional stability. Polycarbonate reinforced with glass gains greatly in tensile strength. The heat deflection temperature is raised to 300°F and mould shrinkage is reduced to 0·001in/in. Impact strength is reduced, however, and the moulding cycle speeded up by the considerably better thermal conductivity. Polycarbonate can be processed by all moulding methods, thermo-forming and machining. Typical applications include street-light glasses (because of heat endurance and high impact strength), domestic crockery (e.g. coffee pots), tubes and tool housings.

3.0 MATERIAL SELECTION AND PRODUCT DESIGN

The large number of sophisticated plastics and the fine points of their capabilities place a great responsibility on the product designer who must specify materials for application.

Selection of the proper material requires analysis of the good points and the weak points of each material considered for the job. No one material will posess all the qualities desired. Undesirable characteristics must be compensated for in design.

Elimination will reduce the field, and final selection may then depend on testing in actual use to prove the endurance and stability of the product.

The following factors should be considered when choosing a plastic material.

3.1 *Elasticity*

If the product requires flexibility, then the choice of material is limited to materials such as urethane/polyester, polyethylene, vinyl, polypropylene, fluorcarbon, silicone, polyurethane, acetal, nylon or some of the rigid plastics that have limited flexibility in a thin section (e.g. thin laminations are quite flexible).

3.2 *Temperature*

Thermal considerations will quickly eliminate many materials. For products operating above 450°F, the silicones, polyamides, hydrocarbon resins, cold mould, glass bonded mica or phospho-asbestos plastics may be required.

Between 250 and 450°F, glass- or mineral-filled phenolics, melamine, alkyd, silicone, nylon, polycarbonate and polypropylene should be evaluated. Domestic appliances like electric irons and toasters use melamine and phenolic handles. The addition of glass fillers to thermoplastics can raise the useful temperature range by as much as 100°F and at the same time shorten the moulding cycle.

In the range 0–212°F a wide selection of materials is available. Low-temperature considerations may eliminate many thermoplastics. Thermosetting materials exhibit minimum embrittlement at low temperatures.

3.3 *Flame resistance*

Insurance requirements on the use of self-extinguishing plastics for contact-carrying members and other components introduce critical material selection problems. All thermosets are self-extinguishing. Nylon, polycarbonate and vinyl are thermoplastics which may be suitable for applications requiring self-extinguishing properties. Cellulose acetate and a.b.s. are also available with these properties. Glass reinforcement improves these materials considerably.

3.4 *Impact*

Impact strengths of plastics are only of comparative value. A better value is impact tensile strength, which can broadly separate materials which can withstand shock loading from those which are poor in this respect.

Comparative tests on sections of similar size, which are moulded in accordance with the proposed product, must be tested to determine the impact performance of a plastics material.

Laminated plastics, glass-filled epoxy, melamine and phenolic are outstanding thermosetting plastics, while polycarbonate and urethane are outstanding thermoplastics. The impact strength of some plastic films is also outstanding.

3.5 *Arc resistance*

Electrical devices often require arc resistance. A high-temperature, high-current arc will ruin many plastics. The more serious cases may require cold-mould phospho-asbestos, glass-bonded mica or mineral-filled fluorcarbon products. Lesser arcing problems may be solved using polysulphore, polyester glass, alkyd, melamine, urea or phenolics. With low-current arcs, general-purpose phenolic and glass-filled nylon or polycarbonate, acetal and urea may be used very satisfactorily.

All circuit-breaker problems must be scrutinised with regard to product performance under short circuit and mechanical shock.

3.6 *Colour*

Urea, melamine, polycarbonate, polypropylene and the phenolics are used in the temperature range above 200°F and up to the materials limitation for good colour stability. Most thermoplastics will be suitable below this range.

3.7 *Transparency*

Maximum transparency is available in acrylic polyolefin and styrene compounds. Many other thermoplastics may have adequate transparency. Polycarbonate and polysulphane provide high-temperature transparency.

3.8 *Applied stress*

Many thermoplastics will craze or crack under certain environmental conditions, so products which are highly stressed mechanically must be checked very carefully. Polypropylene and linear polyethylene offer greater freedom from stress crazing than some other thermoplastics. Thermosets are generally preferable for parts under continuous load.

3.9 *Moisture*

The effects of moisture are well known. For high-moisture applications polysulphane, acrylic, butyrate, glass-bonded mica, mineral-filled phenolic and the fluorcarbons are satisfactory. Impact styrene plus 25% graphite and high-density polyethylene with 15% graphite give long-term performance in water.

3.10 *Surface wear*

Hardness is not necessarily the correct index for scratch resistance. In general the thermosets have the best abrasion resistance. Acrylic and a.b.s. also have good fingernail scratch resistance. Tests simulating actual conditions give the best information. Ultra-high-molecular-weight polythene, urethane, high-density polyethylene, nylon and polyester film give good results.

3.11 *Permeability*

Many plastics rate very poorly in permeability, e.g. polyethylene will pass hydrocarbons and many other chemicals.

3.12 *Dimensional stability*

If absolute dimensional stability is essential then organic plastics are eliminated and ceramics and glass-bonded mica must be considered. Several organic plastics are available which offer very good dimensional stability and are suitable where some age and environmental dimensional changes are permissible. These include polysulphane, mineral-filled phenolic epoxy, rigid vinyl and styrene. Glass fillers improve the dimensional stability of all plastics. If dimensional stability is important then all materials using plasticisers must be avoided. Materials which exhibit substantial moisture absorption are not stable dimensionally.

Many organic plastics show high thermal expansion in comparison with metal mating products. This can cause trouble if tight dimensional relations are to be maintained.

3.13 *Weathering*

Many plastics have a short life when exposed to outdoor conditions. The better materials include acrylic, polyester, alkyd and black linear polyethylene. Black materials are best for outdoor service.

3.14 *Material cost*

Some high-priced materials mould at very high speed and are thus inexpensive to mould. Other materials run automatically, and their adaptability for fully automatic production often justifies the premium.

The production engineer must decide what is demanded by his application and by elimination find a design and material to meet demands at minimum cost.

The ultimate selection of material may be a compromise choice based on the most favourable balance of properties.

In all cases the wrong material is by far the most costly, and the price per pound is by no means the main criterion.

4.0 LAMINATED AND REINFORCED PLASTICS

A laminated structure is formed from layers of material bonded together into a unit. The plastics industry manufactures large quantities of laminated sheets, tubes, rods, etc., using various materials such as paper cloth, asbestos, glass fabric etc., bonded with synthetic resins. Such products are traditionally known as *laminated plastics* when high moulding pressures (1200 to 1500 lbf/in^2) are used, and as *reinforced plastics* when low moulding pressures are employed (0 to 1000 lbf/in^2).

4.1 *Laminated plastics*

The electrical industry makes wide use of the electrical and thermal insulating and the non-magnetic properties of laminated plastics. Small pieces punched from laminated sheets are used in radio and electrical sub-assemblies. Tubes, 5–6 ft in diameter and 7–8 ft long, are used in large transformers.

These are examples of laminated phenolic materials. Copper-surfaced laminated sheets are used for printed circuits. Because of their resistance to chemicals, laminated materials are used to make items of equipment in the chemical, paper and electroplating industries.

Resin-treated wood surfaces and treated fabrics are used to make decorative table tops, which are wear-resistant, impervious to staining by beverages, and burn-resistant. Light-diffusing panels are made from urea resins, pure cellulose and rag papers.

4.1.2 *Resins for laminated materials*

Resins for laminated materials are generally used in a varnish form or a water solution. The varnish is made by dissolving the soluble form of the resin in alcohol. After this the varnish is applied to the laminations. The treated sheets are pressed, causing the resin to flow and bond the adjacent sheets together. The resin becomes very hard, producing a dense, strong, tough substance. Typical resins used are phenolic, melamine and epoxy.

4.1.3 *Filler sheet materials*

Rag paper makes the best filler for lamination material because of its great toughness. Often less costly materials are used, such as kraft paper. Paper selected is of an absorbent type made specially for lamination work. Cloth fillers are used in weights of 1½ oz fabric to a heavy 40 oz canvas.

Sheets of asbestos paper and fabric produce a material having maximum temperature resistance, dimensional stability and resistance to certain chemicals. A glass fabric woven from very fine filaments of glass can be used as a filler to produce a strong material with high resistance to impact, moisture and heat.

4.1.4 *Treating laminated sheets with resin*

Paper, cloth and other lamination materials are received in large rolls and passed through a machine which applies the resin and dries the treated sheet. A squeeze roll controls the amount of resin absorbed and an oven evaporates the alcohol or water from the varnish. This oven advances the cure of the resin so that it will be cured quickly and correctly in the final pressing operation.

4.1.5 *Pressing laminated sheets*

Large hydraulic presses are used to form the finished sheets. A temperature of 300 to 350°F and a pressure of 1200 to 2500 lbf/in^2 are used to cure the resins and bond the sheets. The press platens are chambered to allow circulation of water or steam to provide process heat.

4.1.6 *Making laminated tubes and rods*

Tubes may rolled or moulded. To roll tubing the treated paper is passed over a heated roll and wound on a steel mandrel of the required diameter. This mandrel is centred between three rollers, which apply pressure as the tube is wrapped.

After stoving, the tubes are finally stripped from their mandrels and finished by centreless grinding.

Moulded tubes and rods are made by wrapping the treated paper or cloth on mandrels and placing the assembly in a closed mould to which heat and pressure are applied. Moulded tubes and rods have a greater density but also have a seam or parting line where the mould closes.

4.1.7 *Uses for laminated materials*

In addition to the electrical uses already mentioned, laminated materials, because of their resilience, find employment in quiet, heavy-duty gears.

Cams are made from laminated material containing some graphite. The material saves weight and improves the starting and stopping operations of high-speed cams. Laminated cloth heavy-duty bearings are used in rolling mills because of the shock loads involved. Other uses are for clutches and fan blades. Wide use is made of laminates for decorative finishes.

4.2 *Reinforced plastics*

Reinforced plastics materials occupy a very large section of the plastics industry. They are similar to laminates in many applications, differing mainly by their use of resins which do not require the very high moulding pressures used in making laminated sheet materials. These materials are called *filled plastics.* Reinforcements include glass, boron, carbon, graphite, asbestos, woven and non-woven textiles. Fillers are often particles such as powders, pellets, spheres and needles. Resins used for reinforced plastics include polyester, epoxy, phenolic and silicone, of which a large proportion is polyester.

Catalyst is freshly mixed with resin monomer and filler at the time of moulding and hardens the resin and filler combination without external pressure. Pressure is often used, however, to obtain improved density, good surface finish and a faster cure.

In the curing process a soft gel is initially formed and heat is produced by the chemical reaction. This converts the resin and filler into a hard, integral mass without liberation of volatile materials.

4.2.1 *Resins for reinforced plastics*

Polyesters are the leading resins for reinforced plastics and are comparatively low in cost and easy to mould at low temperatures. They have good mechanical, chemical and electrical properties. Polyesters are mainly used with glass fibre for aircraft parts, motor components, ducting, etc. Epoxy resins give high mechanical and fatigue strength, excellent dimensional stability, corrosion resistance, good inter-laminar bond and very low water absorption. Epoxy glass and epoxy paper combinations are widely used for printed circuits.

4.2.2 *Phenolic resins*

Phenolic resins have high mechanical strength, excellent resistance to high temperature, good thermal insulation, good electrical properties and high chemical resistance. Phenolic is used with glass for high-strength interior aircraft parts, fishing rods, honeycombs, with asbestos for missile parts, and with cotton and paper for safety helmets.

4.2.3 *Melamine resins*

Melamine resins have excellent colour range and retention, good abrasion resistance and good electrical properties. They are resistant to alkalis and flame. Melamine is used with rayon paper for moulded-in decoration of dinnerware, wall tiles and with glass for industrial laminates.

4.2.4 *Silicone resins*

Silicone resins provide the highest electrical properties available in reinforced plastics and are the most heat-stable. They retain strength and electrical characteristics under long exposure from 500–1000°F. Silicone glass is used for electrical insulation, hot-air ducts and other structures in aircraft.

4.2.5 *Reinforcement*

Various types of reinforcement are available to meet product requirement. Glass is one of the most commonly used for reinforced plastic materials, but the stiffness is low. This deficiency has been overcome by using elastically stronger fibres, for example carbon and boron, leading to such remarkable new ultra-strong composites as Rolls-Royce Hyfil.

4.2.6 *Glass fibre*

Glass fibre reinforcement gives outstanding strength-to-weight ratios, high tensile strength, high modulus of elasticity and resilience, and excellent dimensional stability.

Continuous-strand glass gives unidirectional reinforcement. Glass fabric essentially reinforces the object in two directions, while chopped glass strands give random reinforcement. Reinforcing glass mats are lower in cost than fabric and give random reinforcement.

4.2.7 *Asbestos*

Asbestos felts provide maximum tensile and flexural strength, excellent thermal insulation, good abrasion resistance and high impact strength. Asbestos is used for aircraft and missile parts, its short-term heat and flame resistance are excellent (6900°F for 60 s).

4.2.8 *Paper*

Paper is the leading reinforcement for high-pressure laminating and is often used for low-pressure reinforced plastics. It is inexpensive, prints well, and has strength adequate for many applications. Paper is used for circuit boards, for decorative hand-weaving laminates and for furniture.

4.2.9 *Other reinforcements*

Carbon theoretically affords great strength if its atoms are appropriately arranged. This has been achieved by Rolls-Royce with fine threads of carbon embedded in epoxy resin. The threads give stiffness and a marked reduction in weight (compared with titanium) to blades for gas-turbine aero-engines.

BIBLIOGRAPHY

1 J. H. DUBOIS and F. W. JOHN *Plastics.*
2 J. S. WALKER and E. MARTIN *Injection moulding of plastics.*
3 D. FISHLOCK and A. H. COTTRELL *Financial Times.* 3 Dec. 1968.

TOOL DESIGN IN THE PLASTIC INDUSTRY

R. A. Ireland
Witton Moulded Plastics Ltd. (G.E.C.)

SUMMARY

This paper covers some of the many problems which confront the plastic tool designer. Owing to the very large range of components and their widely different methods of manufacture, it is possible to touch briefly only on the basic design requirements. An attempt is made to show the importance in this new industry of close liaison between designer and end user, without which bad designs are produced. The importance of the relationship between 'finished article' design and tool design is also stressed, and a brief indication is given of how this relationship can be improved by plastic material choice. The use of prototype tooling is mentioned briefly.

1.0 INTRODUCTION

It is a sign of the times that a gathering like this should have amongst its speakers a plastic engineer. In the not too distant past the term *plastic* conjured up in most people's minds a substitute material. This early image has now largely disappeared, and it is the current and future value of plastics which will now be considered.

Like other manufacturers, the manufacturer of a plastic article has certain instruments without which he could not do his work. Basically, in the plastic industry they are, (a) a moulding machine, and (b) a moulding tool. It is the latter which is the subject of this paper.

What is required of a plastic moulding tool?

A lot of course depends upon the final product. If one is considering the 'Bucket and Bowl' market then very little is actually required of the moulding tool except speed. Basically, a plastic moulding tool has to manufacture a plastic moulding, but the moulding may have a vast variety of end-uses, and it is here that unfortunately the average moulder has little or no control. Unfortunately it is true that a bad moulder can blame his tools, but conversely a good moulder may have a lot of respect for tool design, and it is most important that a tool designer know exactly what a moulding from a tool is going to do in later life, what it is expected to stand up to, what strains are to be put on it. To know this there must be much closer liaison than exists at present between toolmaker and moulder, and, probably more important still, between moulder and end-user.

For instance, in this country the manufacture of gear wheels in polyacetal resins has been hampered to a great degree by the number of failures which have occurred because, in the absence of tooth loading figures, gears made for many industrial applications were subject to 'creep' under static load. This was blamed on bad moulding techniques, and the words 'plastic gears' have been used with some reservations by instrument makers.

2.0 TOOLS FOR PRODUCTS IN THERMOSETTING RESINS

2.1 *General features*

There are certain general features of tools satisfactory for the production of components in thermosetting resins.

Today there is a considerable variety of machinery available. It is possible to make tools which will work in different machines. But basically, to some degree, the old rule of thumb method applies – 3 tonf/in^2 for a compression tool, 5 tonf/in^2 for a transfer tool, and something in excess of this for a thermosetting injection tool. Before a decision can be taken upon the tonnage required to keep a tool shut it is important to find out how many cavities are needed: as a rule of thumb, *the more cavities one has, the cheaper the final article but the more expensive the tool.* This is not always strictly true. If one is loading inserts the press open time during the loading part of the cycle may well make many impressions uneconomic. Also the sheer physical size of a tool may be a limiting factor, for tool fitting becomes a major headache. However, when this decision is made, the press tonnage is settled.

The next decision is whether the tool should be *open flash,* that is with directly horizontal flash lands, or *positive,* with completely vertical flash lands, or *semi-positive,* a combination of open flash and positive, or *transfer.*

Today it is also possible to injection-mould with a screw pre-plasticiser. This is the most advanced stage of thermosetting moulding at the present time. It requires a completely different approach to toolmaking, and in fact is very much more akin to the toolmaking required for manufacturing a thermoplastic article.

2.2 *Tool design features*

The importance of tool design cannot be too highly stressed.

If inserts are required the mould designer must consider how they are to be fitted into the moulding, how they are to be held, what material is to be used for the pins, whether they are likely to drop into tool faces through accidental breakage of springs or bad fitting by an operator, and if so what damage is likely in the tool.

This, to some degree, will determine the material from which the pins are to be made, and in turn may very well alter the concept of how they are to be fitted to the tool. Importance must also be given to any thin blades that may be necessary in the tool. It may be that the tool should be constructed so that such blades are replaceable. Another factor to be considered is the pressure to be withstood with adequate safety factor, and this applies particularly to the flash land.

Very early in his design thinking the mouldmaker will have decided whether or not the tool is to be capable of fully automatic working. If it is he will make sure that the moulding always stays on the right side of the tool. Today it is usual practice to put stripping gear, either ejectors or stripping plates, on both sides of the tool, so that it is possible to guarantee that mouldings come away from the tool during the open period.

The mould designer must also consider the loading of the tool, and whether to load with preheated pellets, and if so whether they should be specially shaped. Pellets are not always necessarily of the same size when they are in their soft condition, and in fact a ham-fisted moulder can make a large fat column rather than the designed form. Eventually the economics of the process must be affected by such matters.

Consideration must be given to the method of heating the tool. If the moulding factory is steam-heated the problem does not really arise. If, however, steam heating is not available, electric heating has to be used. A base platen may be perfectly adequate on a relatively thin tool but may need to be supplemented by cartridge heaters in certain places. Cartridge heaters require some sort of control, and here the tool designer may bring in the moulding shop electrician and discuss with him where to put thermocouples, how to make them easily accessible, easily replaceable, etc.

2.3 *Tool finish*

The finish required depends upon what is required of the finished article, but it should be remembered that, even if only a 'rough' finish is required, the moulding may prove impossible to get out of the tool unless the metal surface is sufficiently polished.

The 'polish' should really consist of a series of very, very small lines in the line of draw, and is difficult to obtain unless one makes sure that initial machining is done with this requirement in mind. For example, no purpose can be served by turning a component and polishing it on the lathe if the line of draw is at right angles to the turning marks. Because of this it is important that the designer look at the construction of the tool with regard to how it is to be polished.

On large, closed containers a vapour-blasted surface may give easier extraction than a polished surface. This is due basically to the fact that it is possible to make a moulding into a 'piston'. Although the moulding is free to move, directly it does so it is restrained by the vacuum thus created. Quite large presses can be held shut in this way.

It is evidently important to realise how the original design concept bears on the ease or difficulty of manufacturing a tool.

The advent of the spark erosion machine has given another aspect to the question of finish. Unfortunately the normal finish expected from this machine is usually unacceptable by the moulder because of the component extraction problem.

The plastics industry owes a lot to these latest techniques of machining metals, yet the author feels that some of the techniques have created new problems which so far have not been satisfactorily overcome.

2.4 *Tool materials*

Two most important features of tool materials are strength and hardness. It is also important that the metals chosen can be machined in the finished state, and normally this is where the problem arises.

It is undoubtedly true that, although the shrinkage of plastic materials is now much more widely understood, mistakes are still made. Not uncommonly, parts do not show the shrinkage that has been allowed for in the construction of the tool, however clever the moulder may be. The only remedy is for the tool to be remachined, but it is usually uneconomic and undesirable to reduce tool hardness for the purpose. Spark erosion is certainly one way, and grinding is another. The ability to use these two processes, however, depends once again upon the design of the tool. So the tool designer must make sure that it is still possible to get at and machine the parts which are likely to be the most troublesome when the tool is in its finished condition. With this in mind designers now more commonly specify the more exotic materials. Beryllium copper is slowly coming to the forefront in the thermosetting field, as it has been for a few years in thermoplastics.

However, most tools by far are still made from oil- or air-hardening steels, or, even more commonly today, from pre-toughened steels. It is important that the type of steel used be marked on every piece of the mould. Subsequent operations following damage may very well be affected by the initial choice of steel. The material must also readily accept chromium plating.

For certain grades of plastic material it may be necessary to make the tool from grades of steel which have special characteristics in corrosion resistance or abrasion resistance. It is important that this be considered very early in tool design owing to the difficulty of machining some of these special steels.

3.0 TOOLS FOR PRODUCTS IN THERMOPLASTIC RESINS

3.1 *Tool life, core design and gating*

Here the problem is very similar to that which has already been considered. There are certain added complications, and there are also certain factors which make things a little easier for the tool designer.

The required pressures, temperatures etc. must again be taken into account. The fact that a tool generally works in a horizontal plane rather than a vertical plane may also have a bearing on initial design. It is important to remember that the general process is somewhat faster than compression moulding. There are tools used in Britain with cycles as low as one second, and they run possibly 24 hours a day, five days a week. The number of operations performed by them during their life is very considerable. Most of the design time on such tools may be spent on the limitation of wear.

It is also easier to produce mouldings with complicated coring structures in thermoplastic material. This means that the mouldmaker, in order to design a tool with adequate safeguards, becomes a mechanical engineer as well. It may very well be that the actual design of the cavity which makes the moulding is by far the easiest part in the whole evolution of a mould.

Owing to the great variety of materials available in the thermoplastic field, the economics of the tool are greatly affected by the choice of material. For instance, it is important when considering the heating and cooling arrangements to take into account the colour of the components to be produced. A black telephone case, for example, requires a very much higher tool temperature than a grey.

The finish required on a tool is also somewhat dependent upon the end-use of the product. The finish required on, say, a blue washing-machine top is quite different from that required on a white. The blue moulding will show all flow marks etc., whereas the white will hide them quite effectively.

Certain factors must therefore be considered, and possibly one of the most important is the available information on the flow pattern which results from different forms of gating. Here liaison with the moulder is essential. Also shrinkages will depend upon the position of the gates as most polymers used today have a different shrinkage in the direction of flow than across it. Thus a tool must be distorted in one direction to produce a moulding that is distortion-free. It will be seen from these remarks that the position of gating is of paramount importance. This to a great degree is where the injection moulding process differs from any other moulding process today.

3.2 *Tool temperature*

Having determined the position of the gate, one has to consider many other things in tools for thermoplastics. The tool temperature determines the final finish on the moulding, and also affects the final shrinkage, particularly in crystalline materials. It is therefore essential for the designer to determine the operating temperature and to 'build in' the shrinkage accordingly.

It is also important to remember that the tool may not have to be at the same temperature all over. This creates difficulties, for the expansion of the metal varies from one part to another, and here again the designer must 'build in' allowances. When using materials which have a variable ratio of amorphous to crystalline structure it is necessary to control the heat of the tool across its face so that the temperature gradient controls crystallinity.

The old concept of cooling merely the outside bolster of a tool and leaving the cavity to cool by thermal conduction is just not good enough on 90% of the work being done in this country today. The science of tool cooling is gradually becoming understood, and reputable toolrooms are providing tools with improved cooling as experience is gained.

It is interesting to note at this stage the variation in design from one toolmaker to another for a similar component. This can be caused by a number of factors. Usually it is determined by the machinery available in the moulding shop to which the tool is eventually going, but to a degree it is dependent upon a designer's own skill. It could be that designer A has found that by using large amounts of beryllium copper he can reduce the amount of water required to pass through the cavity part of a tool, whereas designer B has found that tools with large amounts of beryllium copper have been returned owing to accidental damage, so it is more expedient for him to use high-quality tool steels, and, because of their poor thermal conductivity, have more waterways in the cavity. Whichever way is used, and whatever the tool material, the main criterion is the surface temperature of the tool when it is in the moulding condition.

It is also possible today, with high-pressure water circuits and hypodermic needles, to inject water up a core pin, and in fact it is possible to cool core pins as thin as $\frac{1}{8}$ in by this method. But these methods are expensive, and only economically acceptable for mouldings which have to be made to a high degree of accuracy.

3.3 *Tool materials*

It is a commercial proposition now to manufacture in material like polyacetal or nylon an article which has tolerances of ± 0·001 in, as long as the tool design allows adjustment to get the mean dimension correct.

Thermoplastics tools give the toolmaker much more latitude in choice of tool materials. It is perfectly feasible to make production tools out of materials such as kirksite, aluminium, or aluminium bronze if they favour economy, heat conduction, or just ease of casting. It should be remembered that internal pressures are around 3–5 tonf/in^2, so these materials, if they are not strong themselves, must be backed up by bolster-work with an adequate safety margin. Certain rules must be obeyed, however, and they are arrived at from the type of material to be used. For instance, if p.v.c. is to be used the tool must in all circumstances be chromium plated, and this applies not only to moulding surfaces but to all surfaces likely to come into contact with the gases given off during moulding.

3.4 *Runner system*

The importance of correct decision regarding number of gates having been mentioned, the problems of getting material from the melt cylinder to the gate will now be considered. In normal circumstances transport is by what is called the *runner system.* Runner systems can take a variety of forms.

The basic concept is this. There is a *sprue* which joins the nozzle on the end of the injection cylinder direct to the gate into the moulding itself. This is satisfactory for a single impression but is not suitable for multiple impressions. The most common way of dealing with multiple impressions is to take a runner through into the plane of the cavities. The runner then becomes part of the moulding and comes away on injection. In a three-plate tool there is a similar situation, but here the runner gear is in an extra plate and the mouldings are fed from a plane other than that of the main parting line of the tool.

More recently this runner system has been built into a hot manifold, and the so-called *hot-runner* tool has come into existence. Certain complications are brought up with hot-runner tools: keeping the runner at the right temperature, and avoiding 'dead' spots in it so that streamline flow is maintained. This system can be taken further, the nozzle itself protruding into the moulding cavity proper. Although there are severe limitations, this is becoming far more common for certain types of article, such as beakers.

Automatic degating can be achieved in numerous ways other than by using a hot nozzle. The most common method is that of the tunnel gate. The material flows through a runner which goes subterraneously into the side of the moulding and is broken off on ejection. The angle and the tapers on the tunnel itself have to be quite accurate and must always conform with certain specifications which vary from one material to another. This method is quite widely used for small components but on larger mouldings troubles can be experienced in getting a gate large enough to fill the component and yet break off neatly during the ejection process.

In any discussion of feed positions the variation of section in a moulding must be considered. Ideally a plastic moulding should be completely uniform, but in practice this is not really possible. Thick sections require a lot more material at somewhat higher pressures than do thin sections. It is therefore important in the initial design of the tool to aim to get the gates as near to these thick sections as possible.

4.0 LOW-PRESSURE TOOL DESIGN

This title can cover a multitude of fields. Basically we are concerned with pressures below ½ tonf/in^2. Polyester dough and premix require approximately ½ tonf/in^2, and of course polyester glass layup and epoxy glass layup are at normal atmospheric pressure. The material can be almost anything which can hold form. In fact most prototype work, and a lot of production work, on polyester glass layup is done on polyester glass or wooden tools. Car bodies, for example, are usually laid up on glass fibre tools, as are boat hulls. A problem with these tools is whether they can be stored under their own weight. All the other problems encountered on the more normal types of moulding tool apply, e.g. flash cut-off, surface finish etc.

The more specialised fields of vacuum forming, blow moulding, and extrusion still have one problem in common, namely that heat must be taken away from a semi-molten or molten material. This means that cooling, and because of this the materials from which the tool is made, are as important as they are in injection moulding. It must also be remembered that the form which must eventually be made from the tool may be as important dimensionally as that made from an injection moulding tool. Because of this the metals to be used must be as stable, and speaking generally the design must be as good as, so-called more accurate injection-moulding tools.

For extrusion a die must be well polished internally to stop sticking or ripping back of the corners of the extrusion. The same applies to the after-finishing jigs. In the past these were always made by the development engineers, but today the actual forming jigs which come beyond the extrusion die itself are just as important, and must be as accurate as the die. Their construction is quite critical, and so is their method of cooling. The designers have problems with corrosion. shrinkage, heat transfer, just as the injection moulder does, and the finesse with which they can now devise dies for very complicated sections has taken their art into the specialist field.

5.0 PROTOTYPE TOOLING

In this country today it is becoming slightly more common to produce a prototype tool before making multi-cavity tools for awkward components. In the States this has been common practice for the last ten or twelve years. There manufacturers apparently are not quite so worried about the capital expenditure involved. However, the prototype can show the designer what shrinkage is to be expected, the flow problems, and whether the mechanics of the tool will be satisfactory in production. It allows experimentation with different gate positions and cooling ideas. It also allows the customer variation in design without too much expense. From the development engineer's point of view it allows experimentation with different machine conditions without fear of damage to an expensive tool. It is important that the customer, the tool designer, and the moulder get together and discuss the cost of the tool and the quantity required. All too often a prototype tool is asked to do far more mouldings than it was originally designed for.

6.0 THE FUTURE

It is quite possible with today's machining techniques to make tool surfaces which resemble leather and leather cloth, wood, and all sorts of different finishes. This is usually done by photo-etching. There is also a process for putting 'wood-grain' on to a tool by using silicone rubber and ceramic to take a cast from a piece of wood, casting the tool surface direct from the cast. By such means it is possible to make curved arms for armchairs in one piece, simulating wood not only in looks but also to the touch. It is possible now to make furniture which looks like wood, feels like wood, and even sounds like wood.

It may appear that the industry has turned full circle. In many instances plastics started as substitutes for wood.

The processes outlined for decorative finishes do not end there. It is possible, by using the same processes, to make items very accurately. By the lost-wax process, making a tool directly from a model, a moulding can be produced exactly like the model.

Today's machining techniques – ultrasonic welding, spark erosion, and even laser beam cutting – have allowed the plastic mould designer to devise moulds to make components which hitherto have been unmachinable. There are numerous examples in the aircraft industry, and the watch and clock industry is slowly changing over to plastic components, gear wheels, cams etc.

Modern welding techniques allow tool repairs hitherto unheard of. It is possible to make tools by welding. One can weld, say, Stellite locally to a tool and thereby get an extremely hard area adjacent to a very soft one. The moulder can use complicated tools with more confidence, and with lower-quality labour, for he knows that if there is an accident and parts are broken, repair though not desirable is not impossible.

A novel way of getting a good shut-out between two halves of a tool is to use one half as an electrode on a spark machine and erode the other half. The result is a very satisfactory face, without the high toolmaking skill normally required.

SESSION 3. DISCUSSION ON THE PAPERS BY R. IREDALE, E. CAPPUCCIO, A. R. BAUMANN, P. J. GILL & J. H. TURNBULL, AND R. A. IRELAND

P. P. LOVE (*Glacier Metal Co.*): There is one plea I would like to make to the designers of assembly machines – could they at least make the products that their machines assemble relatively easy to maintain?

R. IREDALE: I appreciate this. However, there is a tendency today to design products, particularly consumer durables, as throw-away products. It is cheaper to buy a new unit to replace one which is faulty.

I think it desirable in product design to have this throw-away attitude. You do not use screws to fasten pieces together because screws are very difficult and very costly things to use as fastening devices. You use twisted tabs, weldments, press fits, and reduce the cost of assembly, thus making it economic to throw the product away at the end of its useful life.

C. B. PERRY (*Cincinnati Milling Co.*): Mr Iredale, you have been talking about automatic assembly of the kind which is obtainable by mechanisation. How do you feel about a programmable automatic assembly machine in which the capital investment might be amortised over a large variety of applications?

R. IREDALE: That is a very good point. It is time for some new thinking in the development of automatic assembly machines. There are already programmable assembly machines on the market. Notable among them is a series of assembly devices developed at Nottingham University, now being marketed by Hawker-Siddeley. They are programmable heads. You can design assembly machines that are versatile and can be simply retooled – I mean the parts that make contact with, or control the movement of the parts through the machine – then you have a device which can be amortised over several products.

A. TACK (*Rolls-Royce*): I agree wholeheartedly with Mr Iredale's points regarding the requirement for more sound economics in automated assembly, but I think this also applies to many other fields as well, for example in purchase of capital equipment. Mr Cappuccio has made some very good points on the use of d.c.f. in this type of calculation. Perhaps the technique he is suggesting is a little complicated. Graphical techniques have been developed for calculating a d.c.f. return, and I think they would be more suitable for the average buyer of equipment. Probably this is a far less complicated method than the one that is described using computing techniques. Has Mr Cappuccio any comments on this?

E. CAPPUCCIO: I agree with you that to pick the value of greater interest from that formula is quite complicated. I agree with you that, for the first study of a project, we can even use a single formula, and forget the rate of interest, just to find out if there is room for a study. But when we arrive at the moment when we must decide yes or no on the project, which can cost something like \$12 000, I think it is worth making calculations.

W. GREGSON (*Ferranti*): Mr Cappuccio makes the point that, in introducing automatic assembly, there is the problem of training skills. This is a very real problem, which I think is facing us all. The change in these skills is very difficult to forecast, and is very difficult to bring about. Would you like to say a few words on how you achieve satisfactory end-results in this field?

E. CAPPUCCIO: The problem is more than a difficulty in training people to run or maintain a machine. Our problem was to have the supervisors accept the extra effort which is required by an automatic machine.

It is much easier to run six men than a machine. When something goes wrong with the components, or with the regularity of supply, manual labour is very flexible and operators will cooperate in finding a solution. The automatic machine, on the other hand, has a very rigid system and just asks for help. So the main problem is the training of the supervisory staff.

It is true that a machine has a reliability which is never 100%. But it can be a good investment even if it is working at 50% efficiency, if you have considered this fact in your calculation when you decided on the investment. A machine with 100% reliability can be a bad investment.

I think that we are moving to an improvement in the skill of our labour force. Ten years ago it was quite easy for us to find a girl to work a press, just to take a part and put it into a press tool. Now it is almost impossible to find people prepared to accept this kind of work. That is the ultimatum for us. In this sense I think that the increased skill required of the man who actually runs the machine is not a problem. Now the workers are going to be more highly educated when they start work, so I am quite sure this is not the problem.

E. ROSMARIN (*Dexion*): While I fully appreciate the use of air for circuiting controlled devices, what advantage has the system described by Mr. Baumann over the low-pressure fluidic devices which have become such a vogue in this country?

A. R. BAUMANN: What do you mean by *fluidics*? There was a time when the meaning of the word was clear.

These are control devices, digital devices or proportional devices without moving parts. The valve described may be suitable in place of electromechanical relays for pneumatic actuators because it may be cheaper. A box of relays involves transformation from one medium into another twice. Practice has proved that in many applications the valve is cheaper. It is a logic device with more than four inputs, allowing more control for less money than relay control.

J. MURRAY (*Napier College of Science and Technology*): How do you proceed with the task of fault-finding in the pneumatic circuits? Obviously there is nothing similar to an Avometer which could be used.

A. R. BAUMANN: This device serves as its own indicator. If one of the chambers is pressurised it protrudes a little. If there is a break-down you can quickly analyse the state of the device. And if there should be a failure in one of the devices, it is just a question of undoing two screws and putting another device in its place. We did not specially consider an indicator for each system, but perhaps this is a good suggestion to be investigated.

C. W. DEE (*Aerostatic*): With reference to the layouts you indicated in the control systems, did you incorporate any fluidic devices other than the one which you have referred to? In other words, did the complete control system revolve around that single unit?

A. R. BAUMANN: We made a fully fluidic digital control system which has the ability to sort out random inputs. This was done with a turbulence amplifier of the flat type as supplied by Maxam, with 97 elements. This has been running in the laboratory for nearly three years now without failure. We have not made any industrial application of this yet.

J. PRYDE (*Ferranti*): How much does a *nor* device cost and how is the switching performance affected by variations at the input gates themselves? I mean not so much line pressure variation at the inlet but variation between input signals.

Mr BAUMANN: I have been informed that the cost is £7 per position, including all programming, engineering and software. For firms which can solve the problem themselves and do the engineering themselves there is some reduction. Once the development costs are recovered, it is possible to make the price very, very low, say less than £1.

Your second question was the influence of, let's say, pressure-drop on the input. Now, the unit can operate between ½ and 10 atmospheres. Then if we have, say, a supply pressure of 7 atmospheres, the inlet pressure may vary between 1½ and 14 atmospheres. The threshold at 7 atmospheres supply is about 1–1½ atmospheres. But you must not expect such a pressure-drop in a system. Even with 100 ft air lines, there is no trouble at all.

J. R. McINTOSH (*Ferranti*): Has Mr Turnbull any figures on withdrawal torques and the number of re-insertions possible with the Spat System?

J. M. TURNBULL: They are considerably better than self-tapping screws. With the plunged hole there are more threads in engagement, whereas with the normal self-tapper one tends to take it out and put in the next size up. With a Spat screw this is generally not necessary, since the screw always pulls back into the threads on re-insertion.

T. JOHNSTON (*Barr & Stroud*): I work a lot in the defence industry, which conditions my response to many of these new devices. Instead of coming to persuade me to accept them, the originators should approach the people who make Government standards. Has any work been done on this aspect?

Secondly, what is the best way to indicate to the operator where to put the screw?

J. M. TURNBULL: The fastener manufacturers are tied up very much with the International Standards Organisation and also with the national equivalents. Mr Gill is a member of the Standards Organisation. We occasionally give talks to Government bodies.

Placing of the Spat screw is quite simple. Normally you would have something which is pre-drilled being fastened to the sheet metal. In some cases, positioning does not matter, as for example in putting carpets in on certain motor-cars.

J. BRAUN (*'Machine Design & Control'*): You say 'what could be simpler than this?' What have you done towards putting the screw on the end of the Spat gun mechanically?

J. M. TURNBULL: We have a version which is automatically fed. The response to it was not as we anticipated. There are problems with automatic screw feeding. In this particular case there are extra problems because of the extra motions in the gun, but it is available.

F. W. COOPER (*Institution of Production Engineers*): Apart from the question of temperature, which you have dealt with Mr Ireland, there is the elementary problem of the change of colour. I understand that you change the colour and then for three hours afterwards you get throwbacks to the old colour. According to what I am told this is just lived with. You get some red coming out two hours after you started on yellow, and so on. It must give wonderful effects, but is it necessary?

R. A. IRELAND: No, not entirely. We have to get relatively high throughputs. We have machines with high plasticising rates and with complicated internal channels which do not clean very readily. There are two ways of cleaning them. One is to strip the machine. With modern machines you can very easily get the screw out of the barrel for cleaning purposes. Unfortunately, in a big machine the screw may weigh half a ton. It is rather an awkward thing to handle. It is usually very brittle.

We make a lot of telephones. We start off a run with ivory, then go to dark blue, then back *via* green to yellow, then to black. We then take the screw out, clean it and go back to ivory. Now the dyes are incompatible and that is why the blue is in a peculiar place. Unfortunately, industry does not always lend itself to this. Customers never want reds followed by blacks followed by ivories followed by reds. This is our problem and we are slowly solving it.

J. G. SMITH (*Drysdale & Co.*): We are able to use a number of plastic injection mouldings on small-volume production (i.e. one or two off). We have difficulties in making moulds for injection-moulding fairly small components in nylon or polypropylene, the difficulty being the shrinkage rate. We have been unable to get guidance from the materials suppliers. Is there in fact any formula to be used by which you can arrive at a suitable shrinkage rate?

R. A. IRELAND: You have picked the two worst materials out of several thousand that we use. There is no formula. There cannot and never will be a formula.

You can guarantee with amorphous materials a shrinkage of, shall we say, 0·005 in. What you cannot guarantee is a uniform internal pressure in all areas of the tool. When the tool is shut and injection pressure is applied the apparent density will be higher closer to the gate than it will be farthest away from the gate. When you open the tool, of course, this corrects itself. That is one problem of crystalline materials. They are mixtures, and propylene is a real terror in this respect. Round the gate it might be more crystalline than farther away from the gate. The shrinkages in these two areas are different. The variation in shrinkage with nylon can be from 0·010 to 0·070 in.

The thing to do is to make a cheap prototype tool, maybe even a casting for trial purposes. I don't know anyone who has a better solution. American handbooks in general are better in this line than British handbooks.

M. ZVEGINTZOV (*National Research Development Corporation*): The last two speakers touched on what is a most important point of technical industrial philosophy. We in N.R.D.C. have been involved in new materials for ten to fifteen years. What the last two speakers have said reinforces our impression, that there is at present almost a complete dichotomy between the material scientists and engineers. We organise several informal conferences between the two sets, and there is almost a complete lack of comprehension between the material scientists and the engineers.

With the present advance in chemical technology you can really tailor-make any material you like to any design that an engineer could put forward. It is partly a matter of chemistry, partly applied material science, but also it is a matter of what the ultimate user really wants his component to do. Therefore it is a question of the design of the machine which makes the component.

I would like to put this plea to Strathclyde. Here is a wonderful opportunity for the particularly technologically-minded universities – the tailor-making of materials to suit what the design engineer really wants. But it does mean a different concept of training for the engineer.

R. A. IRELAND: I am all for this. There is another point however. When polypropylene first came out in this country I had a very high-up person in the company which first brought it out come to me and say, 'At long last we have got a material that will do all that we say it is going to do, and there will be one grade, one grade only'. Their books, I think, have twenty now.

One of the problems is that the price does not stay stable. The special grades which you really need to use tend to be more expensive. I agree that you have got to have them. Unfortunately it puts the wrong slant on the economics.

F. I. SIMPSON (*Strathclyde University*): Strathclyde has a very strong polymer science department and we have already had discussions with them on the possibility of developing ideas along the line suggested by Mr Zvegintzov.

B. F. SHAW (*Polytechnic School of Management Studies*): We have been asked by the Industrial Training Board of the Plastics and Rubber Processing Industries Training Board to run a course at our School and at Aston University for managers of large and medium-sized companies in these two industries. They do not know what the management training needs are.

Mr Ireland said he had bad operators, and also that there is constant complaint of high costs of materials and components. From my experience, they are all complaining that everybody is trying to cut everybody else's throat. Do you think that it is not only the operator who needs training but also the management? And if so, what are the management needs?

R. A. IRELAND: We have not got bad operators. They are tending to become button-pushers, and this is a sign that the engineering side of our industry is becoming up-to-date. I do think management needs some training.

We are short on the technical side for two reasons. The university graduate, whether chemist or mechanical engineer, tends to go to the material suppliers who can offer him big laboratory facilities. If I call for help from the material supplier, he sends along a polymer chemist who looks at the moulding and he can go and put it right. What he can't do then is test what he has put right, except under lab. conditions. Philips-Eindhoven have one of the best testing laboratories I have ever seen. They do not now make a standard test cup as a moulding for flow length. They make a more complicated moulding because they know that the cup means nothing. In other words, we have not progressed far enough in this line. We need the polymer chemists as mechanical engineers: if you like, we need a mixed breed of animal in the industry now. We need to train senior management as well in many respects.

The price war is one basically of design. We are not making the component to suit plastics, so the plastic component is a little bit expensive compared with its competitor in other materials.

E. G. PRICE (*Council of Industrial Design*): Does Mr Ireland feel that the plastics industry is doing enough to encourage the public to accept plastic materials in their own right, rather than all these slavish copies of other materials, such as imitations of wood?

R. A. IRELAND: Yes, I do. We can now do many things to the surface of plastic to make it look and act like other things. There is a vast amount of plastic that goes into the home and the home still wants wood, but surely the housewife has accepted polyethylene and polypropylene for kitchen utensils? The Formica-type laminate has been accepted for kitchen coverings in any colours, not necessarily wood. Credit must go to the material suppliers here. They have done a lot towards bringing plastics to the designer's attention. The application has got to be right.

PROFESSOR D. S. ROSS (*Strathclyde University*): A comment rather than a question: it is for the designers, not for industry, to create the right product in the material which is best suited for it, and then to advise or to work in conjunction with the material suppliers to get the correct material finish if, for example, it is going to be made to look like wood. Perhaps some terminology might be corrected a little, Mr Ireland. The traditional mechanical engineer does not usually know anything about tool design. This is a production engineering function.

J. R. McINTOSH (*Ferranti*): What is the industry doing, possibly using sophisticated copying techniques or numerical control techniques, to reduce tool-manufacturing or modification times, so that firms like my own, which work on fairly short lead times, can use plastics more than is possible at the present?

R. A. IRELAND: This is a very difficult problem. We have a very big tool-room, and are using new techniques on tool manufacture. What I think is wanted is small firms who are prepared to make prototypes. We do this within our own group, but won't offer it outside at present since it is too expensive. In the U.S. small firms make prototypes, straight from the solid, although not always satisfactorily, but this is probably where one starts. We are not purposely doing anything about it. We are allowing it to happen.

C. W. DEE (*Aerostatic*): What is the feasibility, if we require only one or two parts, of producing an initial model from the solid, as a finished component, and then utilising some form of material by which we can make a mould from which to produce a few components? Is this a feasible operation, or isn't it?

R. A. IRELAND: Certainly it is feasible. Unfortunately, the mouldings will not be exact replicas of the model. They will be undersized because of shrinkage. However, this sort of reproduction is done by the 'lost wax' process. Here one usually makes an acrylic moulding model oversize and forms the mould by electrodeposition round it.

P. P. LOVE (*Glacier Metal Co.*): Mr Ireland referred to the problems arising from incorrectly designed features. Professor Ross said that the mechanical engineer does not know anything about tools, this being a job for the production engineer. Professor Ross, how does the designer avoid building these undesirable features into products, so that they can be made?

Professor D. S. ROSS (*Strathclyde University*): All designers are not good designers. A good designer, I suggest, is one who in addition to having had traditional mechanical engineering design training also has training in what we call *Design for Production.* He gets an appreciation of what is possible with certain kinds of processes. Thus he will avoid some of the gross errors which the poor designer often commits.

P. P. LOVE (*Glacier Metal Co.*): The problem I had when I was a designer was finding out from the production engineer what properties I could use in the design. I found this difficult.

F. W. COOPER (*Institution of Production Engineers*): Would it be possible for a university or college course to be supported by the plastics industry to combine production engineering with an appreciation of plastics?

Professor D. S. ROSS (*Strathclyde University*): One of the problems in the education of engineers is the shortage of time to study many topics which we know to be what is required. What market is there in the plastics industry for people trained in tool design for plastic? We do a little jig and tool design and product design for production and mechanical engineers. But, as Mr Cooper says – some encouragement is required: from the industry, perhaps.

R. A. IRELAND: There is a terrific opening for a good plastics tool designer. But he has also got to be a good plastics designer. We have overcome this problem by having a team of three people: a designer, a plastics engineer and a mechanical engineer.

Dr L. BRUCE ARCHER (*Royal College of Art*): The solution was described in the Zuckerman Report, *Industrial Innovation in Britain*. There were long words saying that it really requires team work. That designing should be done by a team consisting of designer, a production engineer, an economist and whatever other group is necessary.

R. FLEMING (*Hunting Engineering*): I agree with this. Unfortunately many firms are not large enough to support this type of organisation. If we try to integrate within one man the expertises of plastics technology, design and production engineering, we are going against the general trend of the more specialised study of the industrial sciences. But I would put a plea to the specialist industries here for help for the smaller organisation.

E. CAPPUCCIO (*Olivetti*): I am in disagreement with the last two contributors. Looking at the problem from the point of view of big industry it is too easy to say, 'put together the men who know the things and you will have a good result'. While we have to work sheet metal, there is widely diffused knowledge of sheet metal. The diffusion of knowledge of plastics is narrower. So the problem is to try to establish and to keep up to date a set of standards stating the manufacturer's requirements of the designer.

SESSION IV

Manufacturing Technology III

Chairman: Dr C. Timms
Head of Machine Tool Branch
Ministry of Technology

THE ROLE OF DIE CASTINGS IN INDUSTRY

A. G. Wakefield
Birmingham Aluminium Castings (1903) Ltd, Birmingham

SUMMARY

The advantages of die castings are considered and the applications for which they are most suitable enumerated. The importance of expertise is emphasised. In a survey of future possibilities the contributions of process development, instrumentation, mechanisation and automation are discussed. There is allusion to the problem of training.

1.0 INTRODUCTION

It is a fact that quantity production of quality products has been the underlying reason why the people of this country have such a high standard of living. What is more, no production process can be singled out as the one that made such a standard possible. Any method which has shortened the time necessary to convert raw material into a finished part has had some effect, the degree depending upon how fast, how accurate and how practicable the process has proved to be. As one of the fastest and most practical production methods, die casting has made, and is still making, significant contributions to industrial progress.

No other fabricating technique has contributed so much to the economic and quantity production of metal parts. Wherever one may look – in the factory, the office or the home – one is confronted by numerous articles of which die castings are an integral part. The motor-car, the carpet sweeper and other household devices, various types of business machine in the office, store and factory, are but a few of the many end-products incorporating die-cast parts. The aircraft industry depends on precision instruments, hardware, industrial machinery and thousands of other items which in their turn depend upon the production of die-cast components.

From a small beginning, die casting has grown into a mighty industry. Instead of levelling off, production rates are steadily growing. When a process reaches such a high state of perfection there is a tendency for some to think of future progress in the terms of 'refinements'. Such thinking is always fallacious, and especially so when applied to die casting. Many technical improvements must be pursued – the development of satisfactory die materials for high-melting-point alloys, even bigger and better casting machines, improved finishing techniques.

2.0 ADVANTAGES OF DIE CASTINGS

So far as applications are concerned, the so-called limitations of the die-casting process are non-existent. They exist only in the minds of those who do not fully appreciate the potential of this method of production.

Basically it is a process in which metal is forced into a fundamental shape by compressing it into a steel mould. Alloys used in the process are mainly of tin, lead, zinc, aluminium, magnesium and brass. Of these the most commonly employed are zinc and aluminium. I shall therefore confine my discussion to them.

Die castings are recognised throughout the metal-working industry as reliable, versatile savers of manufacturing costs. Manufacturers and users of metal products appreciate the special advantages that are offered by aluminium and zinc die castings, such as low sustained loads, and freedom from deterioration at elevated temperatures.

TABLE 1 COMPARISON OF DIE CASTING WITH OTHER PRODUCTION PROCESSES

Process	Materials	Rate of production	Strength of parts	Complexity
Casting	Lead, tin, zinc, magnesium, aluminium, copper alloys	Very high: on certain components up to 2000 per hour	High unit strength	From simple to very complex
Gravity die casting	Iron, magnesium, aluminium, copper alloys	Relatively low	High, particularly when heat-treated	In general not so complex as die castings unless sand cores are used.
Sand casting	Principally iron, magnesium, aluminium and copper alloys	Low – unless foundries fully mechanised	Less than that of die castings and gravity die castings	From simple to very complex
Drop forging and die pressing	Steel, magnesium, aluminium and copper alloys	Reasonable	Highest of all	Fairly complex
Plastic moulding	Thermoplastic and thermosetting resins	Very high – equal to die castings	Less than parts mentioned above	As die castings, with the advantages that components are self-coloured

2.1 *When die castings are best*

The decision to employ die castings in any application should be based on comparisons with the cost and product of other possible methods. Maximum production, economy and superior product design can be achieved only be using the most suitable material and fabrication process for each casting produced.

A die casting may suit the application best if the answer to any one of the following questions is yes:

1 Is the quantity of parts involved considerable (5000 or more)? *Die casting is characteristically a high-speed production process. For this reason it is naturally suited to economical production on a quantity basis* (see Table 2).
2 Is the tooling for machining expensive? *Die castings usually require very few secondary operations. Reduction of tooling costs means an important saving in overall production*

expense. A relatively small number of castings frequently justifies die casting because the need for costly machine tools is eliminated (see Fig. 1).

3 Do machining, assembling or surface finishing account for an appreciable part of the cost of the finished article? *The use of die castings reduces the time and expense required to complete the product. Assembly is rapid because light metal die castings are uniform and faithful in dimension. Surfaces are smooth as cast, so that many finishing operations are simplified or eliminated* (see Fig. 2).

4 Is a reduction of the investment in machine tools and plant floor space desirable? *Frequently the use of die castings is very advantageous as a measure to conserve plant facilities. The caster supplies castings with the flash trimmed off, and in many cases they are almost ready for assembly. Elimination of the multitude of operations that would be required with other methods can free needed productive capacity for other uses.*

TABLE 2 COST COMPARISON

Process	Appearance and finish	Cost
Die casting	Very good, can be finished with variety of mechanical, plated, chemical or organic finishes.	High equipment cost, high tool cost, low piece cost on high-activity items.
Gravity die casting	Usually machined or ground but left with base metal surface	Low equipment cost, medium die cost. Piece cost between die casting and sand castings.
Sand casting	Inferior to die or gravity castings, machined on ground, left with base metal finish.	Low equipment cost, low tool cost, high piece cost.
Powder metal	Good, but porous, usually left with base metal finish.	Medium equipment and tool cost, low unit cost on high-activity items.
Drop forging and die pressing	Inferior to die casting, usually left in base metal finish.	High equipment cost, high tool cost, reasonably low unit cost on high-activity items.
Plastic moulding	Excellent, can be moulded in variety of colours with excellent finish.	High equipment cost, high tooling cost, low piece cost on high-activity items.

Another outstanding advantage of the die-casting process is that complex shapes can be made that would be difficult, if not impossible, to obtain by any other method – at least in large quantities. By means of sliding die members, undercuts and intricate holes can be formed in the part (see Figs 2, 4, 5 and 6).

2.2 *Pitfalls for the unwary*

Earlier I mentioned superior product design. This is of paramount importance. Any designer who has decided that a casting is the logical choice for a given application is still faced with numerous problems in the design of the casting. If he proceeds with little or no knowledge of the die casting process and its practices, and does not enlist the help of the die casting engineer who knows what is best to do and what to avoid, he will be fortunate indeed if he arrives at the best possible conclusion.

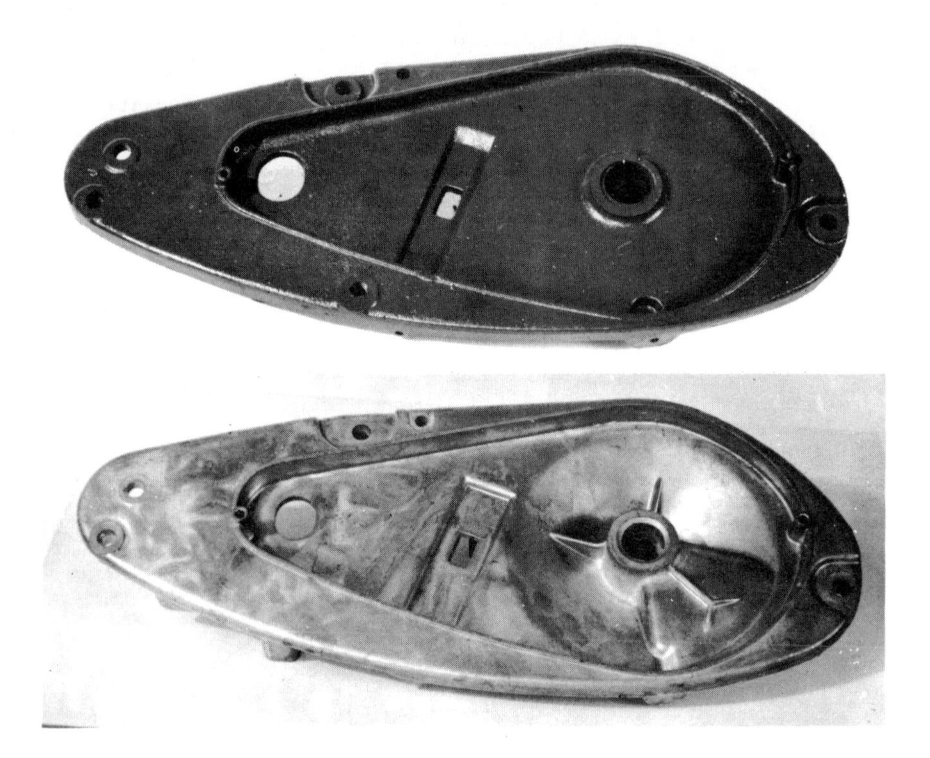

Fig. 1. (Top) Qualcast lownmower side-plate in cast iron. Weight, 7 lb 13 oz. Machining time, 3·2 min. Number of machines required, 12. (Bottom) Same component pressure-die-cast in aluminium. Weight, 1 lb 15 oz. Machining time, 0·47 min. Number of machines required, 3.

More probably in such circumstances he will find that economies which could have been realised are sacrificed. The designer must be aware of the essentials of die castings, for instance the need for ejectors, and the flash which is caused by jointing the area in which the casting is gated. Where called for, subsequent machining can remove evidence of gating and also cater for flash clearance, thereby reducing fettling of the casting to a minimum. It must also be borne in mind that certain essential dimensional features of the casting may suffer with wear and tear of the tools. Similarly, parting lines and the flashes from retractable cores provided solely for casting design reasons are sources of inaccuracies. Further, it is necessary to remember that however accurate the die and excellent its design the casting medium is molten metal and likely to distort during ejection and cooling. Flatness and/or disposition of critical faces can thus be affected. To cater for such variations the Zinc Alloy Diecasters Association, together with the Aluminium Federation, have established over the years a set of engineering standards and tolerances in order to achieve the highest rate of production and a low unit cost. Appreciation of these tolerances is necessary to ensure that, where subsequent machining operations are carried out, the location points selected are subject to the least variation.

To allow for the castings to be withdrawn from the tool, taper is required. In general, for pressure die casting, one should aim for 2°, but for best economy the design should allow maximum taper. Metal on solidification tends to shrink away from the wall of the die cavity and on to die members protruding into the metal, and it would therefore seem that less taper is

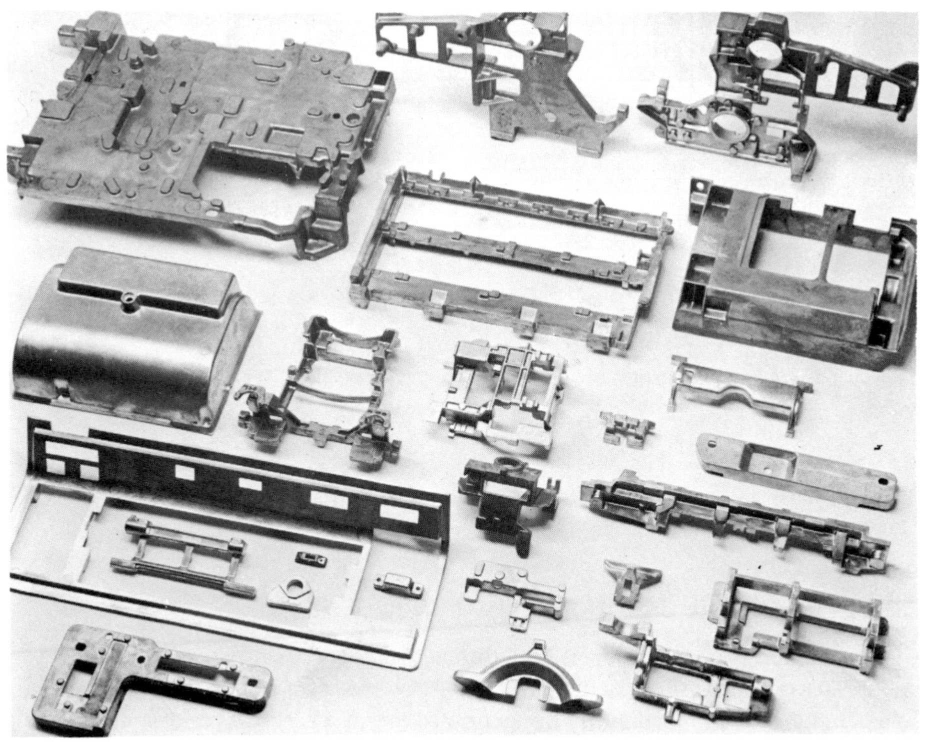

Fig. 2. Use of die castings in a modern teleprinting machine. (Top) The assembly in all its complexity. Machining is minimised. (Bottom) Some of the die castings used in the machine.

Fig. 3. *A* can be die-cast but would need a collapsible metal core. *B*, with an external flange, can be produced with a single-piece core.

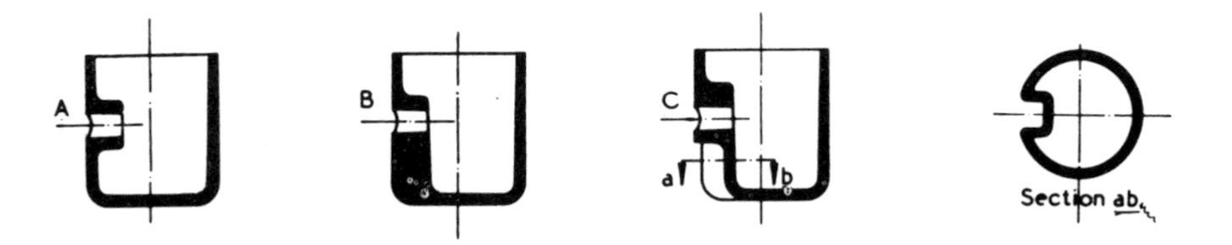

Fig. 4. *A* can be die-cast but would need a collapsible metal core. *B* can be produced with a single-piece core but porosity is likely in the heavy section under the boss. *C* is ideal for uniformity of metal section.

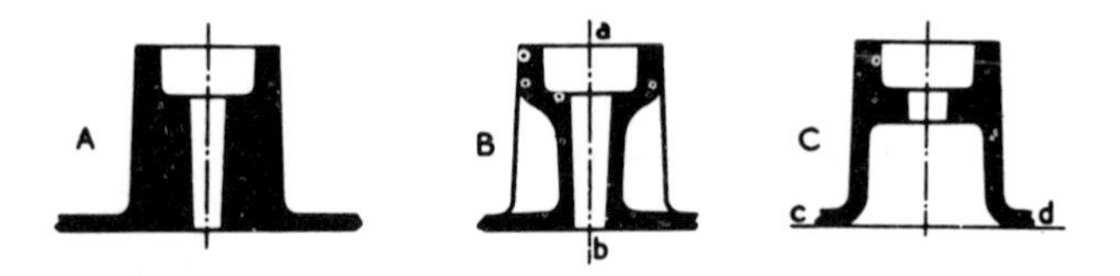

Fig. 5. Heavy sections as at *A* should be avoided. Bosses can be necked and ribbed by jointing die on *a-b* as at *B*. When die is jointed on *c-d* as at *C*, the boss has uniform metal thickness.

Fig. 6. Beading as shown at *A* requires accurate die matching. This can be avoided by design as at *B*, saving cost on the die.

required on outside walls than inside surfaces. However, to assist in manufacture of the tooling, particularly in respect of modelling, it is best to keep the outside taper the same as the inside taper.

3.0 THE FUTURE OF DIE CASTING

Predicting the future of die casting is both difficult and risky.

Process improvement is of course the main key. It is because of continually improved casting techniques that the die casting industry has expanded over the past few years, and will continue to expand. However, those of us who have spent a lifetime in this industry know only too well that it still has its shortcomings, which certainly leave room for further improvement.

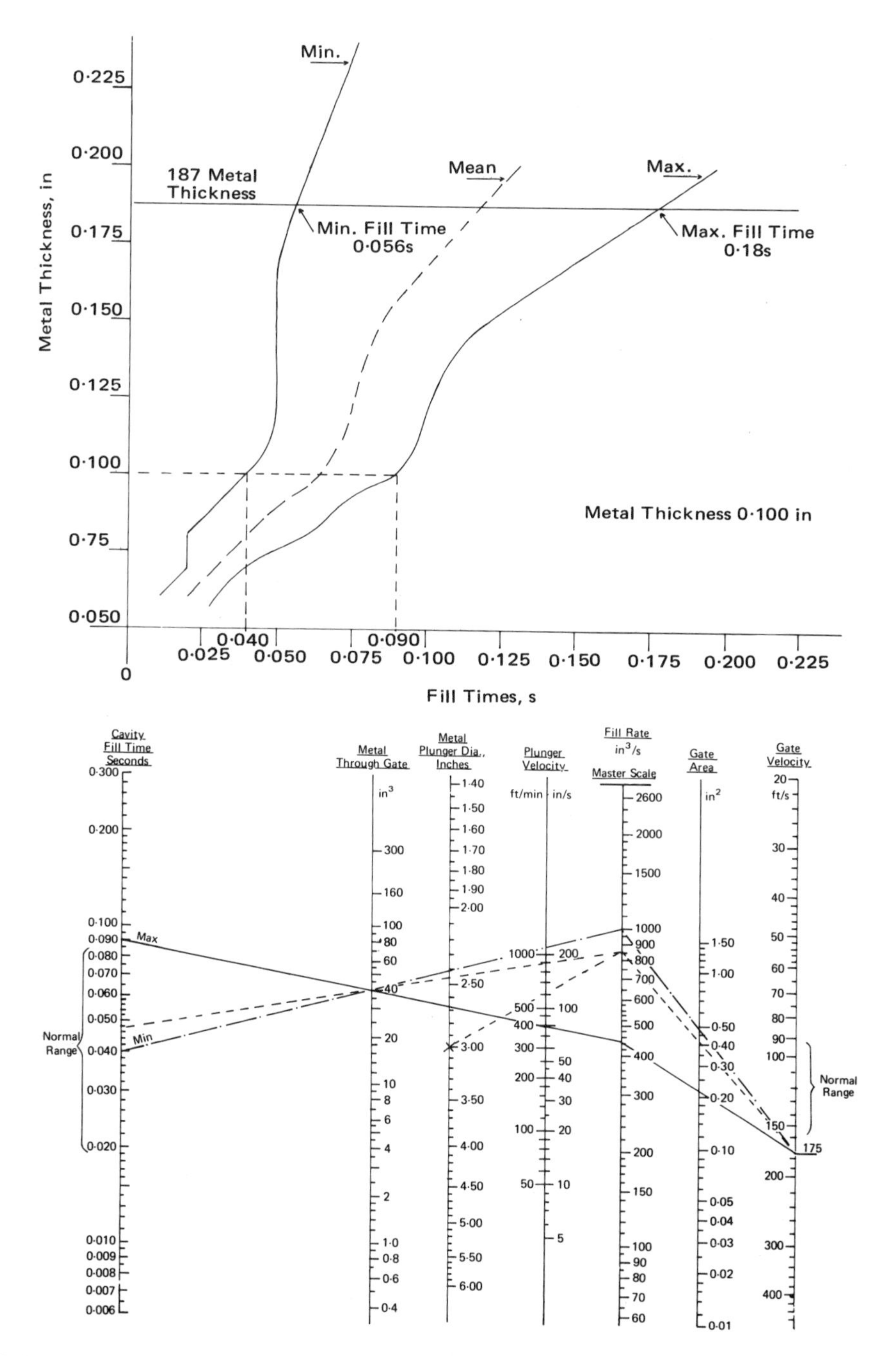

Fig. 7. Scientific approach. From the curves of metal thickness *v.* cavity-filling time a value is read off and marked on the extreme left-hand scale in the nomograph. A line drawn from this point through the appropriate point on the next scale ('metal through gate') to join, on the 'master' scale, a line originating from the appropriate point on the last scale ('gate velocity'), intersects the penultimate scale to indicate the required gate area. The example shown relates to the Qualcast side-plate, Fig. 1.

3.1 *Gap between theory and practice*

We are continually striving to arrive at an established technique. Fortunately, the gap is narrowing between the scientist, who seeks the theoretical goal of ideal and uniform operating conditions, and the die casting engineer, who has to produce castings with dies that operate under variable conditions defying any scientific formula.

For example, the gating of a die casting is still an art and not an established production technique. Although several attempts to arrive at a suitable formula for the size of the gate have been developed, none of the formulae tells where to locate such a gate. Most present-day practices for positioning ingates are based on experience. In the future this must be replaced by a more analytical method. By careful study of metal flow it may be possible for the scientist and die casting engineer to arrive at some formula and basic rules for gating techniques (see Fig. 7).

3.2 *Towards sounder castings*

Pressure die castings have always been subject to porosity. Some use has been made of vacuum to reduce or eliminate air in the die cavity, but even with today's improved die-making technique and intricate sealing, this has proved to be costly and not a sound production proposition.

Without doubt, the more sophisticated die-casting machines of today, employing higher injection pressures, intensifiers, and 3-phase shot control, have contributed to the improvement of the quality of die castings. Intensifiers in particular, which magnify injection pressure some three or four times, have improved the soundness of difficult, chunky castings far beyond what could be achieved by vacuum.

There has been some development in the United States of machines equipped with the Acurad system. This, it is claimed, is to permit the consistent production of stronger, denser components than is possible by conventional high-pressure casting. Main feature of the Acurad process are a secondary plunger, a thicker gate, lower metal-injection velocity, and controlled cooling of the die.

3.3 *How instrumentation can help*

There are many other variables in the die-casting cycle. In the main they are caused by the inability of the operator to keep a steady pace and to repeat continuously within the casting cycle time every operation such as pouring of metal, die lubrication and cleaning. Instrumentation is helping to control the variables of both the machine (casting metal temperature, metal pressure, thermal balance of the die, water cooling temperature) and the operator.

Instrumentation may be used in three ways.

On a machine in normal production, instrumentation may be used for continuous indication, or to record factors which can be measured continuously (such as metal temperature, some local temperature in the die block, and the temperature and flow rate of cooling water). The data relating to the die may be particularly useful in showing when normal conditions are attained after an interruption of operations (see Fig. 8). More extensive instrumentation, recording in detail the pressure fluctuations during the injection stroke, is most likely to be used for establishing optimum conditions, thereafter functioning intermittently to check consistency of operation or diagnose the cause of faulty operation (e.g. malfunctioning of valves).

A second and completely different approach to instrumentation is to use it as an experimental tool in investigating the pressure die-casting process itself. More specialised transducers, not really suitable for continuous use, may be applied to record a wide range of variables. They may give indirect information about factors which are difficult to examine directly, such as the timing and mode of freezing of the metal in the die.

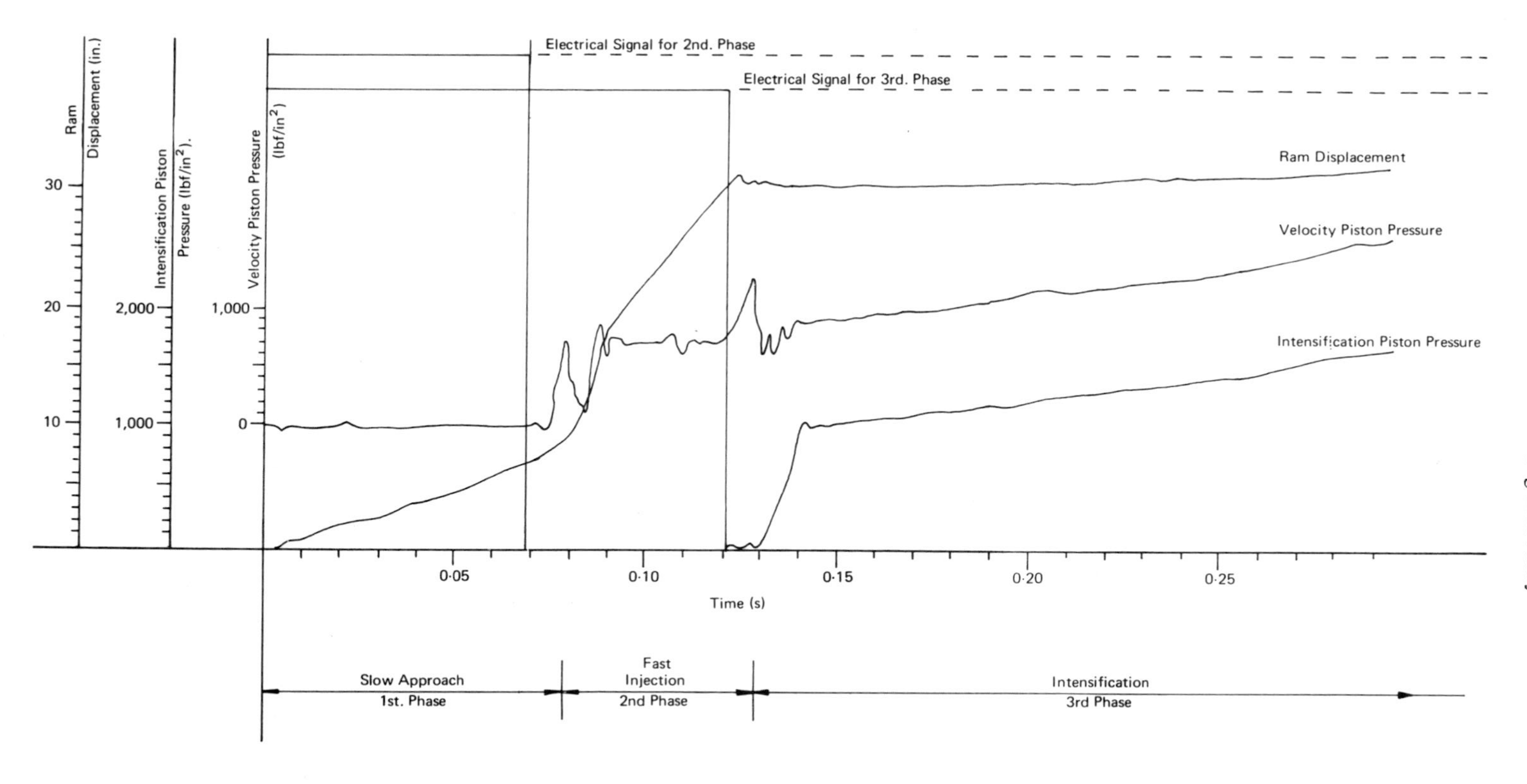

Fig. 8 Typical oscillograph traces for injection phases.

A third use of instrumentation lies in thermal analysis, a relatively new approach to the design of casting dies. An electrical analogue analyser provides direct the optimum position of water cooling channels, and, if necessary, the heat inputs necessary for the best possible thermal balance in the casting die. One of the chief advantages of such equipment is that it permits the assessment of problem areas on the drawing board, speedily allowing the product and die designers to compare notes and select the best solution available.

3.4 *Mechanisation and automation*

The desire to eliminate variables caused by the human element has brought die casting even closer to full mechanisation and automation.

Consider the modern die-casting machine in both its hot-chamber zinc and cold-chamber aluminium forms.

Most modern foundries are using fully automatic zinc die-casting machines, producing castings at a high rate, in some cases in excess of 2000 per hour. Larger castings when ejected are allowed to drop into a tank, usually filled with water. A conveyor belt in turn takes them up to the clipping area. Small components, flash-free, are blown straight from the die impression into an awaiting stillage, the runner having already been broken off during the ejection cycle. Lubrication in this case is fully automatic, using sprays.

The automation of the cold-chamber machine presents more serious problems because metal has to be ladled from the holding pot to the shot sleeve, and because dies for aluminium need more cleaning and lubrication. Over recent years much progress has been made with automatic ladling or metal transfer, particularly on large tonnage machines. One such method is the use of a mechanically tilted ladle.

On the bigger machines full use is also made of automatic metal dispensing. A sealed furnace is pressurised to displace a measured amount of metal through a refractory tube and out to the shot sleeve. One of the more recent developments in this connection is the use for the hot-chamber metal-injection process of working parts, both plunger and cylinder, made in titanium diboride, a high-temperature refractory material. There are difficulties associated with this, but as development proceeds to a satisfactory conclusion it will certainly increase the scope for automation.

The introduction of electronically controlled mechanical handling devices (of which there are two well known makes, the G.K.N. Unimate and the Hawker Siddeley Versatran) will certainly bring full automation a little nearer. Once they have been programmed their movements are accurately performed again and again, continuously. They can be moved from one station to another. All that is necessary is to re-program. The gripping device which holds the casting passes a heat sensing device. This determines whether the casting is present, and helps to ensure that the casting leaves the machine before the next cycle commences.

A further development in die-casting-machine control is a facility for quick set-up and repeatability of optimum casting conditions. This has been achieved with the aid of punched-card programming.

We shall certainly witness in the future toolroom the wider use of numerically controlled machines. At present the use of such equipment is prohibitive for one-offs owing to the high cost of programming. The trend in the major manufacturing industries is to standardise component configuration. Instead of one die being manufactured, several will be made, in some cases multi-impression. They will certainly justify the use of numerically controlled machines.

Spark erosion and other forms of electrical machining are coming to the forefront. I feel sure that most machining will be carried out using these processes with the die material in the fully hardened state, thereby eliminating all the problems suffered in the past from distortion during heat treatment.

Also in the not too distant future we shall see the computer put to greater use. It will concentrate all of the operations in the foundry, and will also aid design, estimating, marketing, etc.

3.5 *Who forms the future?*

Our biggest competition in the world is in the realm of IDEAS. Mechanical handling devices, machines and instrumentation are all very well, but they cannot think. Ideas must come from people and where are these people coming from? They must be trained. Who is training them? Our future lies with them.

EFFECTS OF SPEED IN METAL FORMING

F. W. Travis
University of Strathclyde, Glasgow

SUMMARY

Relevant published literature is examined. An attempt is made to categorise the wide range of speeds employed in the forming of metals, on the basis of the phenomena encountered at different levels of forming speed. Figures are included to illustrate the main points of the text.

1.0 INTRODUCTION

Over the last ten or so years various metal-forming techniques have been introduced and developed. A feature common to them all is high forming speed; the term *high-rate forming* is often used to describe the processes. In the wide range of forming speeds under this heading, however, the workpiece may exhibit very different behaviour.

It is the object of this paper to group the various high-rate and other forming processes according to their forming speed and to the relative importance of the phenomena encountered. Wherever possible, reported advantages and limitations of processes are also discussed. In addition, although not in general a metal-forming operation, very-high-speed impact is included, both for completeness and to show where the processes considered lie within the whole speed spectrum. For simplicity, the latter is grouped in terms of powers of 10 ft/s, i.e. $10^1 - 10^2$ ft/s, $10^2 - 10^3$ ft/s, etc., and whilst a number of processes overlap two groups, each process is placed where it is typically more appropriate.

2.0 FORMING SPEEDS FROM STATIC TO 10 FT/S

In this range lie hydraulic presses, crank or eccentric presses and screw presses, for which platen closing speeds of 0 2, 0 1 – 5 and 0 1 – 5 ft/s respectively and typical mean strain rates of $10^{0\cdot 1}$, $10^{1\cdot 0}$ and $10^{1\cdot 0}$ s^{-1} respectively, are reported[1].

2.1 *Pressing, forging, coining and embossing operations*

No considerations arise of the effects of billet inertia[2,3], or the generation or propagation of stress waves[4,5,6], and strain rate effects are generally either negligible or slight[7].

2.2 *Blanking*

When the deformation of a workpiece is restricted to one small region, as in blanking[8], even modest press speeds can result in very high strain rates within the deforming material. An apparently slow press-blanking operation may therefore involve a much greater strain-rate than would be associated with, say, high-speed turning. With reduction in punch/die clearance, as in close-tolerance or 'fine' blanking, the strain-rate effects are correspondingly accentuated.

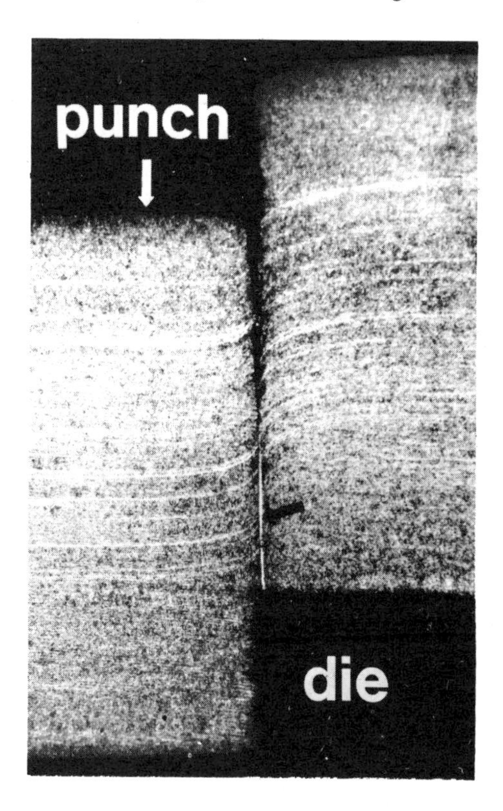

Fig. 1. Effects of thermoplastic instability in the blanking of steel at low punch-die clearance.

This is illustrated by the tests of Zenor and Holloman[9,10] on the blanking of steel at 10 ft/s using a falling-weight apparatus. Heat generated in the shear zone was found to lead to progressive local softening, so that at some point 'thermoplastic instability' developed, and all further shear was concentrated along a very narrow band of material, which rose rapidly in temperature to its melting point. Subsequent chilling of melted material by adjacent, comparatively cold, material, produced a hard martensitic structure, clearly revealed after etching. This is shown in Fig. 1 (arrowed), for the partial dynamic blanking of $\frac{1}{8}$ in thick, flat ground, steel bar (1% C, 1·3% Mn) of hardness 425 HV.

3.0 FORMING SPEEDS FROM 10^1 – 10^2 FT/S

The lower end of this range is occupied by conventional forging machinery, i.e. gravity hammers, power hammers and double-acting hammers, for which platen closing speeds of 12 – 16, 16 – 30 and 30 – 40 ft/s respectively, and typical mean strain rates in the deforming workpiece of $10^{1 \cdot 9}$, $10^{2 \cdot 2}$ and $10^{2 \cdot 3}$ s^{-1} are reported by Jain and Bramley[1]. Following on are high-energy-rate forming (h.e.r.f.) machines, with closing speeds of 30 – 65 ft/s and typical mean strain rates of $10^{2 \cdot 4}$.

The main difference between h.e.r.f. and conventional forging machines is that the former employ platens of comparatively small mass and thus require a high closing speed in order to provide an adequate energy level. The machines are also compact and free-standing, and, as the operating stroke takes only a very small part of the total process time, advantage is taken of stored energy, so that the size of ancillary equipment is greatly reduced. As illustrated by Crawley and Wills[12], the power pack of an h.e.r.f. machine 'may have to deliver between 300 and 400 hp for about 30 ms, and then a tiny fraction of this for the remaining 6 s to complete the work cycle. In order to get around this problem the concept of employing a stored-energy system was evolved. Various materials have been used as the energy storage medium, low-explosives, explosive gases, rubber strips, but nitrogen has been most commonly used[13,14], and a machine has successfuly employed compressed air[15].

The most significant development in h.e.r.f. in recent years, however, has been the development of the *petro-forge* system[15]. Here the energy required to drive the platens is generated by the combustion of a hydrocarbon fuel and air. Fuels employed may be either liquid (petrol, diesel, kerosene) or gaseous (propane, natural gas, town gas). The system is described[15] as being 'essentially a hybrid of an internal combustion engine and a high-speed press, consisting of two sets of components; one set corresponds to those of a petrol engine, (combustion chamber, inlet and outlet valves, spark plug, fuel injector) and the other set to those of a high-energy-rate forming machine (mechanism for the sudden release of energy, ram actuating platen, guidance and structure)'.

3.1 *Hot forging using h.e.r.f. machines*

This operation is discussed elsewhere in connection with the petro-forge machine[1,16], the U.S.I. machine[12], and a special-purpose non-cycling machine using compressed nitrogen[19]. The general impression gained is that the short deformation time associated with these machines reduces the transfer of heat from the billet to the dies, so that thin-walled and finely detailed components can be formed. Die life appears to be inferior to that of conventional forging machines, however. Tooling problems are discussed in detail by Dean[18].

Stress wave effects are not generally considered to be of importance. Forming times, of the order of 5 ms, are long compared with the few tens of microseconds which stress waves take to pass through a workpiece. From analyses of the process [2,3] it is considered that billet inertia may also be neglected. In the hot upset forging of steel rings[19], at platen speeds ranging from 0·07 ft/s to 40 ft/s, under various conditions of lubrication, the ratio of the energy for low-speed tests to the energy for high-speed tests has been found to be approximately 0·1 for a specimen height reduction of 15%, increasing to approximately 0·8 for a reduction of 80%. This has been explained[20] in terms of: (a) strain rate effects, which increase with increasing impact speed, (b) chilling effects, the workpiece losing heat to surrounding dies and suffering increased flow stress (these effects become less with increasing impact speed), (c) adiabatic heating effects within the billet, reducing the flow stress. In all hot-forging operations the above factors are present, but to varying degrees.

3.2 *Blanking and bar cropping*

Blanking[21], and the related operation of bar cropping[22], have been carried out within this speed range, using a petro-forge machine, and blanking has also been carried out using a tup accelerated by a linear motor[23]. Conditions of very high strain rate exist locally in the shear zone, as discussed earlier, with an increased tendency to thermoplastic instability.

3.3 *Impact extrusion*

A linear motor[24] has been used to extrude a metal billet, seated in the mouth of an extrusion die, by impact of a tup at speeds of about 30 ft/s. Under these conditions billet inertia is of great importance, as with too high an extrusion ratio tensile necks can develop in the extruded rod, and rupture may occur. The onset of necking of the product may be predicted theoretically for any impact speed and extrusion ratio[25]. It may be pointed out, however, that mild inertia forces are considered beneficial because they have a straightening influence on the extruded rod[17]. This is discussed in detail by Davies[26].

The impact extrusion of aluminium and copper[27] and steel and titanium[28], using an explosive machine and a compressed-air machine, at impact velocities ranging from 90 to 300 ft/s, has been reported by Austin *et al.* The general conclusions reached were that, at impact speeds below 100 ft/s, tooling problems are not too severe, and that the dimensional accuracy and surface finish of the product are good.

3.4 *Extrusion moulding*

In this process[29] a heated billet is seated in the mouth of an extrusion die and struck by a tup at 60 ft/s. The extruded material, now with a velocity of the order of 1000 ft/s, passes into a closed die-set, where 'the momentum and plasticity of the extruding material are such that intricate shapes can be filled, the speed of filling being sufficiently high to prevent excessive chilling of the extruding material and enabling it to weld into a coherent product, i.e. without laps or folds'. Care has to be taken to avoid using too high a billet temperature or extrusion ratio, which would result in excessive turbulence and porosity in the product.

In addition to the use of a rapidly moving tup for high-speed impact, low-explosive charges have been burned in a specially designed tool[30], to develop pressures of up to 130×10^3 lbf/in^2, in the high-speed extrusion of aluminium and copper[31]. The disadvantages are that charging the tool is a slow procedure, and at, once initiated, combustion of the charge is accelerated on account of the confinement and it is entirely consumed within a few milliseconds. Excessively high billet exit speeds of about 500 ft/s, or inertial necks in partially extruded products, may result.

4.0 FORMING SPEED RANGE $10^2 - 10^3$ FT/S

In this range the inertia of the billet becomes of major importance, strain rate effects are very significant, and regard must be given to the generation and propagation of stress waves in the billet. The effects of speed are emphasised in Fig. 2. On the left is shown a joint secured by a mild steel rivet in predrilled holes in $\frac{1}{8}$ in mild steel plates. The exposed end of the shank (above in Fig. 2) has been struck at approximately 400 ft/s[32]. The shank-end has flowed to form a head, with no distortion of its central regions or the adjacent plate material. In the corresponding static case, shown to the right of Fig. 2, the gross deformation of the rivet head, shank and plates will be noted.

4.1 *Kinetic forming*

This is a new process, basically similar to extrusion except that the extrusion stage is eliminated and the billet simply fired at high speed into a closed die-set[33]. Under the heavy inertia forces generated upon its arrest, the billet material flows into the die-set to form a close-tolerance forging or casting. In addition to the high inertia stresses, there is evidence[33] of stresses due to multiple reflection, within the die housing and the billet, of the intense shock wave developed upon initial impact. To avoid failure under the high transient stresses, and also under the billet inertia stresses[34], and to allow 'venting' of entrapped air[32], close attention must be paid to die design. Fig. 3(a) shows a small aluminium component formed[33] using a

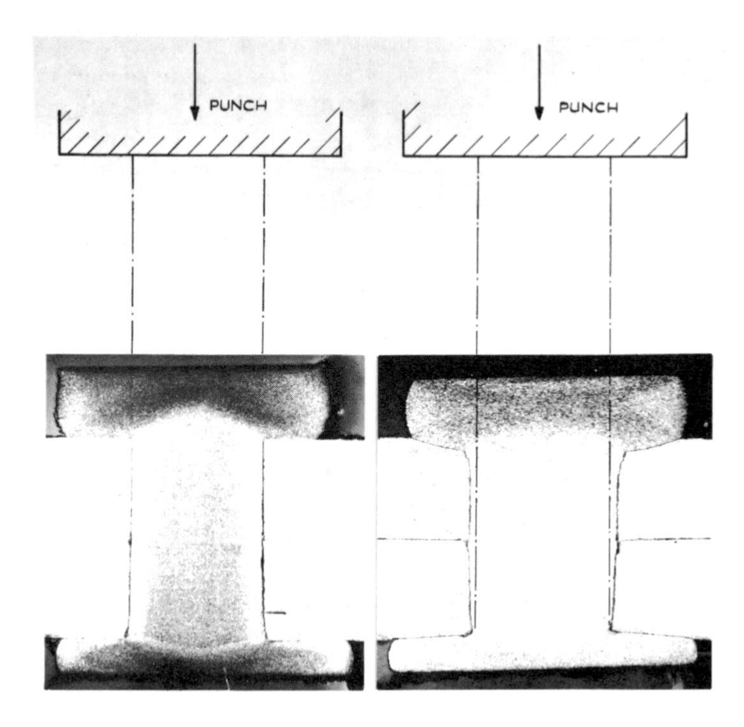

Fig. 2. Dynamically and statically riveted joints, left and right respectively.

rigid steel 'driver' behind the billet to increase the total available energy, at an impact speed of 700 ft/s. Fig. 3(b) shows a tubular product that was formed[34] by firing an aluminium billet at about 1000 ft/s into a toroidal-cross-section die, so that the material was first pierced, and then deflected back upon itself along a circular path, smoothly and without arrest. This makes very

Fig. 3(a). Aluminium component produced by kinetic forming.

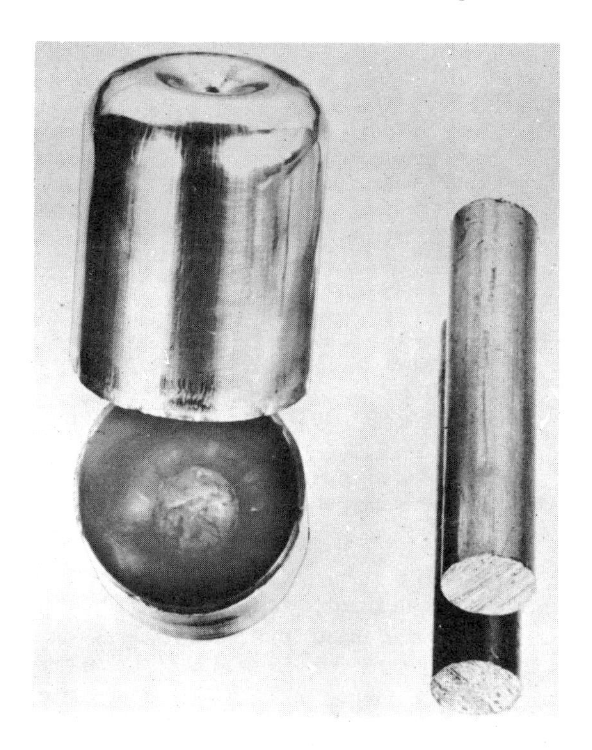

Fig. 3(b). Tubular aluminium component produced by kinetic forming. Inside of component is mirrored.

efficient use of inertia forces. In the reversal of the billet material (i.e. material originally on the billet axis flowing to form the outer walls of the formed tube), some similarity with high-speed cratering (discussed later) will be noted. The rear unconsumed end of the billet may be seen in the mirrored view of the formed tube.

4.2 *Explosive forming*

In this operation[35] a 'high' explosive charge is detonated at some small distance from the workpiece, usually sheet or thin tubular material, a shock wave being transmitted from the charge across the intervening space by, in most cases, immersing the whole assembly in a tank of water. Under the high-intensity short-duration pulse the workpiece is rapidly accelerated to a velocity of about 200 – 600 ft/s, thereafter deforming almost entirely under its own inertia. Owing to long assembly times the process is mainly suited to one-off items, or components which are too large, or of too heavy a section, for forming by conventional means.

Operations basically similar to explosive forming, are electrohydraulic forming[36] and electromagnetic forming[37]. For electrohydraulic forming an underwater shock wave is generated by the rapid discharge of a large, high-voltage capacitor bank through a spark gap, or through a fine wire set in the water. Wire allows some shaping of the shock wave, but necessitates replacement for each operation. For electromagnetic forming a large, high-voltage capacitor bank is discharged through a suitably shaped coil to produce an intense electromagnetic field, which rapidly accelerates the workpiece. A restriction is that, when non-magnetic materials are to be formed, a 'driver' of magnetic material must be employed.

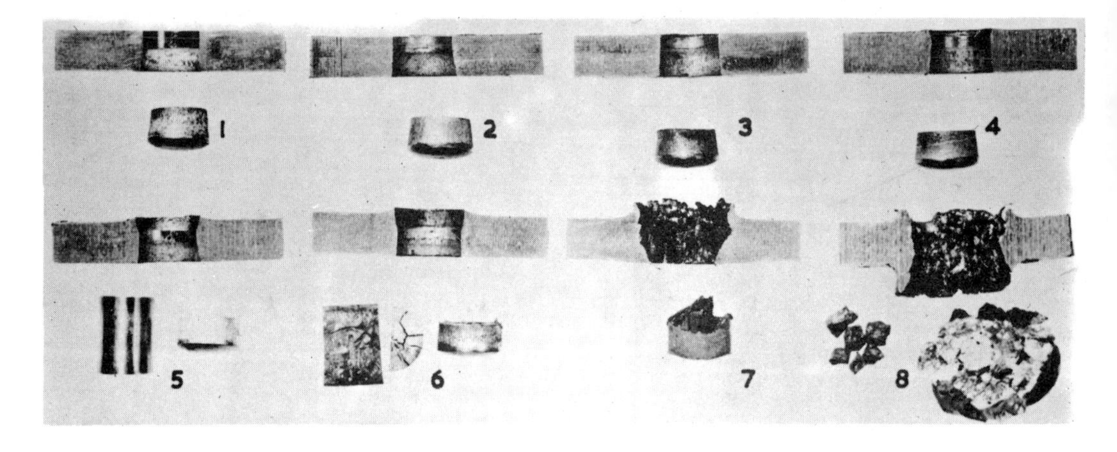

Fig. 4. Copper specimens blanked at increasing punch speed. Specimens 1 to 8 respectively, 0, 252, 438, 793, 930, 1500, 2100 and 2350 ft/s.

Recently experiments have been carried out using explosive mixtures of H_2 and O_2 gas to form tubes[38] and mild steel plates of up to ½ in thickness and 24 in exposed diameter[39]. In the latter case a large tubular concrete tool was used, with the specimen clamped at one end and a source of initiation (a glow plug or powder fuse) at the other. Stoichiometric charge mixtures of H_2 and O_2 at up to 60 lbf/in^2 gauge pressure were used, and the operation was found to be reasonably quiet. Disadvantages were the long charging times involved, and the tendency to scorching of the formed specimen by the hot gases resulting from combustion.

The effects of increasing impact speed, in the very-high-speed blanking of ¼ in thick copper[40], are illustrated in Fig. 4. At an impact speed of around 400 ft/s a band appears at the top of the blanked hole, which increases in depth with increasing impact speed. It is believed that over the early stages of blanking at this level of impact speed the punch is moving faster than the plastic waves. At still higher impact speeds the hole 'craters', forming a 'coronet'. It will be noted that, for the last specimen, the hole produced in the stock is twice the diameter of the punch, on account of the 'cratering' phenomenon.

5.0 FORMING SPEED RANGE 10^3 – 10^4 FT/S

5.1 *Explosive welding*

In this speed range yield stresses are of far less importance in determining material behaviour than inertia stresses. Explosive welding is effected by setting two plates close together, but at a slight inclination – say about 10° – and driving them together forcibly by detonation of a sheet explosive charge. The latter may be on the outer surfaces of both sheets, or merely on one, in which case the assembly must be placed on a large steel anvil to resist the unbalanced forces. Where the direct application of the explosive charge to the plates would be too severe, a 'buffer' of rubber or some similar material is interposed.

In the work of Bahrani *et al.*[41], the characteristic wavy interface of the welded plates is explained using the work of Birkhoff *et al.*[42] (on penetration by shaped charges), where the yield stress of the material is neglected entirely and the process considered as the impact of two fluid jets, obeying Bernoulli's equation. Fig. 5 shows an explosive weld[43] between stellite and

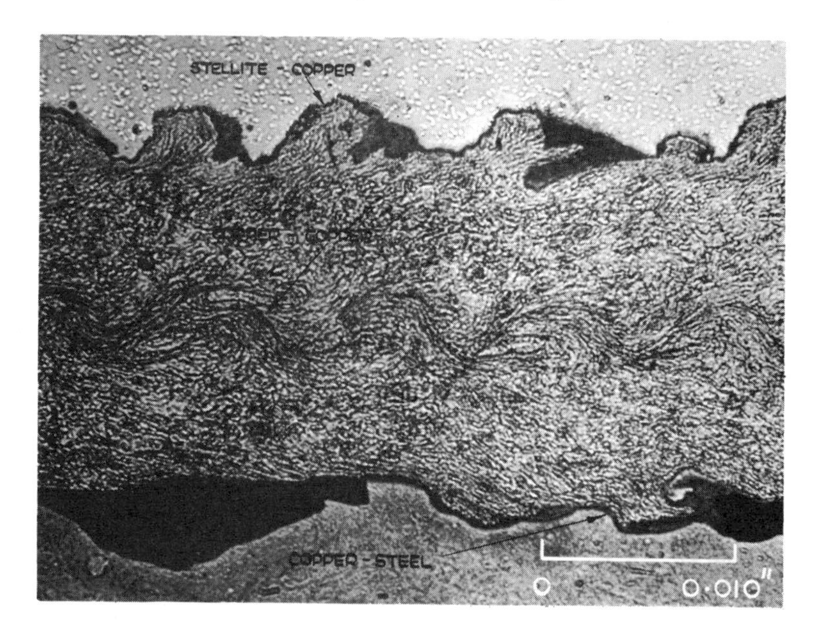

Fig. 5. Explosive welds.

stainless steel, secured by first explosively cladding the stellite and the steel with 0·008 in shim copper, and subsequently explosively welding the clad plates.

The presence of intermetallic compounds at the interfaces will be noted. In general, attempts are made to avoid the formation of intermetallic compounds, or to confine them to local pockets. They are often hard and brittle, and may be detrimental to the strength of the weld where impact, vibration or thermal cycling are involved.

6.0 FORMING SPEED RANGE 10^4 FT/S AND ABOVE

6.1 *Very-high-speed impact*

In this range, inertial stresses and material densities almost entirely determine material behaviour. The 'mud bank' analogy of Eichelberger[44] is appropriate. Eichelberger compared the impact of a high-speed metallic jet on a target plate with the effect of a water hose turned on a bank of soft mud.

Fig. 6 shows a Plasticene block after impact by a multi-coloured Plasticene projectile at about 1500 ft/s. From the hydrodynamic theory of penetration[42], material behaviour is characterised by the non-dimensional quantity $\rho V^2/Y$, where ρ, V and Y are the projectile density, velocity and yield stress respectively. Evaluating this quantity, and assuming an appropriate density and yield stress for steel, one may take the test of Fig. 6 as indicative of the behaviour of a steel projectile striking a steel target as a speed of about 20 000 ft/s.

In accordance with the hydrodynamic theory of penetration the projectile material has suffered lateral reversal in adhering to the walls of the crater. Upon striking the target the forward end of the projectile is progressively eroded. Forward momentum is converted into lateral momentum, which is then absorbed in pushing back surrounding target material to form a crater. [This mechanism accounts for the very high penetration of military shaped charges.

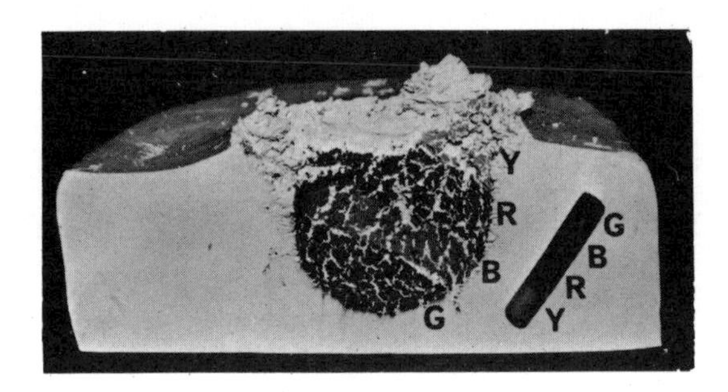

Fig. 6. Result of impact of Plasticene projectile with Plasticene target at 1500 ft/s. A duplicate projectile is shown mounted on the sectioned target at the appropriate inclination. *G* – green, *B* – blue, *R* – red, *Y* – yellow.

The collapse of a metal shell in a high-explosive charge produces a very-high-speed (about 30 000 ft/s) metallic jet.]

6.2 *Ultra-high-speed impact*

At the top end of the impact range, at about 50 000 ft/s, the target and projectile may experience a further phenomenon, an explosive conversion of kinetic energy into heat upon impact[44] , with some vaporisation of the projectile and target material and possibly combustion of the vaporised material in the surrounding atmosphere.

This range may appear to be of no importance, but the advent of space satellites, with reported[45] speeds of about 23 000 ft/s relative to the earth, suggest otherwise. The impact of the earth with meteorites having relative speeds of up to 240 000 ft/s suggests the practical importance of a knowledge of ultra-high-speed impact.

Although its inclusion may not be particularly exact, electron beam welding[46] would appear to fit into this range. It is essentially a process whereby heat is obtained from continual bombardment of a workpiece by electrons, releasing their kinetic energy.

7.0 CONCLUDING REMARKS

Certain of the processes considered in this review are well established and need little explanation, whilst others are at the research and development stage, or are perhaps of only academic interest. However, the author feels that none should be excluded from study and investigation, as knowledge gained thereby may have application to other, related processes. As an illustration, an earlier study of the military use of armour-piercing weapons led to an explanation of the mechanism of explosive welding; the larger process itself arose as a result of failures associated with the unintentional use of overlarge charges in early explosive forming operations.

The theoretical foundations for the explosive forming process, which appeared with the advent of the space age in the 1950s, were laid during extensive studies[47] (initiated by World War I and World War II) of damage resulting from the underwater detonation of mines. The emphasis merely shifted from *deforming* to *forming.* In a similar way, it is felt that an appreciation of lesser-known processes, and of how they fit into the overall pattern, will lead to a better understanding of metal forming in general.

ACKNOWLEDGEMENTS

The author wishes to thank Professor D. S. Ross for his useful discussion of this paper.

REFERENCES

1 S. C. JAIN and A. N. BRAMLEY. 'Characteristics of the high-speed hot forging process'. *Proc. 9th Int. Mach. Tool Des. & Res. Conf.* Birmingham, September, 1968.
2 H. LIPPMANN. 'On the dynamics of forging' *Proc. 7th Int. Mach. Tool Des. & Res. Conf.* Birmingham, September, 1966.
3 M. J. HILLIER. 'Estimation of dynamic forces in very high speed impact forging'. *Trans. Am. Soc. Mech. Engrs. J. Eng. Ind.* 369, 1966.
4 W. GOLDSMITH. *'Impact'.* Arnold Ltd. London, 1960.
5 H. KOLSKY. *'Stress waves in solids'.* Clarendon Press. Oxford, 1953.
6 N. CRISTESCU. *Dynamic Plasticity.* North Holland, Amsterdam, 1967.
7 *Conf. on Properties of Materials at High Rates of Strain.* I. Mech. E. London, 1957.
8 R. A. C. SLATER and W. JOHNSON. 'A survey of the slow and fast blanking of metals at ambient and high temperatures'. *Int. Conf. on Manufacturing Technology, C.I.R.P. – A.S.T.M.E.* Ann Arbor, Michigan, September, 1967.
9 C. ZENER. and C. HOLLOMAN. 'Effect of strain-rate upon plastic flow of steel'. *J. App. Phys.* Vol. 15. p. 22, 1944.
10 C. ZENER. *Fracturing of Metals.* Vol. 3. A.S.M. New York, 1948.
11 R. BALENDRA and F. W. TRAVIS. *Blanking of steel of varying hardness.* To be published.
12 J. CRAWLEY and G. WILLS. 'Production forging by high-energy rate'. *Proc. 7th Int. Mach. Tool Des. & Res. Conf.* Birmingham, September, 1966.
13 H. J. METZLER. 'The development of a high-energy-rate forming machine for research.' *Proc. 9th Int. Mach. Tool Des. & Res. Conf.* Birmingham, September, 1968.
14 P.E.R.A. *Development of the P.E.R.A. high-energy-rate forming machine.* Report No. 131.
15 I. MARLAND, A. J. ORGAN and S. A. TOBIAS. 'Design and development of a compressed-air-driven, counterblow high-energy-rate forming machine'. *Proc. I. Mech. E.* Vol. 180. Part 1, 1965 – 66.
16 L. T. CHAN and S. A. TOBIAS. 'Performance characteristics of petro-forge Mk. I and Mk. II machines'. *Prod. 9th Int. Mach. Tool Des. & Res. Conf.* Birmingham, September, 1968.
17 R. DAVIES and A. N. BRAMLEY. 'Applications of petro-forge machines to high-energy-rate forming of metals'. *Conf. on Modern Manufacturing Techniques.* I. Mech. E. Loughborough, March 1968.
18 T. A. DEAN. 'A comparison of high-rate and conventional forging machines'. *Proc. 7th Int. Mach. Tool Des. & Res. Conf.* Birmingham, September, 1966.
19 A. N. BRAMLEY. 'A discussion of tooling problems in high-energy-rate forging'. *Int. J. Mach. Tool Des. & Res.* Vol. 7. 351, 1967.
20 S. C. JAIN and A. N. BRAMLEY. 'Speed and frictional effects in hot forging'. *Proc. I. Mech. E.* Vol. 2. Part 1. 1967 – 68.
21 R. DAVIES and S. M. DHAWAN. 'A comparison of some strain-rate effects in slow and high-speed blanking'. *Proc. 9th Int. Mach. Tool Des. & Res. Conf.* Birmingham, September, 1968.
22 A. J. ORGAN and P. B. MELLOR. 'Some factors affecting the quality of cropped billets'. *Int. J. Mach. Tool Des. & Res.* Vol. 7. p. 189, 1967.
23 R. A. C. SLATER and W. JOHNSON. 'The effects of temperature, speed and strain-rate on the force and energy required in blanking'. *Int. J. Mech. Sci.* Vol. 9. 271. 1967.
24 W. JOHNSON, E. R. LAITHWAITE and R. A. C. SLATER. 'An experimental impact-extrusion machine driven by a linear induction motor'. *Proc. I. Mech. E.* Vol. 179. Part 1. No. 7 p. 257. 1964 – 65.
25 B. N. COLE and F. BAKHTAR. 'Dynamic effects in very-high-speed impact extrusion'. *Int. J. Mach. Tool Des. & Res.* Vol. 3. p. 77. 1963.
26 R. DAVIES. 'Some effects of very high speeds in impact extrusion'. *Proc. 5th Int. Mach. Tool Des. & Res. Conf.* Manchester, September, 1965.
27 E. R. AUSTIN, R. DAVIES and F. BAKHTAR. 'Extrusion of aluminium and copper' *Proc. I. Med. E.* Vol. 182. Part 1. No. 9, 1967 – 68.
28 E. R. AUSTIN, R. DAVIES and F. BAKHTAR. 'Extrusion of steel and titanium'. *Ibid* 27.
29 R. J. DOWER. 'A preliminary investigation of the extrusion moulding process'. *Proc. 7th Int. Mach. Tool Des. & Res. Conf.* Birmingham, September, 1966.
30 W. JOHNSON and F. W. TRAVIS. 'A tool for explosive hydrodynamic extrusion'. *Proc. I. Mech. E.* Vol. 182. Part 3C. 1967 – 68.

31 F. W. TRAVIS and W. JOHNSON. 'The pressure generated in the explosive hydrodynamic extrusion of aluminium and copper and other phenomena'. *Ibid.* reference 30.
32 F. W. TRAVIS and W. JOHNSON. 'High-speed riveting of mild steel'. *Proc. 9th Int. Mach. Tool Des. & Res. Conf.* Birmingham, September, 1968.
33 F. W. TRAVIS. 'An investigation into kinetic forming'. *Int. J. Mach. Tool Des. & Res.* Vol. 9 p. 51. 1969.
34 R. BALENDRA and F. W. TRAVIS. 'Kinetic forming of tubes'. To be published.
35 A. G. THURMAN and A. A. EZRA. 'The analysis and design of an explosive forming facility'. *Proc. 9th Int. Mach. Tool Des. & Res. Conf.* Birmingham, September, 1968.
36 P.E.R.A. *Electrohydraulic forming.* Report No. 192. June, 1969.
37 S. T. S. AL-HASSANI, J. L. DUNCAN and W. JOHNSON. 'The influence of electrical and geometrical parameters in magnetic forming'. *Proc. 8th Int. Mach. Tool Des. & Res. Conf.* Manchester, September, 1967.
38 W. A. POYNTON, F. W. TRAVIS and W. JOHNSON 'The free radial expansion of thin cylindrical brass tubes using explosive gas mixtures'. *Int. J. Mech. Sci.* Vol. 10. p. 385. 1968.
39 W. A. POYNTON, F. W. TRAVIS and W. JOHNSON. 'The use of a large tool in the forming of metal by explosive gases'. *Proc. 9th Int. Mach. Tool Des. & Res. Conf.* Birmingham, September, 1968.
40 W. JOHNSON and F. W. TRAVIS. 'High-speed blanking of copper'. *Proc. I. Mech. E.* Vol. 180. Part 31. 1965 – 66.
41 A. S. BAHRANI, T. J. BLACK and B. CROSSLAND. 'The Mechanics of wave formation in explosive welding'. *Proc. R. Soc.* Vol. A296. p. 123. 1967.
42 G. BIRKHOFF, D. P. MACDOUGALL, E. M. PUGH and G. I. TAYLOR. 'Explosives with lines cavities'. *J. App. Phys.* Vol. 19. p. 563. 1948.
43 F. W. TRAVIS and W. JOHNSON. 'Explosive welding of stellite to stainless steel' *Proc. 8th Int. Mach. Tool Des. & Res. Conf.*, Manchester, September, 1967.
44 R. J. EICHELBERGER. 'Behaviour of materials under dynamic loading'. p. 155, *Am. Soc. Mech. Engrs.*, 1965.
45 M. E. VAN VALKENBURG, W. G. CLAY and J. H. HUTH. 'Impact phonomena at high speeds'. *J. App. Phys.* Vol. 27. p. 1123. 1956.
46 M. A. COOK. *The science of high explosives.* Rheinhold, New York, 1958.
47 O.N.R. *Underwater explosion research.* Vol. 3. Washington, 1950.

LIQUID BULGE FORMING

Takashi Ogura
Nippon Bulge Industries Ltd, Tokyo

SUMMARY

Liquid bulge forming is a cold pressing technique. A tubular blank is deformed in a die by pressurising liquid within the blank. This report describes the general ideas of the process, the equipment, and examples of components experimentally developed for low-cost production.

1.0 INTRODUCTION

The liquid bulge process is for cold-pressing metal pipes, tubes and other cylindrical products outwards into dies. The energy is provided by high-pressure liquid in the cylindrical workpiece. Various liquids, including soft metals such as lead, low-melting-point alloys, organic material like rubber, polyethylene glycol and so on, are used as pressure media. For generation of pressure there are also various methods, including mechanical means, powder explosion and electric discharge explosion. As a pressure medium we use mineral oil. A hydraulic press generates the pressure.

The reasons for the choice of mineral oil and a hydraulic press are mainly these:

a In order to control the thickness of the deformed wall, and to obtain substantial expansion, independent axial compression is possible against the hydraulic pressure.
b Auxiliary steps can be made with the dies during forming.
c Hydraulic pressure can easily and accurately be measured and controlled.
d The cost of consumable material can be minimised during processing.
e Safe operation is guaranteed.

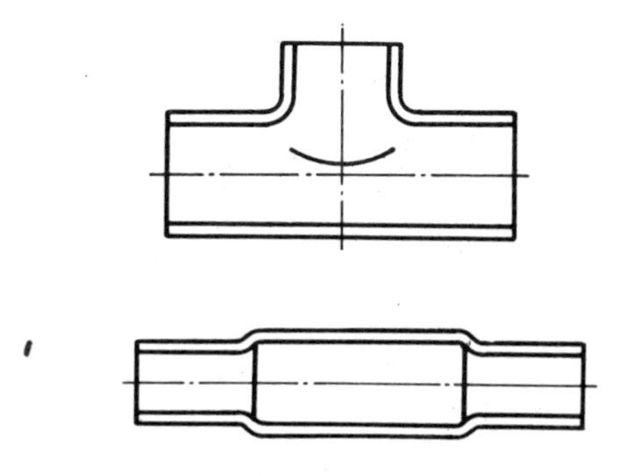

Fig. 1. Two categories of bulge forming.

The liquid bulge process falls into two categories according to the shape of the product. In one category part of a cross-section is made to project or branch. In the other category the flow of metal can be seen all round the cross-section.

The tee shown in Fig. 1, a pipe fitting, is a typical example of the first category. Others are various bicycle parts and automotive rear-axle transmission housings. In order to have enough wall thickness as well as considerable expansion during their formation it is necessary to compress the tubular blanks axially.

Stepped hollow shafts, as shown in Fig. 1, are typical of the second category. Here formation is mainly by hydraulic pressure. Sometimes, however, axial compression is also required. Other examples of the second category are bellows, flexible joints and hubs for bicycles. They are first bulged with the hydraulic press, then axial compression is applied to form the part completely.

The hydraulic bulge process requires a minimum of operations for comparatively complex-shaped tubular products which are, at present, mechanically finished after casting, hot forging and welding.

The hydraulic pressure process has not been used in the past for lack of means to generate ultra-high pressure, difficulty of control, and lack of a simple yet positive sealing method for both ends of the tubular blanks.

Below is an outline of the liquid bulge process, its method, its equipment, and some of the forms that we have studied in Japan for the past two years. Nippon Bulge Industries Ltd are at present producing about 300 000 tees and other shapes, in various materials, from 12 mm pipe to 300 mm tube, by means of four bulge-forming presses.

2.0 LOCAL OR SECTIONAL BULGING

2.1 *Components with one branch*

A typical example is a tee as shown in Fig. 1. Tees are normally produced by casting or by a special hot-forging process because of the basic requirement that a relatively long branch

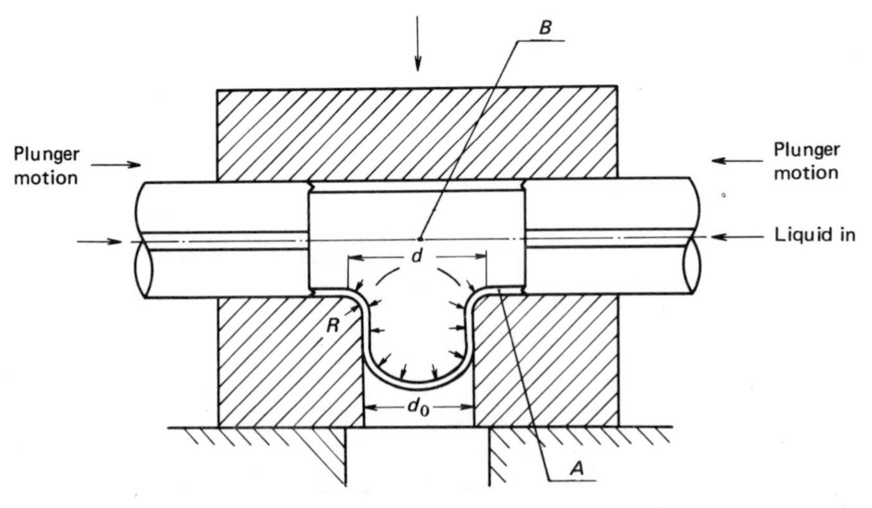

Fig. 2. Forming a tee.

should have the same wall thickness as the main tube. General bulge-forming procedures for tees are as follows.

A metal tube of specified length is placed in the lower half of a split die. The die is then closed with a hydraulic press. Liquid is injected into the tube, the ends of which are sealed by a pair of hydraulically powered plungers with specially designed tips. Hydraulic pressure is then built up inside the tube by an intensifier. When pressure is sufficient to start the bulging, the ends of the tube are pushed inward, causing the tube to assume the contours of the die cavity. In Fig. 2 the pipe wall in zone A is flowing into the branch cavity of the dies. Meanwhile the pipe is being pushed inward by the plungers while maintaining intimate contact with both the main and branch cavities because of the internal liquid pressure. The pipe wall in zone B (in a plane perpendicular to that of the paper) is subjected to severe radial deformation due to the combined stress created by the axial compression and the tension provided by the radially exerted liquid pressure, causing the branch end to be bulge-formed.

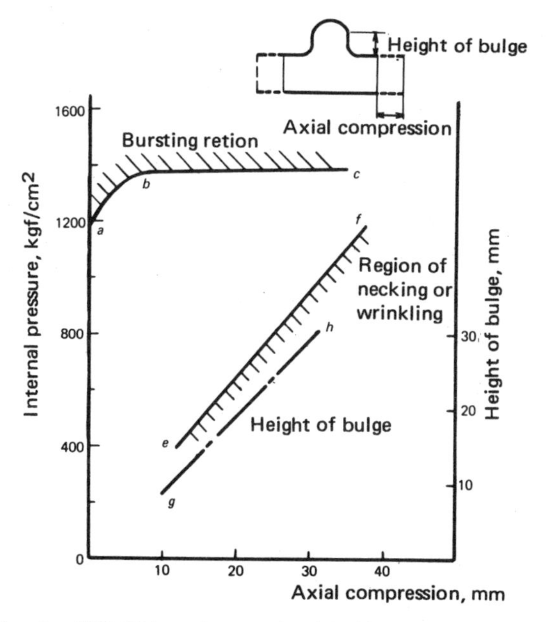

Fig. 3. Formable region for STP 30A carbon steel tube, 40 mm outside diameter, 2 mm wall.

It may readily be appreciated that the formability of the workpiece is directly related to the rate of pressure intensification and the rate of axial compression. Fig. 3 shows the 'formable' region of a tubular blank in relation to pressure and axial compression. Pressures in excess of those represented by curve a–b–c will burst the bulge tip open. If the pressure with respect to the amount of compression is insufficient, either a neck will form, as shown in Fig. 4, or wrinkles, as shown also. Straight line e–f gives the relationship between axial compression and the minimum pressure required to form a bulge without necking.

The initial value of internal pressure, 0–a, approximately equals that obtained from a liquid cup test on a tubular blank with diameter d as shown in Fig. 2. As the pipe wall begins to flow into the branch cavity along radius R, accompanied by axial compression of the blank, diameter d decreases and the bursting pressure increases accordingly, as shown by line a–b. The bursting

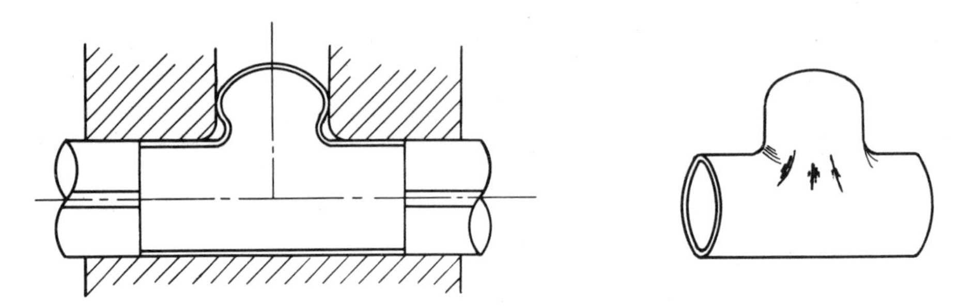

Fig. 4. Left – necking. Right – wrinkling.

pressure becomes virtually constant and stays so once diameter d has reached the specified value d_0. On the other hand, the most important factor determining the limits of necking is radius R. The wall thickness gradually increases towards zone A because the inward movement of pipe material is resisted by friction with the die cavities, and the drag increases with increasing internal pressure. The gradually increasing wall thickness of the blank at radius R is accompanied by gradually increasing resistance to bending under radial liquid pressure, causing necking as shown in Fig. 4. Wrinkles tend to collect in zone B owing to unbalance between the axial compressive force and the circumferential tensile force caused by liquid pressure. Wrinkles can therefore be eliminated by increasing the liquid pressure with respect to the rate of axial compression. Whether necks or wrinkles form depends upon the shape of the component to be made and the material.

Thus the bulge forming of a particular component is possible only within a region which is

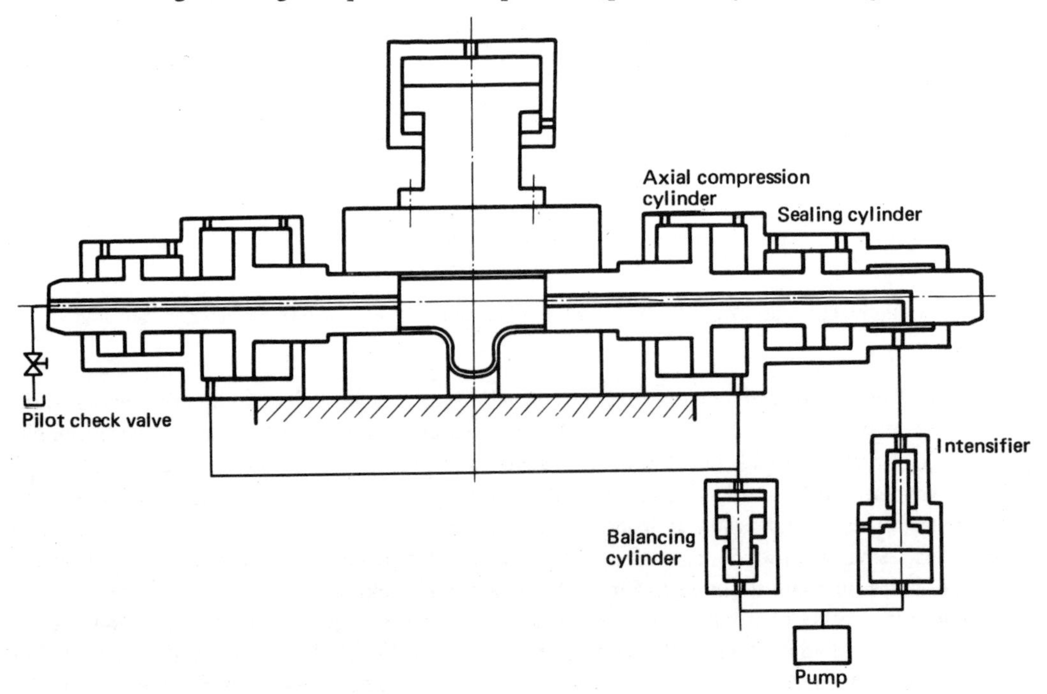

Fig. 5. Bulge-forming press for tee components.

bounded by the bursting line above and the necking or wrinkling line below. The difficulty of bulge-forming for the particular component is judged on the area of this 'formable' region.

The height of the bulge is nearly proportional to the axial compression. The inward movement of the blank is shown in Fig. 3 by straight line g–h, of which the slope is mainly dependent on radius R (Fig. 2), the length of blank and the material.

The bulge-forming press shown diagrammatically in Fig. 5 has been designed to press tubular blanks of different diameters, wall thickness and materials as required by a frequently changing production schedule.

Tees made by presses of this type are shown in Fig. 6.

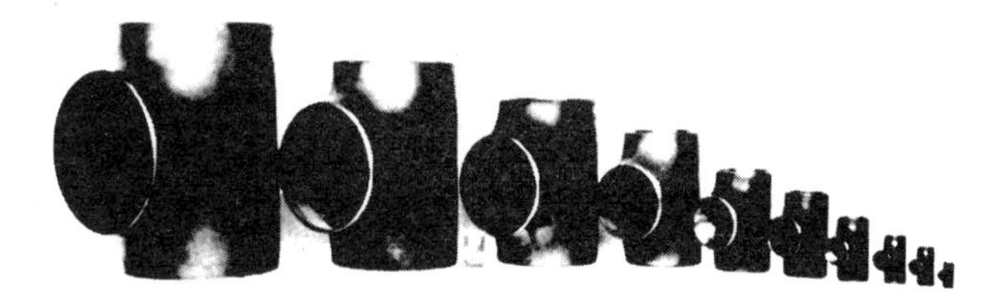

Fig. 6. Tees bulge-formed on presses of type shown in Fig. 5.

2.2 *Two axially aligned branches*

The head lug of a bicycle frame is a typical example. Refer to Fig. 7. When a component with two axially aligned branches is formed, only the pipe wall in zone A flows into the branch cavities whereas that occupying zone C stays still. Hence the height of bulge obtainable for a given axial compression is reduced to about half that available in the bulge-forming of a

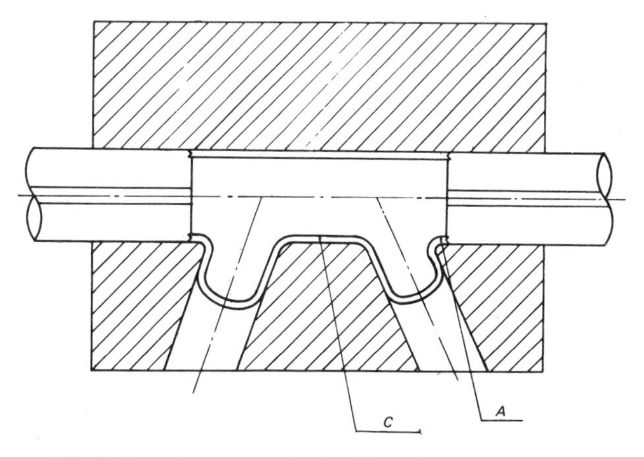

Fig. 7. Forming process for head lug of a bicycle frame.

component with one branch. Conversely, to give two branches the same height as in the case of a single bulge (Fig. 3), the blank must be compressed twice as much. The same relationship between the bursting pressure and the axial compression applies, but because of the necking or wrinkling limits with respect to axial compression, which is almost doubly severe, it is not practical to hope for a component with long branches in a row.

2.3 *Two circumferentially aligned branches*

Crosses or X-pieces such as pipe joints and automotive rear-axle transmission housings are typical examples.

The manner of deformation during bulge-forming of this type of component is considerably different from that of a tee. In a tee that portion of the tubular blank in the vicinity of the branch cavity flows into it, while the portion opposite the cavity is stationary and is thickened only by the lengthwise compression exerted on the pipe ends. Hence the deformation resistance offered by the plastic flow of the tube wall differs greatly at different points on the circumference, and this is obviously one of the causes of the wrinkles which tend to collect in zone B. Since a cross-piece is quite symmetrical so is the manner of plastic flow of the pipe wall, and there is less variation in deformation resistance over the circumference and less axial compressive force is required to form the bulges. Naturally the bursting limits applicable here are the same as for a tee of corresponding diameter.

After successive experiments with gradually increasing radii we have successfully test-formed a central part of an automotive rear-axle transmission housing as shown in Fig. 8.

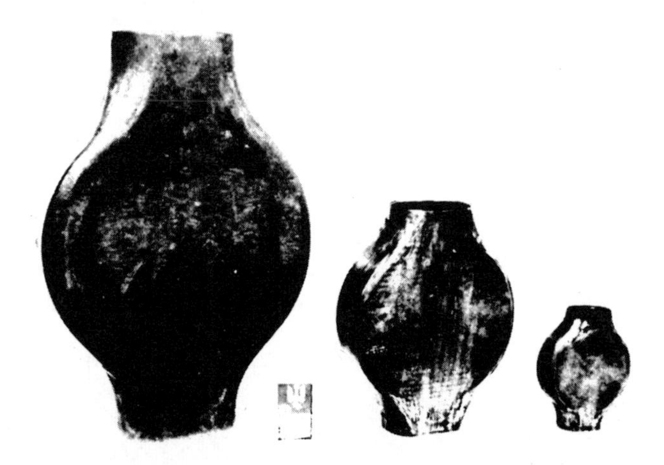

Fig. 8. Bulge-formed automotive rear-axle transmission housing. Left, for 2 ton truck. Centre, for Japanese car. Respectively, tubes of 132 mm outside diameter, and 6 mm wall thickness, and 96 mm outside diameter, and 3 mm wall thickness, in STP 38 carbon steel. On the right is the first test piece, made to half scale.

Note that, as the radii are large, the branches assume the shape of a disc with the axial length spanning the base of the two radii (corresponding to R in Fig. 2), the disc having more than twice the diameter of the original blank. The formable region of such a component is very small, and forming is very difficult accordingly. This is because the effect of axial compression is virtually nullified and the bursting pressures are considerably lower than in a tee. Certain modifications of the dies and adaptation of forming procedures are required, depending on the shape and dimensions of the branched parts.

2.4 *Four branches*

A hanger lug used on a bicycle frame has four branches as shown in Fig. 9. The larger two branches (32·6 mm outside diameter) align circumferentially in the centre quite close to each other. The smaller two branches (26 mm outside diameter) align axially at a certain distance

Fig. 9. Bulge-formed hanger lug for bicycle frame.

from the centre. Hence two different sets of bursting limits apply to the two pairs of branches, as shown by curve *A* for the smaller branches and curve *B* for the larger branches in Fig. 10.

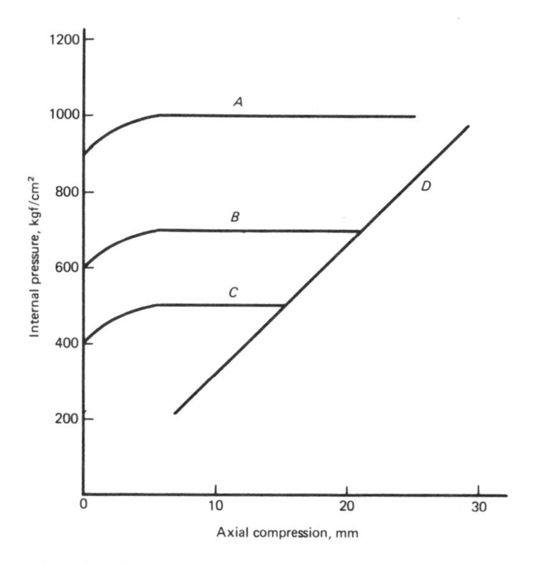

Fig. 10. Formable region for four-branch part in STP 30A carbon steel tube, 40 mm outside diameter. 2 mm wall thickness.

The bursting limits for the larger branches were measured with the two branches set apart so as to determine the relation between the individual diameters and the bursting limits. Actually, however, the close proximity of the two branches demands that the corresponding die cavities be merged into one big hole where they meet the main cavity. Because of this augmented projected area of the merged branch cavities, the bursting limits for the larger branches are brought down to such levels as are shown by curve *C*. The formable region, thus confined to the small area contained by curve *C* and line *D*, does not permit axial compression of the blank for any distance of practical value.

In order to solve this problem two stoppers are provided. They slide in the larger branch cavities, as shown in Fig. 11, to support the tips of the branches. The stoppers are guided by

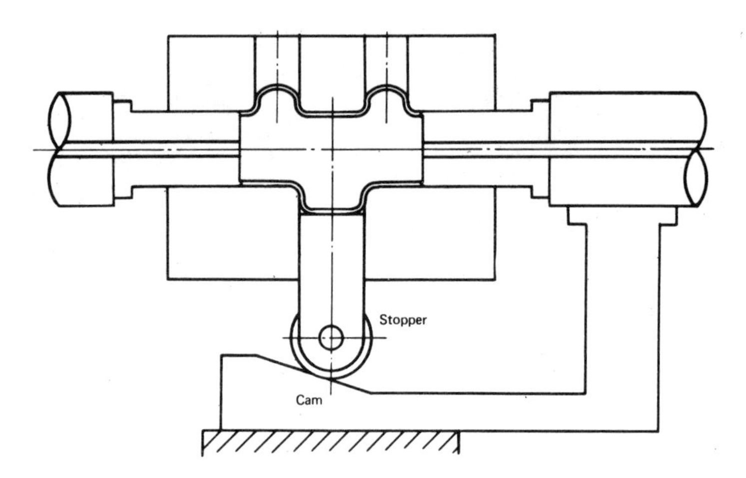

Fig. 11. Stopper and cam to prevent bursting.

cams directly connected to the plungers. Thus the blank is gradually and controllably allowed to extend into the larger cavities in proper co-ordination with the inward movement of the plungers and without fear of bursting. The cams are so designed that the axial compression and the length of the branches will increase generally as shown in Fig. 3. The formable region is thus enlarged on the upper side to the limits of curve A, permitting uniform extension of all four branches.

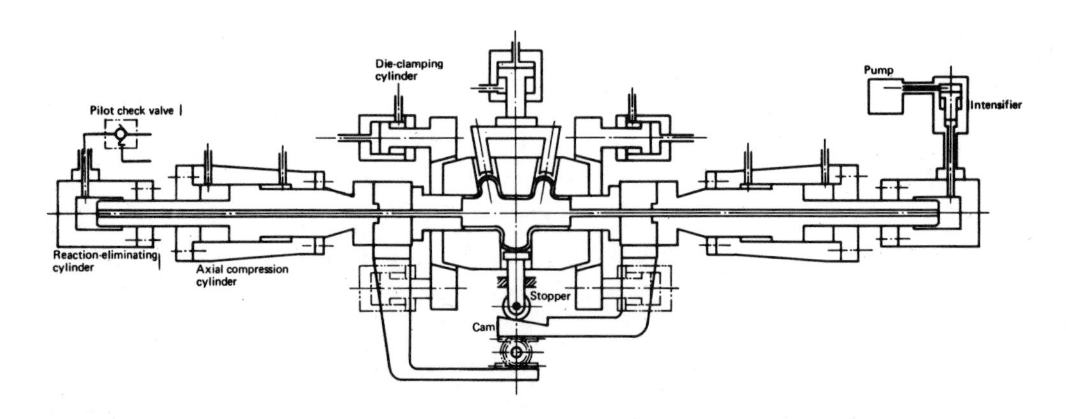

Fig. 12. Bulge-forming press for hanger lugs.

The bulge-forming press for this type of component is shown diagrammatically in Fig. 12. The hydraulic circuit is simplified compared with that given in Fig. 5 because this is a special-purpose machine, designed for one kind of tubular blank exclusively.

A bulge-formed hanger lug and a finished hanger lug are shown in Fig. 9.

3.0 OVERALL OR CIRCUMFERENTIAL BULGING

This kind of bulging is for forming stepped hollow shafts of various designs and for components such as the front handles of bicycles. The process can be further classified as follows.

1 Radial deformation by internal liquid pressure alone.
2 Deformation by internal liquid pressure plus axial compressive force on pipe ends.
3 Deformation by internal liquid pressure accompanied by lengthwise shift of die members.

Bulge-forming by liquid pressure inside a tubular blank is the most common practice. Generally speaking, as far as tubular parts with relatively thin walls are concerned, the bulge ratio or expansion ratio $(D-d)/d$ is determined by the strain at the ultimate strenth point on the nominal stress-strain diagram for the material (d = blank diameter and D = diameter to which blank is to be expanded).

If the axial length of that portion of the blank which is subjected to expansion is kept within about twice the diameter of the blank, the expansion ratio approaches the nominal elongation obtained in a tensile test on the particular material. Consequently the maximum bulgeable diameter D is larger in this case.

Since there is a definite limit to D in either case, bulge-forming by internal liquid pressure alone cannot be expected to compete favourably with conventional tube drawing in the forming of simple shapes. This is mainly due to the relatively high initial cost of equipment.

When liquid bulge-forming is accompanied by axial compression of the blank, which is relatively thin-walled, the expansion ratio jumps to 1·2 times or twice the nominal elongation, provided that the length of the expanded portion of the blank is less than twice the diameter of the blank.

Some components require axial shift of a die member or members during the forming operation, e.g. bellows and flexible joints. These components, by the very nature of their shapes, do not require a high expansion ratio in the sense of the term as used in the last few paragraphs, but they demand a considerable margin lengthwise which cannot be provided by axial compression applied at the tube ends.

A tubular blank is inserted in a series of ring-shaped dies, properly spaced, and liquid under pressure is introduced into the blank to bulge-form those sections of the blank which are not in contact with die rings. $(D-d)/d$ is such that the circumferential elongation required is well within the capacity of the blank, so, within the limits of the nominal elongation of the material, the expansion ratio in this case is restricted by the surface area of the finished component. To assist in this connection the die rings are made to close in while liquid pressure is being applied internally.

As this is a well known art we shall limit ourselves here to some of our experimental applications.

3.1 *Stepped hollow shaft*

We have attempted to bulge-form the shafts of small electric motors of the kind shown in Fig. 1. As is well known, the solid centre of a shaft contributes little to its torsional or bending strength. So far as deformation is concerned a solid shaft in torsion or flexure is equivalent to a tube (commonly called thin-walled pipe) of 110% the outside diameter. The saving of weight and material cost would be great if all solid shafts could be replaced by tubing. Experiments have been conducted with some success, but the new method of shaft forming is not in practical use at present.

The experiments were conducted with tubular blanks of outside diameter 21·7 mm and wall thickness 1·8 mm (carbon steel tube, tensile strength 36 kgf/mm^2, elongation after annealing 39%) which was formed as shown in Fig. 1.

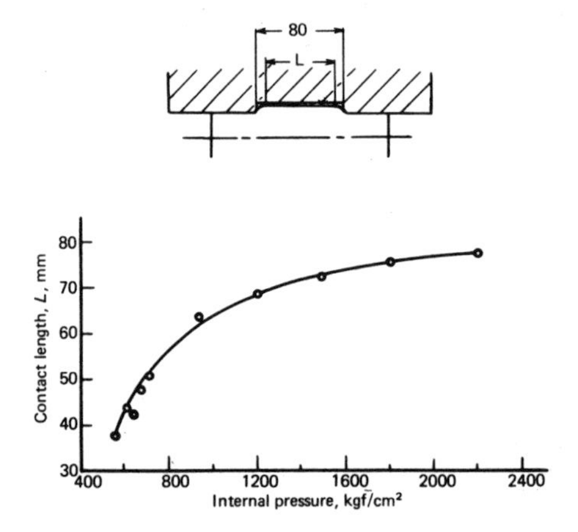

Fig. 13. Relationship between contact length and internal pressure. Diagram shows difficulty at relatively sharp corner.

Radial expansion is relatively easy but the coining of the tube wall to the relatively sharp corner of the stepped section of the die cavity was not successful, as shown in Fig. 13. The corner radius is critical because the inner race of a ball bearing must be tightly fitted to it in the assembly of a motor. To solve this problem, a pair of axially movable edging dies was contrived. They are hydraulically actuated to set the required radius accurately.

It is now possible to force-fit the tubular shaft into a component in which the shaft is to be set, and to form the radius at the same time, as shown in Fig. 14. The main dies are here replaced by the component in which the shaft is to be mounted, with the edging dies on each side.

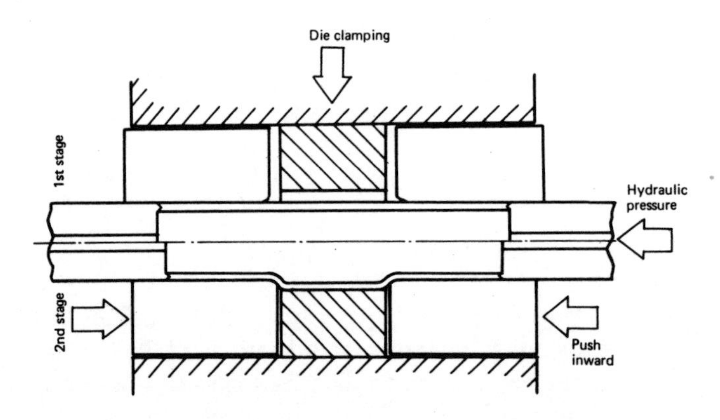

Fig. 14. Simultaneous formation of sharp corner and mounting.

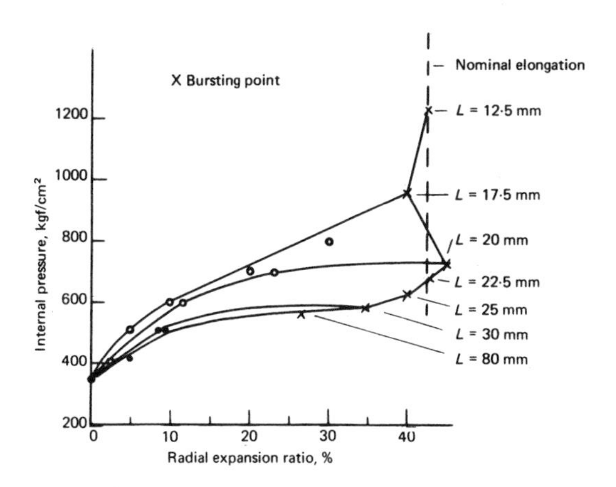

Fig. 15. Relationship between internal pressure and expansion ratio.

Fig. 15 shows the relationship between liquid pressure and radial expansion ratio with respect to various contact lengths, *L*. In the experiment the tubular blank was allowed to expand freely under internal pressure until it burst. When *L* is large the expansion ratio at bursting is relatively small, and nearly equals the strain at the ultimate strength point on a nominal stress-strain diagram. With decreasing *L* the expansion ratio increases and approaches the nominal elongation.

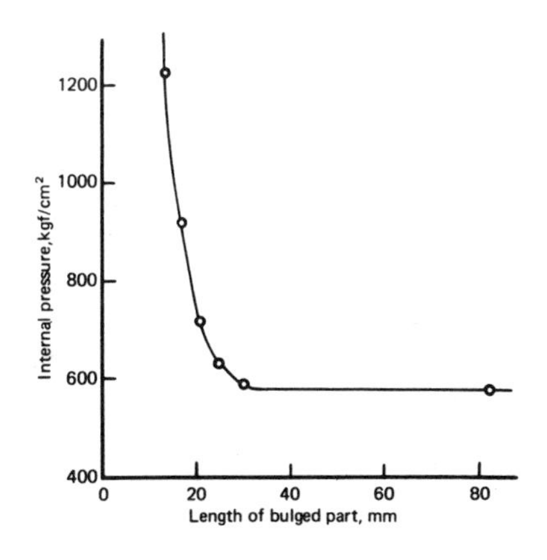

Fig. 16. Relationship between bursting pressure and length of bulged part.

The same results are expressed in different terms in Fig. 16. There bursting pressure is plotted against length of blank bulged by internal pressure. It will be readily seen that the bursting pressure is virtually constant as long as *L* is more than twice the diameter *d* of the original blank. With decreasing *L* the bursting pressure jumps up abruptly, showing that the blank can withstand extremely high pressures with small *L*.

This experiment was conducted with a tubular blank having the same dimensions and properties as that used for the motor shaft. Further experiments with blanks of other diameter and wall thickness are due.

Bulge-forming under both liquid pressure and axial compression can only be used for components with expansion length L under the sloping section of the curve shown in Fig. 16. Sideways compression of a component longer than twice the diameter of the blank will result in an insufficient bulge and failure to obtain the desired shape.

3.2 *Free-wheel hub*

Analytically, the free-wheel hub shown in Fig. 17(a) can be considered in the three parts illustrated in Figs. 17(b), (c) and (d). By spot-welding these parts the manufacturer can avoid the costly conventional forging and subsequent machining. Part (b), hereafter referred to as the outer pipe, is bulge-formed. Part (c), called the inner pipe, is formed by swaging, while part (d) can easily be drawn on a press. Swaging and drawing are not new and are left out of the present discussion.

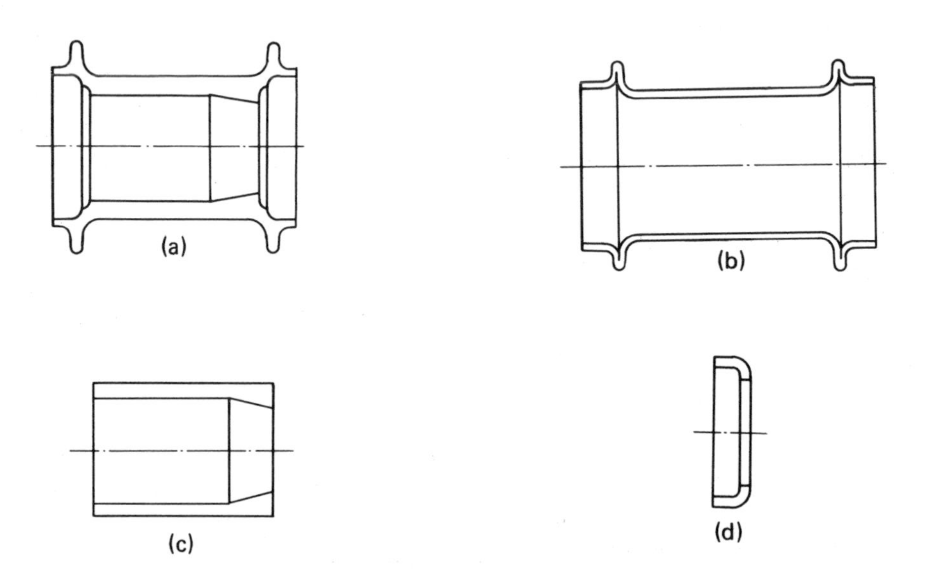

Fig. 17. Hub components.

A tubular blank of outer diameter 38 mm and wall thickness 1·6 mm is bulged as shown in Fig. 18. After proper bulges have been obtained, the hydraulically operated cylinder dies are tripped and closed in toward the centre, pressing the bulged sections of the blank against the split dies to form the flanges.

The bulge-forming press used for this operation is basically the same as the presses previously mentioned, with the difference that the forces required from the plungers are rather small and the plungers must be able to accelerate simultaneously with the advance of the cylinder dies to keep the blank sealed at both ends.

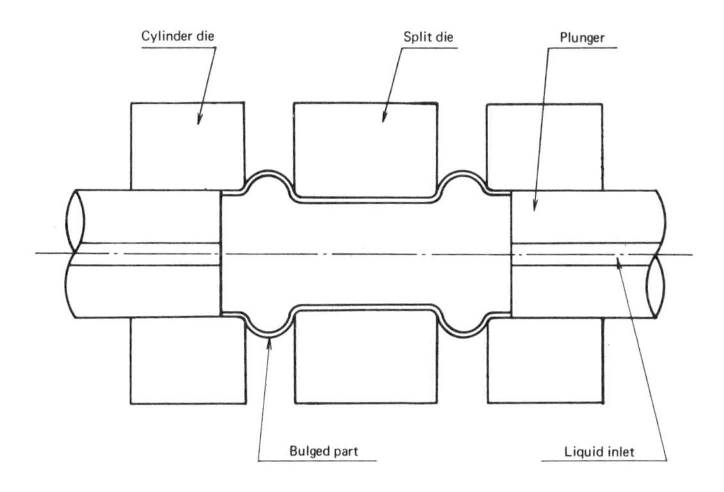

Fig. 18. First-stage bulging for shell of hub.

4.0 SEALING

Since liquid at 300 to 3000 kgf/cm^2 is used in the bulge-forming processes described here, special care must be taken in choice of sealing method. It is particularly necessary in an automatic bulge-forming press to provide easy but steady means for making the tubular blank oil-tight. Generally speaking, high-pressure liquid is retained by sealing with rubber, plastics, soft metals or a metallic device on which the full sealing force is borne by a loop-like area so small that the bearing pressure exceeds the pressure of the liquid. At the experimental stage of bulge-forming, O-rings or cup-shaped seals of synthetic rubber were mostly used. For bulge-forming tees these proved to be impractical, partly because axial compression caused such wear and tear that the seals had to be replaced quite frequently.

This problem, which is of considerable practical importance, was solved by giving the tips of the plungers a special shape. Each plunger is machined and ground with a ridge of triangular section at the tips, running parallel to the circumference of the plunger and forming a ring. The small annular area of the pipe ends, cut into by the triangular section, bears the full force of the plungers, resulting in an extremely high pressure spread all over the small sealing surface. The height chosen for the ridge depends on the surface roughness of the ends of the tubular blank and the squareness of these ends with the axial centre-line of the blank.

5.0 CONCLUSION

The bulge-forming method, its equipment and a part of its application have been studied by a team including the author.

All the blanks for the products were of pipe and tubular form, but blanks of non-circular cross-section and cylindrical blanks with a bottom can also be processed. Pipes welded by reliable methods can also be used.

The research was carried out by the Government Industrial Research Institute at Nagoya, Japan. Various bulge-formed products are being manufactured by Nippon Bulge Industries Ltd, Tokyo, Japan.

ELECTROPAINTING

D. B. Bruce
Pinchin Johnson Paints, Birmingham

SUMMARY

Electropainting is distinguished from other painting processes. The physico-chemical phenomena are described. Types of paint which can be applied by means of the technique are stated. The scope of the method is discussed and its utility in industry assessed. Electropainting plant layout is considered in general terms.

1.0 INTRODUCTION

Paint application technology has required that paints have a viscosity such that they flow readily in the applying apparatus, but, once applied to the substrate, flow only sufficiently to provide a smooth surface. This requirement has been only partially met, so defects in paint films result. In electropainting the paint dispersion has a very low viscosity, but, in the act of deposition, the paint is effectively separated from dispersing 'solvent' so that a very great increase in viscosity occurs. The initial film is fairly smooth and only slight flow during stoving gives the required degree of smoothness in the final film. Electropainting is essentially an electrolytic chemical reaction in which the metal substrate and the paint dispersion are the reactants. Thus the nature of the substrate and the paint play important roles in determining the quality of the reaction product.

Electropainting is distinguished from other techniques of applying paints in that it is a chemical process. In this paper it is proposed to touch on the following topics.

- The electropainting process, including the chemical and physico-chemical phenomena.
- The types of paint which are being applied by this technique, the main industrial outlets for electropainting, and the advantages to be gained.
- The general layout of an electropainting plant.

2.0 ELECTROPAINTING

2.1 *The electropainting process*

All electropaints in current commercial use are based on acidic organic resins which can be dispersed or dissolved in water by neutralising, in part or in whole, the acid function. The resin dispersion is thus composed of anionic macromolecules together with the cations corresponding to the neutralising base used (e.g. diethylammonium, sodium potassium). When such a dispersion is subjected to electrolysis the following main reactions take place.

At the anode. (i) Hydrogen ions are generated and interact with the resin anions in the vicinity to precipitate the acidic resin, which is insoluble in this environment[1]. (ii) Gaseous oxygen is then formed at the anode. (iii) Depending on the nature of the anode, normally metallic, ions corresponding to the metal may be generated and will interact with the resin anions to form metal resinate. Thus steel anodes give Fe^{++}, zinc anodes give Zn^{++}, but platinum yields only hydrogen ions as in (i).

At the cathode. Cations corresponding to the neutralising base are discharged but immediately react with water to reform the same ionic species and liberate hydrogen gas. Providing the cathode is not made of a reactive metal, no attack on the cathode occurs.

It is clear that reactions (i) and (iii) lead to precipitation of resin in the near vicinity of the anode. Thus, if the article to be painted is made the anode of such an electrolytic cell as we have considered, the passage of electric current will, in favourable circumstances, lead to the deposition of paint resin on the article.

Consider now the circumstances which must be favourable to obtain a coating. The 'free acid' form of the resin must adhere to the anode. The anode must be a conductor of electricity, for otherwise no electrolysis can occur. The relative movement of the anode and the paint must not be so rapid that the freshly precipitated resin is stripped from the anode surface. The rate of formation of oxygen at the anode surface must not be so great that the freshly deposited resin is torn away from the anode surface by the growing gas bubbles as they break away. The current applied must be direct, for otherwise the resin deposited in acid form during a positive cycle would be redissolved by the base released during the following negative cycle. The amount of ripple which can be tolerated depends on the resin system being used. 5–10% ripple is certainly satisfactory, and in some cases much more is acceptable.

For the sake of simplicity we have dealt only with resin solutions. For painting, however, pigmentation must be introduced. The pigment particles are dispersed in the resin solution in such a way that each particle or agglomeration of particles is surrounded by a layer of resin micelles. It is not therefore necessary for the pigment particles to move under the influence of the electric field towards the anode in order to be deposited, as would be the case in simple electrophoresis. The pigment particles are taken for a ride, so to speak, by the resin micelles, and plenty of the latter are always present at the anode surface owing to the continuous agitation of the paint bath.

It is always possible that, in the process of paint manufacture, some pigment particles may escape wetting out by resin and may exist alone in the paint dispersion. Depending on the pigment type and the overall composition of the paint such particles may be cationic. On their discharge at the cathode flocculation may occur, pigment aggregates being swept off the cathode surface back into the paint bath. There they may fall on horizontal surfaces to give rough deposits.

2.2 *Process parameters*

The amount of paint deposited depends almost directly on the number of coulombs of electricity passed. The thickness of the film does not, however, vary directly with the duration of the electrolysis at constant voltages[2]. It follows that the current density must vary. The type of variation found in practice is shown in Fig. 1. Typical values for the various parameters are:

- Initial current density, 3 – 5 A/ft^2
- Time to minimum current, 30 – 60 s
- Applied voltage, 50 – 500 V

The curve of Fig. 1 relates to a very simple cell in which the anode and cathode are flat plates. The change in current density is due of course to the progressive insulation of the anode

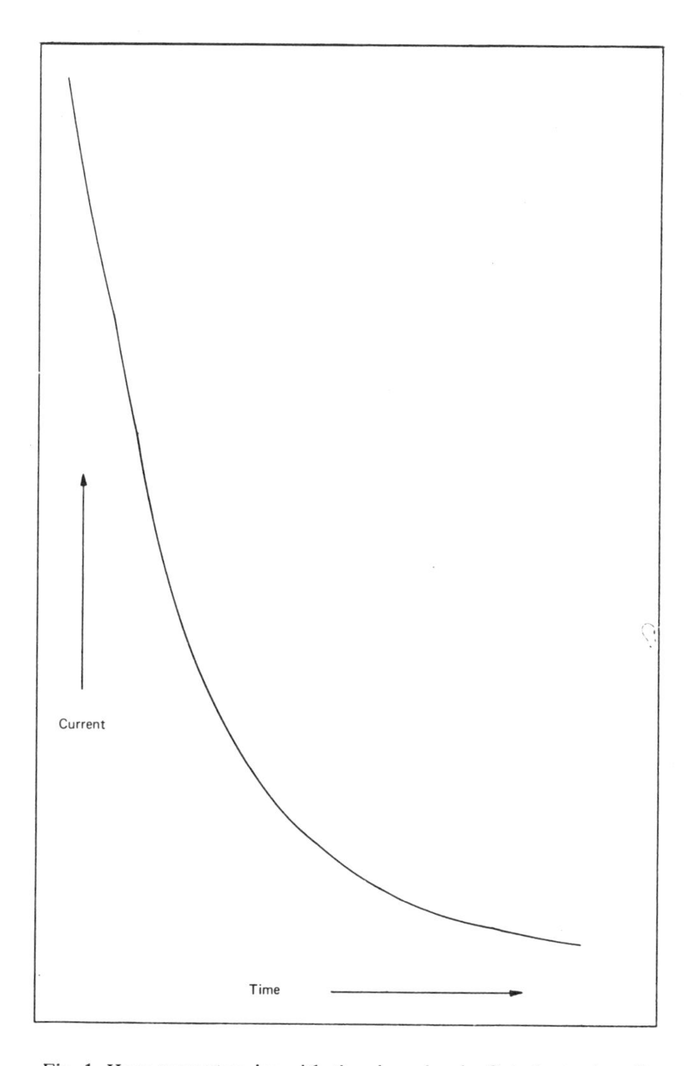

Fig. 1. How current varies with time in a simple, flat-electrode cell.

surface by the depositing paint. Even in such a simple arrangement, however, the shape of the current/time curve can vary between very wide limits, depending on the nature of the paint, the composition of the substrate, the applied voltage, and the paint temperature. Some systems never develop any further resistance as the film is progressively applied. Others develop virtually infinite resistance before a film of useful thickness has been laid down. The ideal to be aimed at is the sudden attainment of infinite resistance when a chosen film thickness has been laid down. Some modern electropaints approach the ideal. The applied voltage is important since, if it is too low the paint deposit is often spongy, conductive and non-self-limiting, whereas if the voltage is too high there is excessive 'gassing' [anode reaction (ii) in Section 2.1 above] which prevents the building-up of an insulating layer of paint.

The 'ideal' behaviour described makes possible one of the main advantages of electropainting, viz. the even deposition (constant thickness) of paint all over an article of complex shape. When for example a tube is used as the anode, the initial electric field has a shape such that current flows only to the outside of the tube. Once an insulating layer has been formed there, however, the field penetrates progressively into the tube until all the tube surface has been painted[3]. Under carefully controlled experimental conditions the painting of a narrow tube can be used as a useful test of the 'throwing power' of an electropaint[4].

The nature of the substrate can have a profound effect on the development of paint film resistance. A typical series of curves for one paint, using mild steel, zinc and platinum anodes but otherwise under identical conditions, is shown in Fig. 2.

It must be recognised that for another paint system the curves might be quite different – even in the reverse order. For the system shown, however, it is clear that, on a mild steel substrate, very good throwing power would be obtained, whereas on platinum only indifferent throwing power could be expected.

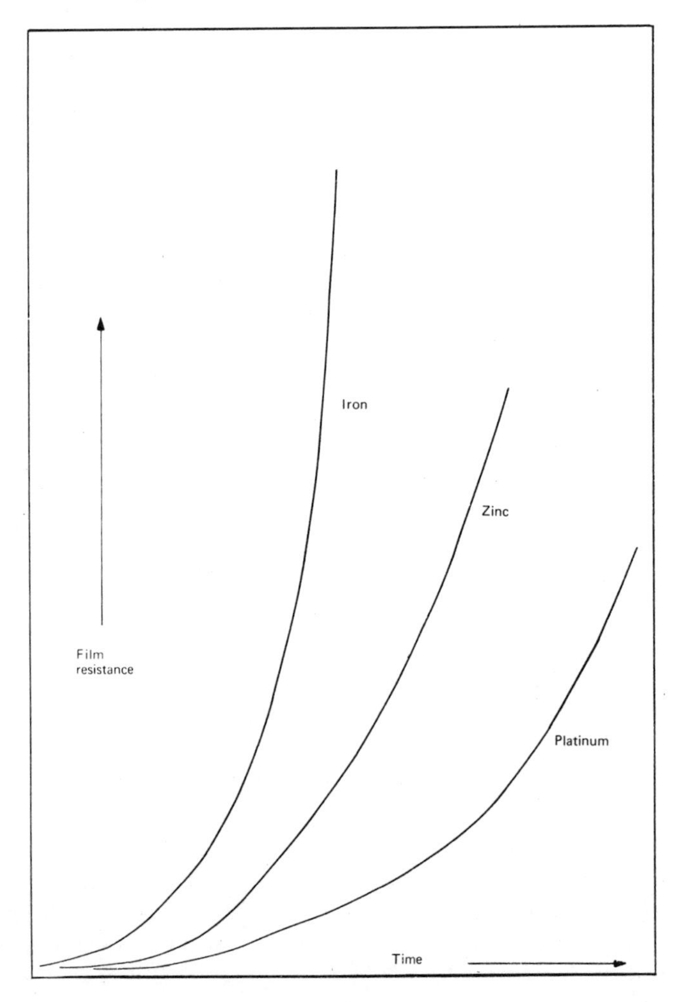

Fig. 2. Variation of film resistance with time and anode metal.

The maximum voltage which can be used for any given paint system depends on the rate of evolution of oxygen as described above. It is normally called the *rupture voltage.* This is not an absolute figure since it will depend on the geometry of the test cell. The minimum voltage usable, often called the *threshold voltage,* is similarly not absolute, but in practice it is determined by observing the voltage at which the rate of deposition of coherent film becomes negligible. Clearly, for high throwing power one would aim for high rupture voltage and low threshold voltage.

2.3 *Process control*

It is obvious that, if allowed to continue, the electrode processes described in Section 2.1 would lead to a continuous denudation of the bath with respect to acidic resin but to no change in the neutralising base concentration. The pH of the bath would therefore increase. One consequence of this would be a fall-off in the efficiency of deposition (measured in terms of grammes deposited per coulomb of electricity) since the paint bath composition would be changing towards that of a paint stripper for acidic resins. Some means must therefore be sought for making fresh paint additions to the bath in such a way as to keep the composition sensibly constant. Various methods have been proposed.

Control by evaporation of excess base. If, for example, ammonia is used as the neutralising base then any increase in its concentration relative to that of acidic resin will increase its vapour pressure and therefore its rate of evaporation. One might hope to feed the bath with fully neutralised resin and rely on ammonia evaporation to maintain the base balance. In practice this method has not been satisfactory.

Control by ion-exchange resins. If the paint bath solution is circulated through a suitable ion-exchange resin column, excess base can be removed. This process has been found to be difficult to control and expensive in skilled labour.

Control by base-deficient feed. If the bath is fed with incompletely neutralised resin then the excess base present in the operating bath is used up in completing neutralisation. This method has found widespread use. Its main advantage is efficient utilisation of base – only adventitious losses have to be made good. Its disadvantage is that, in general, base-deficient feeds are less easily dispersed in the bath since the base needed to render them fully soluble is dispersed throughout the total volume of the bath. Special mixing equipment may be necessary. Poor dispersion can lead to rough coatings owing to undispersed 'bits'.

Control by membranes. If the cathode is contained in a box one side of which, facing the anode, is closed by a permeable membrane, then the liberated base, chemically equivalent to the deposited resin, is contained in the box and does not return to the paint bath. The acid/base ratio in the bath is thus held sensibly constant and the bath may be fed with fully neutralised resin (paint) which is readily dispersed. The base discharged in the 'cathode box' can be removed by flushing the box with demineralised water. (If an ion-selective membrane impervious to anions is used, the flushing may be done with ordinary water.) The main advantage of the system is the simplicity of operation; the main disadvantage is the relatively inefficient use of neutralising base.

At the present time the control methods in use are base-deficient feed and membrane control. Both methods have their supporters. It seems unlikely at present that either system will prove to be an outright winner.

Since electropainting is a chemical process (and in fact a continuous one) it is natural that the build-up of contaminants in the system can be a problem. Contamination can arise from a variety of sources. For example, atmospheric CO_2 is always present in solution, and probably in combination with the base used to neutralise the acidic resin of the paint. Inorganic ions may be introduced to the bath either from poor-quality demineralised water (used in paint make-up) or from imperfectly rinsed workpieces in the pre-treatment section of the plant (see Section 4). Low-molecular-weight organic ions may build up owing to resin breakdown due to hydrolysis or to oxidation processes[5].

Whatever the source of ionic contamination the general effect is to increase the conductivity of the paint and to increase the proportion of current consumed in generating oxygen at the anode. The rupture voltage and efficiency of deposition fall. Clearly, then, the avoidance of ionic contamination is important. Its effect is less (other things being equal) if the rate of use of the paint is high, since fresh, uncontaminated paint is then being introduced at a high rate and the equilibrium level of contamination tends to be low.

When a workpiece is withdrawn from the bath three paint layers may be distinguished: (a) the coherent deposited paint film, (b) the semi-coagulated film ('cream coat') which, with further passage of current, would have become part of (a), and (c) the dip coat, adhering owing to viscosity and surface tension, and with a composition equal to that of the main bath solution.

In order to get the best films for overall performance – particularly where overcoating with other paint systems is required – it is desirable to rinse off coats (b) and (c). Demineralised water must be used for this purpose for otherwise inorganic salts will be left behind on the surface, leading to inter-coat adhesion problems. It is also desirable to blow off any demineralised rinse-water, since any droplets left behind may, during stoving and curing of the applied paint film, leach out the more water-soluble components of the resin and again lead to inter-coat adhesion problems.

3.0 INDUSTRIAL ELECTROPAINT AND ITS ADVANTAGES

3.1 *Types of electropaint*

The following resin types have found commercial use: (i) water-soluble alkyds, (ii) maleinised oils, (iii) water-soluble acrylics, and (iv) epoxy esters.

In some cases such dispersible resins have been used to emulsify other non-soluble resins. The emulsions can be applied readily by electrodeposition since the soluble resin deposits in the usual way while the emulsified resin is co-deposited. This is due to de-stabilisation of the emulsion consequent upon the conversion of the soluble resin anions into free-acid form. It is interesting to note that the electrodeposition of resins is not a new idea[6], but that commercial realisation of the technique had to await the advance of resin technology in providing stable resin systems.

3.2 *Scope of electropainting method*

The specific advantages of the electropainting method are:

a Automatic application.

b By suitable choice of paint an even film can be laid down in enclosed areas of complicated workpieces (e.g. box sections of motor-cars) which would be inefficiently coated by conventional techniques.

c Good coverage of edges and freedom from runs.

It is clear, therefore, that the advantages obtained by using electropaints derive principally from the efficiency of the technique of application. The basic film properties of electropaints are not markedly superior to those of conventional paints.

Examples of the successful application of electropaints include: (i) motor-car bodies, (ii) wheels, (iii) small metal pressings with many re-entrant angles, (iv) petrol tanks (interior and exterior simultaneously), and (v) domestic appliances.

As with most novel and fashionable techniques there can be a tendency for electropainting to be applied inappropriately. The guiding principles of technical adequacy and economic justification should be applied when electropainting is being considered.

Other things being equal, electropaint plants are more costly than, for example, simple paint-dipping plants. It is the author's opinion that, where simple dipping can give a film of satisfactory performance, electropainting should not be considered.

Perhaps the simplest example of the real advantage of electropainting is in motor-car wheels. These can be jigged in a fairly high-density configuration so that a relatively small plant can produce a high output. Penetration of the welded areas is markedly better by electropainting than by other techniques, and no 'fat edge' is produced at the lower part of the periphery of the wheel.

The most impressive example, on the other hand, is the automatic painting of an entire car body. Here again the excellent penetration of seam-welded areas, coupled with the complete coverage of the interiors of box sections gives results which can be seen (or rather *not* seen) on the increasingly salted roads of North America, Europe and Britain. It seems likely that, in perhaps three years' time, it will be difficult to buy a new volume-production car that has not had its first coat electropainted.

Can the second or enamel coat be successfully electropainted? Or indeed, can a one-coat finish be obtained by electropainting? In the author's opinion the answer to the first question at the present time is no, and to the second a qualified yes.

If a second coat is to be applied by electropainting then the first coat must be an electrical conductor, either from the beginning or following treatment. If the first electropainted film is an electrical conductor then the property of 'throwing power' must be substantially abandoned for that first film. Furthermore, if the second film is to be efficiently applied by electropainting, then the conductive property of the first film must be uniform. In my opinion this is not feasible in the present state of the technology.

One-coat finishes by electropainting already exist. Their production depends on substrates of uniform electrochemical properties, without which film thickness and/or colour will vary owing to chemical reactions between substrate and paint films at their interface during painting. Such variations may be quite unimportant for some end-uses.

4.0 PLANT LAY-OUT

Most electropainting plants consist of pre-treatment plant, an electropainting tank including rinse section, and an oven.

4.1 *Pre-treatment plant*

The treatment of metal articles before painting is just as important for electropainting as it is for conventional paint application. A phosphate or other coating is no more and no less valuable for an electropaint film than for any other. The important requirement for *all* types of paint is a clean surface; the specially desirable feature for electropaint is a surface of uniform chemical reactivity, because the application process involves that reactivity.

In practice conventional phosphate pre-treatment has proved successful. It ensures a clean and reasonably uniform surface. Most manufacturers prefer a fairly lightweight zinc phosphate coating (Ca 150–200 mg/ft^2) but iron phosphate has also found favour.

During the act of deposition as described in Section 2.0 acid conditions obtain at the site of chemical reaction. Under these conditions some solution of phosphate coatings occurs, and to meet these circumstances some phosphate coatings relatively resistant to acid solution have been developed. In general, however, no migration has been detected of dissolved phosphate coating into the main paint bath. After the final stage of phosphating a demineralised water rinse is included to ensure that no water-soluble salts are carried over into the electropainting bath.

4.2 *Electropainting tank*

The features which distinguish an electropaint bath from an ordinary dip tank are as follows.

Electrical connections. It is becoming more and more common practice to have the tank lined with an insulating layer (epoxy coating or p.v.c.), the workpiece (anode) directly connected electrically to the conveyor mechanism and earthed, and the cathode live. With these arrangements a plant which is safe to operate is readily designed.

Heat exchange. In a plant which may be drawing around 1000A at, say, 300 V, it is obvious that a great deal of heat has to be dissipated. This is done by circulating the paint through an indirect heat exchanger which is supplied with cold or refrigerated water as the heat-exchange medium.

Cathode boxes are arranged along each side of the electropainting tank where the membrane control system is employed.

4.3 *Oven and ancillary equipment*

Following electropainting the article may be stoved directly in some cases. More commonly the 'dip' and 'cream' coats are removed by rinsing first with town water and then with demineralised water. Surplus water droplets are blown off with compressed air and the article then stoved.

REFERENCES

1 FINN and MELL. *J. Oil. Col. Chem. Assoc.* 47 (3) 219, 1964
BECK. *Farbe u Lack* 72 (3) 218, 1966

2 FRAGEN. *Farbe u Lack* 70, 271 – 279, 1964

3 MAISCH. *Industrie – Lackier – Betrieb* 35, 3 – 8, 1967

4 BREMER *et al. J. Paint Technol.* 39 (512) 551, 1967

5 SULLIVAN. *J. Paint Technol.* 38, (499), 424, 1966

6 DAVEY. U.S. Patent 1,294,627,1919;

PLATING TECHNOLOGY IN MANUFACTURING INDUSTRY

C. R. Darby
W. Canning & Co. Ltd

SUMMARY

The author describes the present position of automatic plating plant, particularly noting recent developments in mechanised and programmed equipment and the preparation of programs. Electroplating processes in manufacturing industries are reviewed and the present position of plating technology is outlined with reference to recent developments. The value of zinc and cadmium coatings for protection and of nickel/chromium coatings for decoration are dealt with in some detail, together with typical process sequences. Hard chromium plating and other engineering applications are briefly considered. A typical hard-chrome process sequence and tank layout is taken to illustrate a programming graph. Reference is made to design requirements for effective plating of components.

1.0 INTRODUCTION

Mechanical processing is now the accepted method for mass-production electroplating. Manual handling of articles through series of tanks is now, in general, restricted to small-scale application and certain special techniques.

An automatic or semi-automatic electroplating plant is essentially a transfer system by which the articles – held on plating racks (jigs) or, if small, carried in bulk in plating barrels – are conveyed through a series of solutions. The process sequence comprises:

1 Pre-treatment including cleaning, pickling (if necessary) and rinsing.
2 Electroplating.
3 Post-treatment including final rinsing and drying.

The pre-treatment sequence for any process will vary with the material to be plated (e.g. steel, zinc-base die-castings, copper or copper alloy, aluminium or ABS plastic), the surface condition of that material, and to some extent the deposit to be applied.

Tables 1 and 2, later in the paper, illustrate respectively typical process sequences employed on the zinc-plating of steel and on the copper-, nickel- and chromium-plating of zinc-base die-castings.

Two basic designs of plating equipment are available for fitting into the production line:

1 Fixed-sequence return-type automatic plants.
2 Variable-sequence transporter-type plants, which may be either fully programmed or semi-automatic, manually controlled.

The choice depends upon production requirements. The first design is suitable for the mass-production plating of considerable numbers of articles of a similar type requiring identical treatment, the second where variability of process and/or plating thickness are required, or where the range or size of components varies widely. This is particularly the case for the smaller manufacturer and the trade plater.

In addition there are, of course, specialised types of plant not in general use in manufacturing industry, and hence not considered here.

2.0 FIXED-SEQUENCE PLANTS

The fixed-sequence plant embodies a central lifting and transfer system which carries the cathode tracks supporting the flight arms, and through which the current for cleaning and plating is fed to the work racks (or barrels). The plant forms a single unit. The process tanks are arranged in a U shape round the conveyor system, with load and unload positions adjacent.

The transfer system may be pneumatic, hydraulic or electromechanical in operation, depending upon the output, the rack size or work load, and the process requirements.

Fully automatic fixed-sequence plants are the most economical for plating where the range of work requires identical treatment. At any moment every station on the plant is full, and the operator is kept uniformly busy loading and unloading. The plant can provide for automatic loading and unloading of plating racks, accepting and returning the plating racks to and from the shop conveyor. The shop conveyor carries the racks to the racking-up area, which need not necessarily be adjacent to the plant. Fig. 1 illustrates a fixed-sequence plant for copper-, nickel- and chromium-plating.

The immersion time in each process is a function of the number of arms in that tank and the output of the plant in work arms per hour.

$$T_p = \frac{60N}{P} - C$$

where T_p = immersion time (min), P = plant output (arms/h), N = number of arms in process tank, and C = change-over time between processes, a constant for a particular plant and usually of the order of ½ min.

It is possible to vary the output and hence the immersion times in all tanks pro rata, but the plants are made for a specific production purpose and output, and the plant is not suitable for major variations in plating time or process sequence. It is also possible to include, at the design stage, mechanism to permit some variation in the fixed process sequence by the use of 'skip' or 'delayed set-down' devices; or to vary the plating time by double indexing or half indexing in the plating section (thus halving the plating time or obtaining twice the plating time).

Nevertheless, fixed-sequence plants are relatively inflexible. If variation in process sequence, process or plating times is required, or where the possibility of alternative post-treatments or various base metals has to be considered, or where facilities are required to increase output at a later date, programmed automatic plants are preferred. In particular, the application of fixed-sequence plants to barrel plating is limited where the work varies enormously in its surface area/weight ratio, in the pre-treatment it requires, and in the specified deposit thickness. To take the surface area per lb alone, typical material for barrel zinc plating can vary from 30 to over 600 in^2/lb. If the barrel is loaded to the maximum permissible weight, each time with the same total amperage on the barrel (a function of barrel design and perforation), the total cathode area and hence the plating time will vary enormously.

Fig. 1. Fixed-sequence automatic plant for nickel and chromium plating.

3.0 VARIABLE-SEQUENCE PROGRAMMED AUTOMATIC PLANTS

These comprise one or more lines of process tanks, at either side of or over which are rails upon which transporters traverse the length of the plant. These transporters carry flight arms (from which the plating racks are suspended) or plating barrels. The transporter lift/lower and traverse movements operate under the instruction of a programmed controller. The flight arms are not rigidly attached to the transporter – when a particular flight arm or barrel is lowered into the tank it remains there whilst the transporter carries out other operations as directed by the programmer. The side elevation of a transporter is shown in Fig. 2.

The advantage of this type of plant is that, as the arms carrying the components are not mechanically linked (as in the previously-described automatic plant), it is possible to vary the immersion times or the route sequence of operations in one section without necessarily altering the immersion times on the remainder of the plant. Thus differing finishes can be produced from one plant and also changes in specification can be made. Provision for program variation, however, results in a reduction in the overall efficiency of the plant, in that there will be occasions when the equipment is not fully utilised.

As the work arm remains in one position in the plating tanks for the whole of the process time 'cell plating' can be carried out using specially formed anodes if required, e.g. for nickel and chromium plating of bumper bars. Programmed plant may also be used where components are too large for processing by fixed-sequence automatic equipment.

Various layouts of process tanks are possible, depending on site conditions, work flow and process sequences. Some arrangements are shown in Fig. 3. Fig. 3(a) illustrates in-line layout with loading at one end and unloading at the other, while the in-line layout in Fig. 3(b) has loading and unloading stations at the same end. The latter is of special interest in that the tank sequences do not follow the process sequence. The tanks are laid out to give optimum utilisation of the transporter(s) and to permit future expansion. For this reason the plating stations are normally at the far end, away from the load/unload end of the plant. Additional plating stations can then be added without disrupting the plant, the cleaning and swilling cycle being adequate for this expansion. A typical programming graph based on a plant layout of this type is shown later (Fig. 5).

'Return' layout, in which work is loaded at one point, progressed around the plant and unloaded at the end of the second line, is illustrated in Fig. 3(c). A variation of the 'return' layout appears in Fig. 3 (d) – side transfer for the flight bar or barrel so that it can leave the line for loading and unloading.

The three-line plant in Fig. 3 (e) has a central cleaning section from which work passes to the appropriate outside processing line. This type of layout permits many variations, with additional by-pass transfers for inter-process operations and alternatively one or more 'legs' extending beyond the cross-transfer unit for additional processes and/or auxiliary unloading.

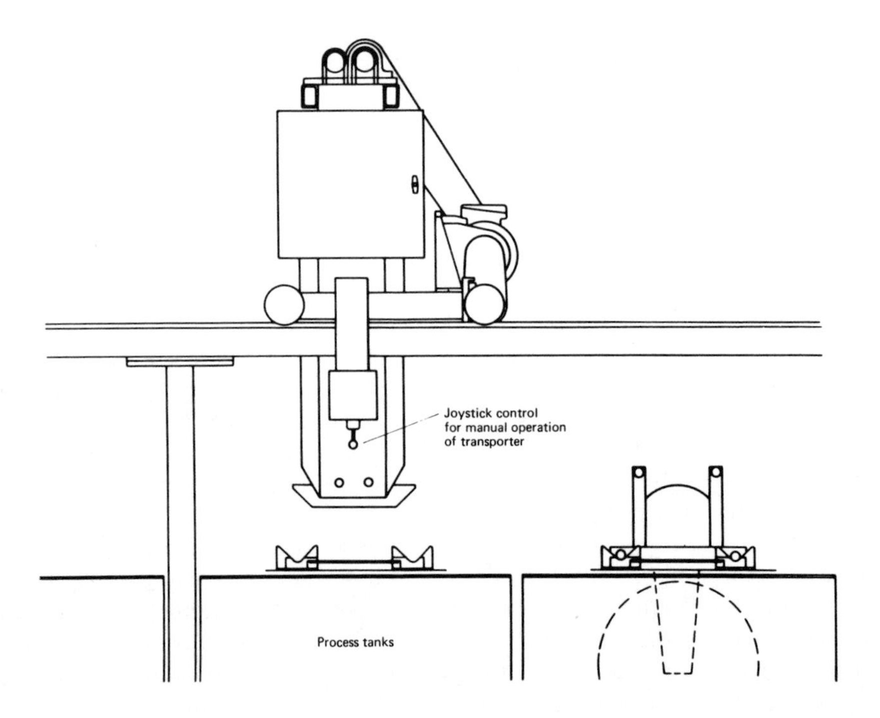

Fig. 2. Side elevation of transporter for programmed plant.

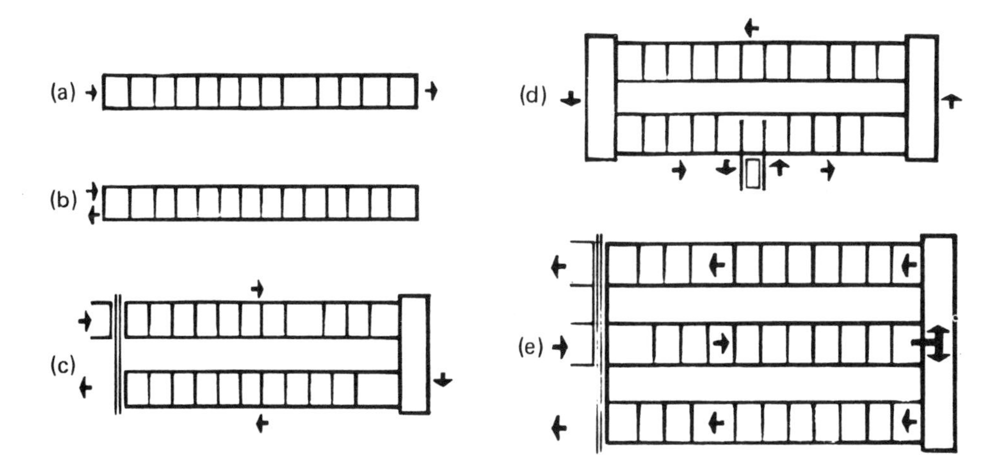

Fig. 3. Typical layouts for programmed plating plant.

3.1 *Semi-automatic working*

Each transporter is provided with a joy-stick control for manual operation. When the plant is not supplied with a programmer but manually operated the plant is known as semi-automatic.

A recently developed low-cost alternative to barrel plants with relatively small output, and to rack plant up to 6ft wide, is a light transporter carried on rails mounted on the two longitudinal sides of the process tanks. The lift/lower operations are still electrical, but the transporter is pushed by hand from station to station.

4.0 PROGRAM CONTROLLERS

Two main types of program controller have been developed to meet production and process requirements: preset program controllers and random selection program controllers.

4.1 *Controllers with preset program*

These are sometimes referred to as 'fixed' program controllers as only one program is applied to the machine at a time. Different programs may be available and the controllers are designed to permit their rapid change.

Program units employing different information storage systems are available. These include rotary-cam-drum, plastic- or punched-card and solid-state-circuit devices.

Typical of the storage systems now used is the solid-state-circuit controller in which a tape is read by means of a photo-electric cell system and the use of mechanical switches is eliminated. Each transporter has its own reader and all of them are synchronised at the commencement of each cycle. The tape incorporates twenty tracks which are allocated to control the lift/lower, traverse left and right movements of the transporter and the stop positions at the various process tanks. The program is punched as a series of holes in the tape. The tape is stepped past a continuous light beam, the holes admitting light to the photo-receivers which issue instructions for the movement of the transporter. When the movement is completed the tape is stepped on to the next set of instructions, i.e. each movement of the transporter is completed before the reader progresses to its next set of instructions. The tape is a continuous loop so that at the end of one cycle it automatically commences the next cycle.

Fig. 4 illustrates part of a preset program controller. The view shows the tape and reader.

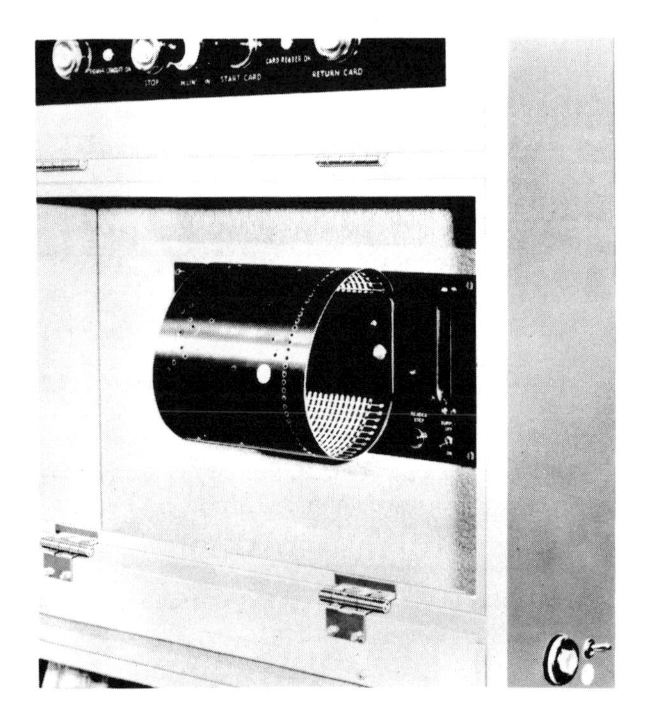

Fig. 4. Part of preset program controller – the tape reader.

The program for a preset controller is usually for one particular plating sequence. It is possible to have a program comprising two plating sequences, e.g. zinc and nickel/chrome, the components being loaded to a pattern. Alternatively it is possible to have one finish but two types of cleaning sequence. In all cases, however, the work must be batched and loaded to the pattern for the particular program.

Where work can be batched this type of system provides simply and efficiently a high degree of flexibility, together with the normal advantages of automatic plating plant.

4.2 *Random-selection program controllers*

Random-selection program controllers are employed where it would not be practical to batch or pattern-load work, and where it is necessary to provide, on individual work carriers or barrels, for variation in the process sequence and/or immersion times. This situation can arise where:

1 Variations exist in the basis metal to be treated, necessitating alternative cleaning sequences.

2 Racks and barrels are to be handled on the same plant.
3 Alternative finishes are required, e.g. nickel and zinc.
4 Alternative post-plating treatments are required, e.g. bright and full passivation.
5 Process times need to be varied to meet differing treatment, thickness or work-area requirements.

When a work load is placed on the plant the required route and time variations are fed into the memory of the controller by the operator, who presses the appropriate route and time selection buttons on a control desk adjacent to the loading station.

With the random-selection controller all transporter movements are initiated by the timing units associated with the various process stations and located in the program controller.

At each position the next destination to which the load must move is known, and the instructions to make the move are built into the memory device.

Since the work carriers are not moving to a preset pattern, as in a fixed-program plant, before accepting the instruction to make the move the controller also checks that the destination is free to receive the load. If this clearance is not received the call is stored until the route is clear, and a visual indication is given that a move is pending.

If several process stations time out simultaneously and issue signals calling the requisite transporter, a priority check unit decides which signal to handle. Three levels of priority are provided for each transporter. These cater for processes on which the specified immersion times must not be greatly exceeded. A top-priority call will override any other call, providing the transporter is not actually carrying out a transfer.

In the case of processes such as passivation, where it is essential that the immersion time be not exceeded, a facility is provided to 'lock' the transporter on to the work load. This means that when the transporter deposits the load in the station, it remains with it, ignoring all other calls until the process is complete and the work load has been transferred to the next non-critical process.

Each process station is provided (in the programmer cubicle) with a timer which can be preset to any value within the selected range. Where a choice of times is required, a multiple timer is provided.

With this type of control the actual immersion times are subject to some variation depending upon the position and availability of the transporter, e.g. a transporter carrying work will not accept a call; and a transporter will always respond to a call having a higher priority.

4.3 *Program preparation*

To calculate the number of transporters required, and to provide the information necessary to prepare the program, a graph of movements (the program graph) is drawn up for each processing sequence required.

The output of the plant in flight arms per hour or barrels per hour having been determined, and hence the time cycle on which to base the diagram, the movement of the first transporter may be 'plotted' to maintain the times of essential processes (i.e. cleaning and plating), the swill times being adjusted accordingly. The object is to cover as many tanks as possible in the time cycle and hence keep the number of transporters to a minimum. The second and subsequent transporter movements are determined in similar fashion.

A typical program graph is shown in Fig. 5. This indicates the immersion time at each tank and the movements which the transporters must undertake in order to carry out the required process sequence. From this diagram the program card is cut or punched accordingly. Note that the process stages are listed against the vertical axis of the diagram and the time cycle in minutes as the horizontal axis of the diagram. It must be explained that the tanks are laid out in one line, with loading and unloading at one end. The layout is as in Fig. 3(b). The process sequence is listed in two columns on the graph for convenience only, to indicate the process sequence in relation to the tank layout.

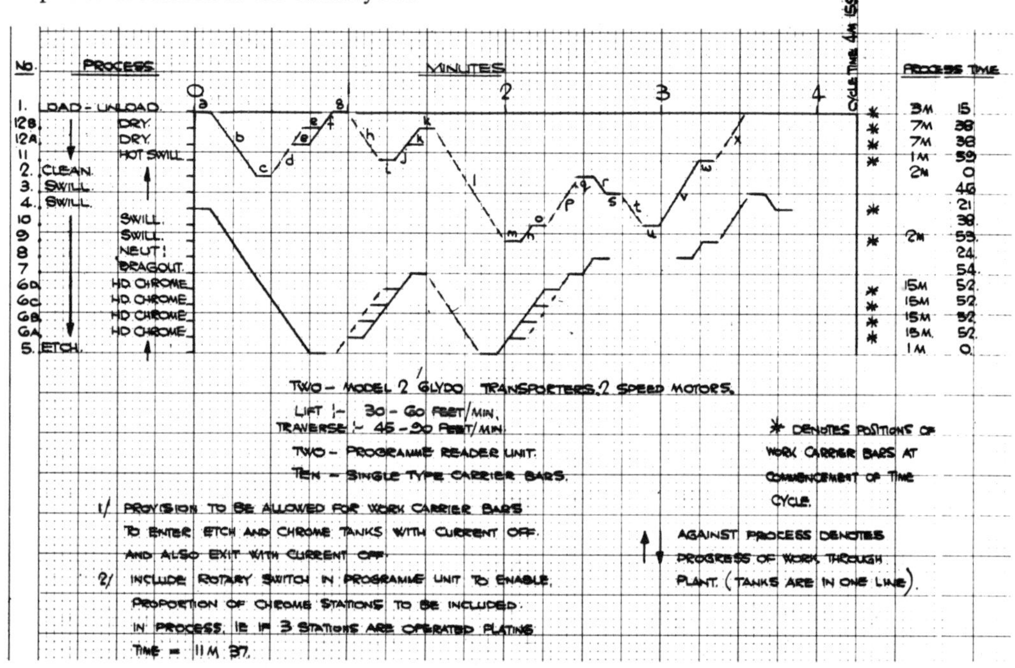

Fig. 5. Typical program graph for hard chromium plating plant.

The interpretation of this type of graph is as follows:

- a New load of work lifted out of station 1, time 6 s.
- b Work taken to process 2, time 18 s.
- c Work lowered into process 2, time 6 s.
- d Transporter traverses empty to process 12B, time 12 s.
- e Finished work lifted out of process 12B, time 6 s.
- f Finished work taken to station 1, time 6 s.
- g Work lowered into station 1, time 6 s.
- h Transporter traverses empty to process 11, time 12 s.
- i Work lifted from process 11, time 6 s.
- j Work taken to process 12B, time 9 s.
- k Work lowered into process 12B, time 6 s.
- l Transporter traverses empty to process 9, time 27 s.
- m Work lifted from process 9, time 6 s.
- n Work taken to process 10, time 4 s.
- o Work lowered into process 10, time 6 s.
- p Transporter traverses empty to process 2, time 12 s.
- q Work lifted from process 2, time 6 s.

The remainder of the graph for the first transporter, and similarly for the second transporter, can be followed accordingly. It will be noted, for example, that between c and q a time of 2 min has elapsed, which gives the immersion time in process 2. If a different cleaning time were required an alternative pattern of movements would have to be drawn up.

For stages where the immersion time exceeds a single cycle time, multi-station tanks are included, e.g. stations 6A, 6B, 6C, 6D on the graph, and also stations 12A, 12B. When working on program the controller directs the transporter to the multi-station tank and an additional relay system selects the particular station into which the work is to be lowered.

5.0 PLATING PROCESSES

Electroplating must be considered an essential stage in the manufacture of an article and not an operation carried out after manufacture in order to provide a surface finish.

In manufacturing industry electroplating provides:

1 Protection against corrosion.
2 An improved surface appearance.
3 Special surface properties, for example hardness, chemical resistance, electrical conductivity.

5.1 *Protective finishes*

Zinc and cadmium plating are used extensively in manufacturing industries to provide a rust-proof finish on iron and steel. Bright plating solutions are normally employed so that a decorative effect is obtained in addition to protection.

In urban and industrial atmospheres zinc provides better performance in protecting steel than cadmium. When the behaviour of coatings of similar thickness is compared, cadmium is found better than zinc in marine conditions.

Zinc is by far the major finish of the two, and in many applications is replacing cadmium because of its lower cost.

In the automotive industry and engineering fields zinc is used extensively as a low-cost protective finish on fasteners (including screws, nuts and bolts), steel pressings and parts of small mechanical assemblies, many of which were formerly left in the raw steel condition. Barrel zinc-plating of fasteners in particular is a major manufacturing activity.

The bright zinc deposit also provides an attractive selling finish and simplifies assembly. The plated components are more pleasant to handle than those in plain steel and the need for greasing to provide superficial protection against corrosion is avoided. Fig. 6 illustrates the underside of a record changer, showing the lever system which is bright-zinc-plated and then fully passivated.

For general protection purposes it is usual to apply zinc deposits having from 8 to 25 μm (0·0003 to 0·001 in) minimum thickness, depending upon the application: the usual commercial deposit of zinc is a nominal 8 μm (0·003 in). Cadmium coating thicknesses vary from 5 to 10 μm (0·0002 to 0·0004 in) thickness. For threaded components the thickness varies from 4 μm (0·00015 in) for small-diameter parts for 10 μm (0·004 in) for larger threaded diameters of say 20 mm (¾ in).

The relevant B.S. specifications are B.S.1706: 1960 for general protective purposes and Parts 1 and 2 of B.S.3382: 1961 for electroplated coatings on threaded components.

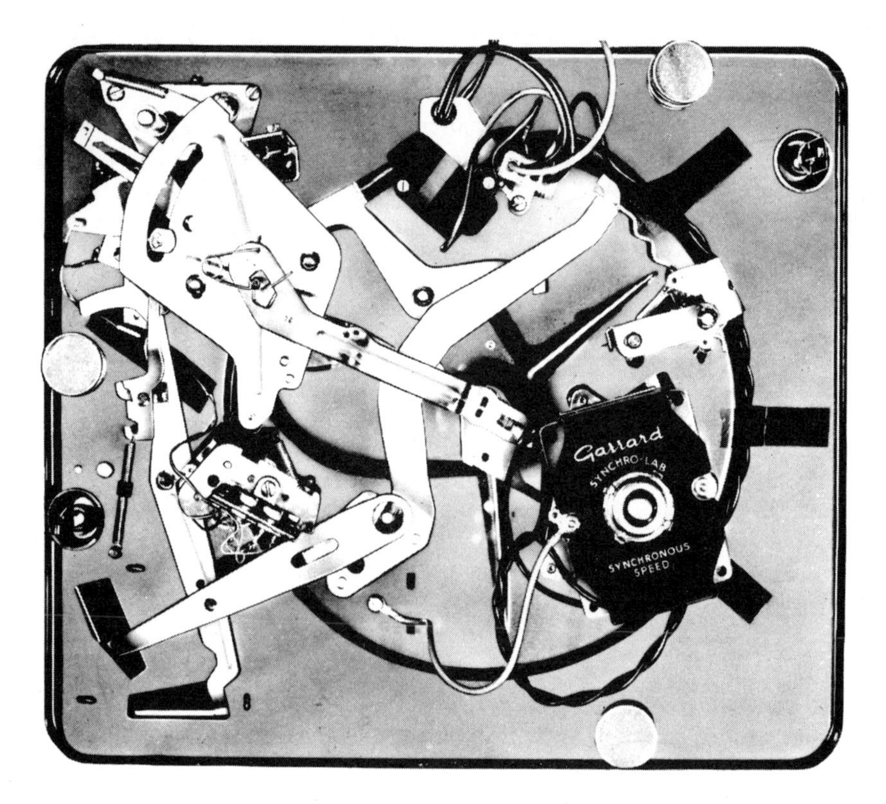

Fig. 6. Underside of Garrard record-changer.

To increase the protective value of zinc and cadmium plating to give maximum corrosion resistance a passivation process is carried out after the plating operation. In the case of high-tensile steels which are heat-treated following plating to minimise hydrogen embrittlement, the heat treatment should be carried out *before* passivating.

Passivation processes may be divided into two main groups, bright and full.

Bright passivation is employed on bright zinc, and to a lesser extent on bright cadmium, where some increased resistance to corrosion and finger-marking is required whilst a bright decorative appearance is retained.

The standard bright passivation on zinc for manufacturing purposes gives a light blue colour to the zinc deposit, which resembles bright chrome. It has in the past been called 'imitation chrome' and is sometimes specified as a decorative finish in its own right.

Full passivation puts a coloured film on zinc and cadmium. It gives a high resistance to atmospheric corrosion and greatly increases the protective value of the coating. It maximises protection against corrosion where a coloured effect is acceptable.

There are in addition iridescent passivation treatments for use where a full passivation finish would not be acceptable but where greater resistance to corrosion is required than that provided by bright passivation.

A typical process sequence for zinc plating of steel components is shown in Table 1. Here 13, 14 and 15, 16 are alternatives. Output is 150 jigs/h (75 arms/h) and time cycle 48 s (change-over 30 s)

TABLE 1. ZINC PLATING STEEL IN FIXED-SEQUENCE TWO-LINE AUTOMATIC PLANT

Process number	Process	Number of arms	Process time
1	Hot soak clean	5	3 min 30 s
2	Hot anodic clean	5	3 min 30 s
3	Cold swill	1	18 s
4	Cold swill	1	18 s
5	50% HCl acid dip	3	1 min 54 s
6	Cold swill	1	18 s
7	Cold swill	1	18 s
8	Cold anodic clean	3	1 min 54 s
9	Cold swill	1	18 s
10	Bright zinc plate	16	12 min 18 s
11	Cold swill	1	18 s
12	Cold swill	1	18 s
13	Blue passivate	1	18 s
14	Cold swill	1	18 s
15	Full passivate	1	18 s
16	Cold swill	1	18 s
17	Cold swill	1	18 s
18	Warm swill	1	18 s
19	Drying oven	9	6 min 42 s

Standard formulations are employed for zinc and cadmium plating solutions. Recent developments have lain in providing more economical addition agents and in the newer range of passivation processes, particularly the light blue passivation finish. Low-cyanide and cyanide-free zinc-plating solutions have been developed for areas where effluent disposal is a particular problem.

5.2 *Decorative finishes*

For a decorative finish it is usual to apply a deposit of nickel followed by a deposit of bright chromium. This finish, generally known as 'bright chromium plate' provides a combination of protection against corrosion, resistance to wear, tolerance to high temperatures and decorative appeal. The nickel deposit gives protection to the basis metal and the chromium layer serves to preserve the appearance of the nickel deposit and also to improve the protective value of the coating system.

A bright nickel-chrome finish is the more usual but considerable use is now made of satin nickel-chrome finishes. For a satin or semi-matt finish a satin nickel-plating solution may be employed, or the nickel deposit may be finished mechanically to give a satin or semi-bright effect.

Before nickel-plating zinc-base die-castings it is necessary to apply an initial deposit of copper in order to prevent chemical attack on the zinc alloy by the nickel-plating solution. For metals such as aluminium special pre-treatment sequences are necessary.

A typical process sequence for the nickel and chromium plating of zinc-base die-castings is shown in Table 2. Output is 120 jigs/h (60 arms/h) and time cycle 60 s (change-over 30 s).

TABLE 2. NICKEL AND CHROMIUM PLATING ZINC-BASE DIE-CASTINGS IN FIXED-SEQUENCE TWO-LINE AUTOMATIC PLANT

Process number	Process	Number of arms	Process time
1	Hot cathodic clean	2	1 min 30 s
2	Cold swill	1	30 s
3	Hot anodic clean	2	1 min 30 s
4	Cold swill	1	30 s
5	Cold swill	1	30 s
6	2½% HF acid dip	1	30 s
7	Cold swill	1	30 s
8	Cold swill	1	30 s
9	Cyanide copper flash	3	2 min 30 s
10	Cold swill	1	30 s
11	Cold swill	1	30 s
12	Pyro-phosphate copper plate	9	8 min 30 s
13	Cold swill	1	30 s
14	Cold swill	1	30 s
15	Semi-bright nickel plate	26	25 min 30 s
16	Bright nickel plate	11	10 min 30 s
17	Cold swill	1	30 s
18	Cold swill	1	30 s
19	Bright chrome plate	9	8 min 30 s
20	Drag-out	1	30 s
21	Neutralise	1	30 s
22	Cold swill	1	30 s
23	Cold swill	1	30 s
24	Hot swill	1	30 s
25	Drying oven	6	5 min 30 s

The thickness requirements for nickel and chromium plating (B.S.1224: 1965) are given in Table 3. The specification covers four service grades.

Grade 1 Severely corrosive conditions, e.g. those encountered by external components of motor-cars.

Grade 2 Intermittent exposure outdoors, e.g. as experienced by perambulator parts.

Grade 3 Service indoors in places where condensation may occur, e.g. kitchens and bathrooms.

Grade 4 Service indoors in warm, dry atmospheres, e.g. offices.

Note that B.S.1224: 1965 permits the lowering of the nickel thickness on steel components to Grades 1 and 2 from 30 to 25μm (0·0012 to 0·0010 in), if a minimum thickness of 12·5μm (0·0005 in) of copper is applied. Note also that, on aluminium or aluminium alloy components, crack-free chromium is not permitted.

TABLE 3. THICKNESS REQUIREMENTS FOR NICKEL AND CHROMIUM PLATING

Minimum thickness of nickel				
Basis metal	Service grade 1	Service grade 2	Service grade 3	Service grade 4
Steel	0·0012 in*	0·0012 in†	0·0008 in	0·0004 in
	30 μm	30 μm	20 μm	10 μm
Zinc base	0·0010 in*	0·0010 in†	0·0006 in	0·0003 in
	25μm	25μm	15 μm	8 μm
Copper and copper alloy	0·0009 in	0·0006 in	0·0004 in	0·0003 in
	23μm	15μm	10 μm	8 μm
Aluminium or aluminium alloy	0·0012 in‡	0·0012 in	0·0008 in	0·0004 in
	30 μm	30 μm	20 μm	10 μm

Minimum thickness of chromium		
Regular (conventional) chromium	0·000 01 in	0·25μm
Crack-free chromium	0·000 03 in	0·8 μm
Micro-cracked chromium	0·000 03 in	0·8 μm

* Duplex nickel or polished nickel and any of the chromium deposits, or bright nickel followed by crack-free or micro-cracked chromium.

† Bright nickel and regular chromium.

‡ Where bright nickel is employed it must be followed by micro-cracked chromium;

In recent years enquiry into methods of improving the corrosion resistance of nickel chromium coatings has led to the development of duplex nickel, micro-cracked chromium and micro-porous chromium.

For duplex nickel deposits an initial layer of low-sulphur semi-bright nickel is applied, followed by fully bright nickel. The usual ratio of deposits is 70% semi-bright nickel to 30% bright nickel. Duplex nickel can provide improved resistance to corrosion particularly in marine, rural and suburban conditions. Its use can also give worth-while production advantages on components such as car bumpers.

The basis of the protection which duplex nickel provides is that the sulphur content results in a difference in potential between the nickel deposits, so that the upper layer is dissolved preferentially when in contact with electrolytes such as rain-water, road mud, fog or other condensation. Any resulting corrosion pit will penetrate the coating till it reaches the interface between the two nickel layers. Any subsequent corrosion will occur in the top layer only. This delays attack on the basis metal and so prolongs the life of plated parts.

With a crack-free chromium plating solution a bright chrome deposit of three to four times the conventional thickness can be applied, free from normal surface cracking. The improved chrome deposit so obtained, applied to a normal thickness of nickel, gives a better finish with a considerably higher corrosion resistance.

For maximum resistance to atmospheric corrosion the use of micro-cracked chromium is preferred.

With micro-cracked chromium, a very large number of fine cracks (30 to 80/mm, 700 to 2000/in) is produced in the chrome deposit. The corrosion current, developed at breaks in the chromium surface, is thus distributed over a very wide area instead of being concentrated at a few points. Under highly corrosive conditions, therefore, very many small pits are produced which do not notably affect the appearance of the surface, instead of a small number of deep pits which could result in early failure of the surface finish. Because of the multitude of cracks already present, the underlying nickel is much less likely to be cracked than with conventional bright chromium plate.

Micro-porous chromium produces a protective effect similar to that of micro-cracked chromium, but, instead of a final crack pattern, a multitude of very fine holes or pores is produced in the chromium deposit by co-depositing an inert material in a very thin final nickel layer following duplex nickel plating.

5.3 *Cathodic passivation of nickel chromium deposits*

Treatment of decorative nickel-chromium-plated articles in a cathodic chromate passivation solution, as recently developed by the Battelle Memorial Institute, increases resistance to atmospheric corrosion.

5.4 *Black chromium*

Black chromium is now being employed on a commercial scale for the production of an attractive alternative to bright chromium on articles such as builders' hardware, door fittings and office furniture, It is also being considered as a non-glare finish for automobile interior fittings and body trim.

For black chromium plating a special solution is employed, and the process replaces the usual bright chromium plating after bright nickel plating.

Black chromium is hard and resistant to wear, heat and corrosive environments. The colour is retained in service and there is no need for any further protection as in the case of chemical finishes.

6.0 ENGINEERING APPLICATIONS OF PLATING

6.1 *Hard chromium plating*

Hard chromium deposits are widely used for abrasion-resistant wearing surfaces and for building up undersized and worn parts. As a general rule, a finished thickness of 0·005 in (0·13 mm) is ample for most purposes, and in many cases thin deposits of 0·0005 to 0·002 in (13 to 50 μm) are sufficient to give protection agains wear or prevent seizing of moving parts.

Hard chromium plating is widely used for facing gauges, for cutting tools, dies and moulds.

Components, such as piston rings and cylinder liners, crankshafts for marine and aero engines, hydraulic and oleo rams, gears and other articles are plated to a thickness of 0·005 in (0·13 mm) as standard procedure to improve their wearing qualities and to resist corrosion.

A typical process sequence for hard chromium plating is shown in the program graph, Fig. 5. The process numbers should be followed as the tank sequence in this instance is not laid out to follow the process sequence, for reasons given in the paragraphs on layout of programmed plant, Section 3.0, Fig.3(b).

6.2 *Copper plating*

Brief mention has been made of copper as an undercoat for zinc-base die-castings prior to nickel and chromium plating. It may also be used as an undercoat for steel to save nickel. See Table 3 and the penultimate sentence of the related paragraph, Section 5.2.

Apart from such purposes, copper plating has important industrial applications. It is used extensively as a 'resist' in case-hardening to prevent carburisation of those parts of an article which are to remain soft, and is deposited on knuckle pins to prevent fretting.

Copper is also the most suitable metal for the production of articles by electroforming, a special application of electroplating. There are products of electroforming which could not be made by conventional manufacturing techniques.

6.3 *Tin plating*

Tin plating is used in the nitriding of steels, being applied as a 'resist' in the same manner as copper to prevent carburisation of selected areas in case-hardening.

6.4 *Nickel plating*

Heavy nickel deposits are applied to engineering components in order to provide surfaces which are resistant to corrosion, wear, and high-temperature scaling. Other applications are the building up of over-machined or worn surfaces and the production of electroforms for use as moulds and press tools.

6.5 *Electro-less nickel plating*

Chemical immersion deposition (which is not electroplating) is used for coating on to metal and is a recent development in the plating field.

Electro-less nickel is particularly suitable for components of complex shape and where it is very important to obtain an even distribution of metal, for example in pipes, blind tubes, the interiors of vessels and screws. The rate of deposition varies from 0·0003 to 0·0007 in/h (7·5 to 17 5 μm/h depending upon the operating temperature. The deposit contains phosphorus and is therefore much harder than conventional nickel plating. The hardness can be increased by post-plating heat treatment.

7.0 COMPONENTS FOR PLATING

Design for plating has been covered by several booklets [1,2,3] and reference should be made to these for a detailed study.

7.1 *Shape*

The thickness of a plated deposit is dependent upon the current density and the plating time. With the majority of articles the current density will vary over the surface, being higher at edges and points than in recessed areas. The more complex the shape of the article, the greater are these variations likely to be.

The thickness of deposit is estimated from the surface area of the article, the current applied, and the plating time. This will be the average value over the whole of the surface, and at some points the thickness will be greater than the average value, and at others, as in recesses, less than the average value.

Most plating specifications call for a given minimum thickness on the significant surfaces, generally those areas which can be touched with a 1 in (25 mm) ball. In order to ensure that the required minimum thickness is obtained it is necessary to apply an average thickness which is greater than the minimum required. This allowance will vary. For example, it may be 50%, i.e. 0·0015 in (38 μm) average thickness as against a 0·001 in (25 μm) minimum thickness.

Therefore, to reduce costs and to improve the distribution, deep recesses should be avoided and corners should be radiused. The significant surface (where the specification will apply) must be marked on the drawing.

7.2 *Fabrication*

Carry-over of solution from one process to another must be minimised. This is essential from a cost point of view, to avoid excessive loss of solution, contamination of one process by another, and excess of effluent with attendant problems.

In manufacture, seams and rolled edges in which the solution can be trapped should be avoided. If a rolled edge is essential it should either be completely closed or left well open. Apart from the danger of contamination between processes, the final drying of the article is extremely difficult.

Steel pressings with a rim should have a drain hole in the rim. Moreover, it should be laid down that the component must be jigged with the drain hole downwards.

Drainage holes should be provided at the lowest parts of tubular components. The tubes should have well rounded corners when formed, sharp bends being avoided to improve plating distribution.

7.3 *Dimensions*

The effect of plating on the dimensions of a component must, in certain cases, be considered. Engineering applications of 'hard' chrome and 'heavy' nickel are a case in point. Screw threads pose particular problems. They have been discussed in detail by Wallbank and Layton[4].

7.4 *Method of suspension*

Provision must be made in the design/manufacturing stage of the component for a means of suspension of the component on a jig. This can be a hole, thread, lug or a part of the interior surface where the thickness of the deposit is unimportant. The jigging of steel pressings for zinc-plating is easy, simple hooks on the jig normally being all that is necessary. It is surprising how many steel pressings have no holes. The provision of a simple hole is invaluable.

The positioning of articles in order to reduce variation in the current density over the surface is an important consideration when designing a plating jig.

By improving the distribution on a jig by fitting side shields, or by mounting components closer together at edges of jigs, one can make considerable cost savings.

7.5 *Drag-out*

A particular aspect of cost reduction to be considered is control of the drag-out. This can be minimised by adequate drainage time between processes. In the case of automatic plants a dwell time can be allowed above the process tanks, and in barrel plants the barrels can rotate during the lifting period.

Drag-out recovery should be considered. In addition to reducing wastage it conserves swill water and reduces the quantity of effluent.

The questions of deposit distribution over a jig, drag-out and associated cost reduction problems have been investigated in detail by Bouckley and Watson[5].

8.0 CONCLUSION

The foregoing examples of the present technology in plating do not cover every aspect of progress but are representative of applications.

Further developments can be expected to give better protective and decorative finishes more economically. With future increases in the use of plastics an extension in the use of electroplating can be foreseen.

REFERENCES

1. *Design for Metal Finishing.* Institute of Metal Finishing, London, 1960.

2. D. N. LAYTON. *Design for Electroplating.* International Nickel Company (Mond) Ltd, London, 1961.

3. *Notes for designers of zinc alloy die castings to be electroplated.* Zinc Alloy Die Casters Association, London, 1968.

4. A. W. WALLBANK and D. N. LAYTON. 'Plating of Screw Threads'. *Trans. Inst. Metal Finishing,* Vol. 32, 1955, pp. 308–325.

5. D. BOUCKLEY and S. A. WATSON. 'The optimum utilisation of nickel in electrodeposition'. *Electroplating and Metal Finishing,* Vol. 20, October 1967, pp. 303–310; November 1967, pp. 348–353.

SESSION 4. DISCUSSION ON THE PAPERS BY A. G. WAKEFIELD, F. W. TRAVIS, T. OGURA, D. B. BRUCE AND C. R. DARBY

T. JOHNSTON (*Barr & Stroud*): As a user of small quantities of aluminium die castings I stress a small point: that of getting into production. After dimensional proving of a first sample the subsequent batches for production differ because the die in which the proof casting is made is not in the production shop. I can see the high cost of putting it on to a production machine and getting the die heated to the right temperature, etc., to run off the one casting. What hope is there of bringing a machine quickly to optimum conditions?

A. G. WAKEFIELD: This sampling procedure is a problem. If the sample is made from a cold die it will be undersized, and if made from a hot die it will be oversized. Generally speaking, a tool is made in a soft state and we sample it in a soft state just in case any corrections are necessary. On approval we harden the die. Distortions take place and we do get some slight discrepancies.

M. T. WATKINS (*National Engineering Laboratory*): Dr Travis showed the firing of a billet into a die, giving rise to a very complex shape. There were some complications about the manner in which the material flowed, whether it was molten or whether it was plastic. In the Accurad process mentioned by Mr Wakefield, is there a possibility that the end of the billet, to which the second ram was applied, was in the plastic state? What would happen if the original billet had been completely in the plastic state? Would the cavity be filled, and would this have given a product which was in the raw condition rather than in the casting condition?

A. G. WAKEFIELD: I think one of the very original thoughts that put the Americans on to the process was that, with the ordinary diecasting process, the solidification time is so short that any streaking that takes place cannot be counteracted. One company was thinking of shooting a charge into the slug. The Americans realised that what was missing was a secondary plunger in the form of a missile which would do the same job. This has proved very successful, but it is a difficult production proposition. One plunger working at a temperature of about 400°C gives rise to seizure. A secondary plunger will greatly increase down time. I have seen pressure die castings 6 in square, $\frac{3}{8}$ in thick, solid, with not a flaw in them and no surface defects whatever.

M. T. WATKINS (*National Engineering Laboratory*): Do you think that that is the future of pressure die casting, and will it no longer be known as pressure die casting?

A. G. WAKEFIELD: No, this process will only be used in certain fields. It is too slow and expensive. However, one can cast intricate porting channels with the pressure process which one cannot with the gravity process.

D. B. LLOYD (*Hoare & Co.*): Could Mr Wakefield give any idea on what the value of the output of the die casting industry is in the U.K.?

A. G. WAKEFIELD: Sorry, I do not have the figures to hand.

E. ROSMARIN (*Dexion*): Just as a comment on this, in the *Diecasting Journal* there is a complete breakdown of the production capacity of the U.K., Europe and the U.S.A.

J. C. MORRIS (*Cincinnati Milling Machines*): What experience has the speaker in encouraging customers to change from cast iron to aluminium components? If a customer makes such a change, is it true to say that a lot of the machining disappears?

A. G. WAKEFIELD: I have a tremendous amount of experience in trying to talk customers into changing from iron, plastics and steel pressings, to aluminium, with little success. It is a question of cost. A product that has been made in iron can be made in aluminium. Generally speaking there is no cost saving, unless that item is designed initially as an aluminium die casting or an aluminium gravity die casting. In general there is a cost reduction in machining, since it is quicker to machine aluminium. Pressure die casting is far more accurate and fewer machining operations are required. However, in one firm an engineer said, 'I am pleased to say I have just been given a project. It is going to be a casting, it is about 6 in long, about 3 in square and it has got a hole straight up the middle. What would be the price of it in aluminium?'. Now, gentlemen, what could I do?

D. L. JELLEY (*Belmos Peebles*): I sympathise with that. If designers would design from scratch for the material which they are going to use there would be significant advantages. But before this a designer wants some rough idea of the order of cost, to see whether in fact the effort of considering the design is justified in that material.

A. G. WAKEFIELD: When I started to ask the engineer further questions, he said, 'Well, first of all, it is a burner head'. Now, aluminium melts at 600°, and there was the answer. They had to stop with iron.

P. P. LOVE (*Glacier Metal Co.*): I wonder if I can press Mr Wakefield on this question? The engineer knows that cast iron costs so many pence per pound, and that is a formulation for the cost of an iron casting. Now, can't the die casters give a rough estimate of pence per equivalent pound of cast iron? It does not seem to me that that should be too difficult.

A. G. WAKEFIELD: We are in an industry that produces many types of components. One may weigh only half an ounce. The cost may be £20 or £30 per pound of aluminium. A transmission case weighs 21 lbs and the cost may be only 4s or 5s a pound. I do agree that to a certain extent it could be formulated, but I think it might be misleading.

C. W. DEE (*Aerostatic*): Take a casting of iron and replace it with aluminium. Go a stage further and say, this casting is going to be subject to years of stresses and loads. The aluminium counterpart becomes a very much more intricate component. The result is that our die costs go up through the roof. So how can you replace a casting subject to specific load and stress requirements with an aluminium casting and say you can reduce the costs?

A. G. WAKEFIELD: If we were simply to convert from iron there would be no cost saving whatsoever. First of all we have to reduce the aluminium content without sacrificing strength, and this is where design plays a fantastic part. In general, we find only a very slight cost saving on a lot of iron-to-aluminium conversion. The biggest cost saving really is the nuisance factor which has been removed. To produce pressurised die castings you do not need a great deal of room. All you need is the machine.

C. W. DEE (*Aerostatic*): One of the hidden costs that I meant was the more intricate die which one has to produce. Therefore the cost of the die must go up through the roof.

A. G. WAKEFIELD: Not necessarily, if the cost is spread over, say, 5000 components per week. It costs an awful lot of money to produce iron castings with the sophisticated equipment required.

J. J. PATERSON (*Rolls-Royce*): I am particularly interested in numerical control. Can you give me some indication of how much, if any, work is being done to provide castings – sand, die and gravity – with precision lugs which should allow immediate mounting on a machine without any other orientation?

A. G. WAKEFIELD: With pressure die casting this is not a problem because accuracy and surface finish are adequate for numerically controlled machining. For gravity casting and sand casting we make a simple jig set-up and we machine the selected area for location.

M. T. WATKINS (*National Engineering Laboratory*): There are two points on Mr Ogura's paper as presented by Dr F. W. Travis. I think there must be some interrelation between the internal pressure and the end movement of the rams. There must be some system in this somewhere which relates the two. Secondly, would Dr Travis comment on the system of sealing which is described there?

Dr F. W. TRAVIS: The method of sealing is to have on the end of the piston a vee-shaped annular projection. It might be just as effective to put another plug inside. Ogura's method requires that you turn the end of the tubes. You have to develop a high force before you develop any sealing.

J. JOLLY (*Rolls-Royce*): Could I ask Dr Travis for the reference to the American paper he quoted in discussing Mr Ogura's paper?

Dr F. W. TRAVIS: International Conference on Manufacturing Technology, Ann Arbor, Michigan, September 1967, 'The Use of Compensating Stresses in Difficult Metal Working Operations', T.N.O., Delft.

Dr J. A. McGEOUGH (*University of Strathclyde*): Dr Bruce mentioned agitation of the paint bath. In other electrochemical processes such agitation usually results in the formation of a hydrodynamic boundary layer on the electrodes and this often affects the surface finish which is achieved. Are similar effects noted in electropainting?

Dr D. B. BRUCE: No. I think they have not been noticed because we are obliged to have agitation in the paint bath. The reason is that the pigment is too willing to settle to the bottom of the bath and we really do have to keep it agitated. It is important to have the correct amount of agitation to keep the finish right as well. If you make the agitation far too severe you start washing off the paint film. You may change the pigmentation of the paint film, and the pigment binder ratio, giving different appearances on the paint film.

Dr J. A. MCGEOUGH (*University of Strathclyde*): What would be a typical rate of agitation?

Dr D. B. BRUCE: This is an extremely difficult question to answer. It is very easy to say six times an hour, so that if you have a 20 000 gallon bath you are pumping the paint at 120 000 gallons an hour. It is possible to have very great agitation at some parts of the bath and practically no agitation at other parts. Hence some parts of the bath come feet deep in pigment and some parts of the articles painted are affected by excessive agitation.

I have been campaigning for some time for some new definitions of agitation in paint baths. I have so far only coined the unit of measurement called the *turb*, but I do not know its dimensions. I would be very grateful if somebody in the engineering line would come forward with some ideas on this. It is very badly needed.

D. L. JELLEY (*Belmos Peebles*): Car manufacturers are only using electropainting as undercoating. With electropainting imperfections are not disguised in the same way as with conventional painting. Is there any further development in electropainting which would enable it to be used as a final finish and which would disguise imperfections on the surface that is being painted?

Dr D. B. BRUCE: Everybody would like to see this. The advantages of even deposition militate very greatly against getting the kind of thing that you are asking for. If you are asking for levelling, then almost inevitably you are going to diminish flowing power. Another way would be a two-coat electrodeposition. This is not feasible at this time because, if the first layer is made conductive to allow for a second deposition, then all that happens to the flowing power happens again.

E. ROSMARIN (*Dexion*): Could Dr Bruce give any indication of the relative difficulty of painting steel, aluminium and Mazak by electrodeposition, and would he consider it feasible to paint these products in the same bath?

Dr D. B. BRUCE: There is no real difficulty in painting Mazak or steel. Aluminium is the real brute. Some aluminium alloys paint very nicely indeed. Others are extremely difficult. It is a matter of getting the pre-treatment right. Can we paint all articles in the same bath? The answer is a qualified yes. It is highly unlikely that all kinds of articles would come out looking the same.

B. F. SHAW (*Polytechnic School of Management Studies*): Would Mr Darby say how much development there is in plating plastics?

C. R. DARBY: The main difference between plating plastics and plating metal is that you must make the plastic metallic before you can plate it and therefore you have a long pre-treatment sequence. This today is quite well known. There is an etch, an activator, a sensitisor, and an electro-nickel deposition. Then it can be treated entirely as a metallic article. There is a certain amount of success on polypropylene. There are one or two production plants, but most plants are on a pilot scale at present.

SPEECH

B. C. Harrison, C.B.E.

at the University of Strathclyde,
Thursday evening 4 September 1969

In giving this talk, which was prepared several days before I saw the papers, I feel like a man attending a crowded resort. I am in danger of treading on other people's feet and on papers. However I intend to go forward with tonight's task, hoping to tread upon some virgin sand, a minimum of papers, and no toes.

I do find that many of the things about which I intended to talk have already been said, particularly by the speakers on the first day. Nevertheless, the fact that they spoke in some depth does not stop me from saying the things again, because they are very important. They are mostly matters of commercial management, and deal with innovation at industrial level. I am NOT presuming to do a summing-up.

In commerce, the motivation is the making of money. You, as individuals, may be motivated by a lot of different driving forces, amongst which will be the earning of your own living. This may, or may not, rank high in your own motivation. You may be doing what you are doing because of a keen vocational interest, because your work is rewarding and satisfying. You may be doing what you are doing because you are one of the fortunate ones who have a private source of income and can follow an interest which overrides all others that you have. But there is not the slightest doubt that in business, whatever the business, the fact is that one's company is in it to make money.

Now in business for making profit one has very many factors to consider.

It is no good innovating and making a product unless you have already satisfied yourself that there is a market or that a market can be created. It is of material importance to form a sound idea of the size of that market. If it is international, and surely it should be, consideration must be given to environment, freight, language, system of measurement, skill of user, delivery of raw materials and disposal of products and by-products, and many other such items.

It is a fact of life that very often novel ideas occur to several people at the same time. Perhaps that is not so remarkable when one considers that very often an idea evolves in the mind because of the need to solve a problem. Evolution makes it apparent that there is a problem which needs a solution, and consequently different people in different parts of the world start to apply themselves to finding the answer to the same problem. If a solution occurs to an individual, or a group of individuals, then it is important that the completion of the design and the commencement of manufacture is proceeded with as quickly as possible so as to have the product on the market before any competitors. It must therefore be designed quickly, it must be designed without faults, and it must be designed at an attractive cost, and not over-designed.

I believe it was Henry Ford who said 'an engineer is a man that can make a thing for a dollar which any fool can make for two'. In this competitive world you must be careful because if you make your product for a dollar your competitor may make it for ninety cents, and a month earlier than you.

It is one of the strange things of life that seldom are creative minds cost-conscious. It is essential, therefore, that very early in the development of a product, contact is made with production engineers, whether they be in your own company or experts from an outside supplier, so that the product is designed for economical manufacture. This is integration.

It is at this stage that a notional cost of design development and manufacture can be formed. The policies of absorbing those costs into selling price vary from company to company, but the object should be to refer the ultimate selling price to the marketing people for their approval. Before quantity production begins, that is, when the design is finalised, a firm cost should be established, and again the marketing people should be told of the selling price. This is their final opportunity to confirm that a market exists and that they can sell in that market.

Seldom is a designer experienced as a production engineer. It is very desirable that he should be, but this is idealistic. If designers were good production engineers then there would be no need for value analysis. Every successful piece of value analysis is a reflection upon the designer. The field of production engineering is so wide, and is expanding, growing and altering so fast, that it is difficult even for full-time production engineers to keep up to date: so it is not reasonable to expect designers to be first-class production engineers too. The designer should work closely with the production engineer as he goes on with his design. The production engineer can study alternative means of production so that the design can be adjusted to accommodate alternative courses of manufacture or different materials.

Value engineering can cause serious delay, but without that delay the project may flounder because of production difficulties, or because the ultimate cost turns out not to be competitive, particularly if there are other manufacturers entering the field at the same time as one's own product is marketed.

Speed is of great importance. You want to be first in the market. You do not make money until the goods are sold and paid for. The customer does not pay until he is satisfied. A designer would like to try alternative solutions to his problems. He must compromise, sometimes reserving his alternative ideas for phase 2 of the product, when he can refine his design.

One of the many interesting things being discussed at this conference is computer-aided design. This not only makes it possible for the relevant design work to be done more quickly and more accurately, but it allows alternative courses to be explored, with the result that the design is the best of all which are explored. In fact, if the design is thoroughly well carried out one questions the need for the building of a prototype, but so often the prototype reveals mistakes in design or performance which have to be corrected before quantity production can commence. It is the production engineer's responsibility continually to be calling to the attention of the designers new developments as they become available.

It is equally the designer's responsibility to keep himself aware of new materials, new proprietary goods, as well as new techniques of design. If he intends using new methods he must ensure that the manufacturing plant is advised so as to give the necessary service. The more designers can know of new processes, of new materials, and the problems which beset the production engineer, the more quickly the product can reach the market, the more reliable it will be, and more attractive its costs. In other words, good team-work is required.

An idea is conceived in one mind alone, but several competent minds, working together, fertilise one another, and the outcome is better ideas. This method of working is, I believe, well known to designers, but it should be practised by designers together with production engineers right from the inception of design, so that the best ideas, both of design and manufacture, can be incorporated right from the beginning, with the object of producing a completely satisfactory design, made by the best manufacturing methods, at a price which is competitive and which would be a challenge to any others trying to enter the same market. The designer who says 'it is my job to design and the production engineer's to make' is out of date. He does not know his job. He is not cost-conscious and must have his outlook changed.

Dr Bruce Archer's report of a psychologist's comment that he saw 'joy in the staff working in a multi-disciplined environment' appealed to me as being realistic and desirable.

I believe that the prototype, when made, should not only test the design, but should be used as far as possible to test any new methods which the production engineers wish to incorporate in the new product. When the designer determines the accuracy and the quality of the product he is not always aware of the problems which he is setting the production engineer. Likewise, he is not always aware of the real necessity, or otherwise, for tolerances, both with regard to dimension and to surface finish. There is generally a tendency to err on the safe side and to make tolerances too tight, but this is usually very expensive. The practice of running in is often no more than correcting finish and fits, and is probably more costly. Experienced production engineers frequently can advise on these matters.

It is the production engineer's responsibility to acquire the necessary equipment for measurement and the maintenance of quality. Should any new process be involved which necessitates such new equipment, the production engineer should be brought in early so that any testing which he has to do can be carried out in good time.

It is essential that, very early, a complete plan be evolved. That plan must not only be associated with the design of the product, at least one cost check, the manufacture of the prototype, and the tooling to enable quantity production to be started, but must also concern itself with many other matters. For example, the briefing of the sales force, which has already indicated the size and problems of the market, and for which catalogue matter and other descriptive literature must be prepared. Spares service must be established, demonstrators and service men trained, maintenance manuals developed. The language probelm must be dealt with in many of these items.

In order to make sure that all these things proceed according to an overall planned timetable, thought should be given to them very early by management. These things do not necessarily start when design starts, but it is a general responsibility of management to ensure that all are started at the appropriate time, that on the one hand the knowledge necessary to start them is available when it is required and on the other hand they are all monitored and completed. Thus management must ensure the perfection of the timetable, so that when the appropriate stage of manufacture and marketing is reached there are no unnecessary, and therefore irritating, delays.

One of the most satisfactory methods of achieving this is to have a critical path analysis made of the whole project, including design, production engineering, manufacture, and all matters associated with marketing. Such an analysis should ensure that the items which have to be bought from outside are ordered on time, both for the prototype and for quantity production, whether they be material, literature or educational matter. These must not be ordered too early so that knowledge gained in the making and testing of the prototype is wasted, but not ordered too late so that quantity production is delayed. Frequently this involves reserving capacity with suppliers whilst the specification of the goods to be obtained from outside is confirmed.

Reference has been made to computer-aided design. For this there must be access to a computer and suitable programs. Critical path analysis has been mentioned. To get fast and frequent monitoring of progress a computer is essential, and so are frequent reviews.

In today's world of fierce competition, speed, accuracy, cost-consciousness and quality are of paramount importance. A company which cannot provide the resources of equipment, and men of high calibre, cannot be leader. In other words, today the advantages lie with large organisations which can afford such resources. Nevertheless, there are small firms which are successful. One usually finds that they are full of dedicated men, men of infectious enthusiasm, with determination to succeed and the ability to overcome difficulties.

Management must be prepared to take risks. However, the better the management the fewer the items upon which it is ill-informed and therefore the smaller the risk.

I don't know what all those present do in their daily work. I hope many of you are designers, adding to your knowledge of design methods and techniques, and, very importantly, adding to your production engineering knowledge of methods and materials. The conference will surely reinforce and probably add to the knowledge of all production engineers present, and I hope give ideas to those in general management, and perhaps to those in the field of education. Many of the matters discussed at this conference, and some of those I have mentioned, involve change, and resistance to change must be overcome.

It is said in advocacy of long-range planning that if you do not look ahead you will discover your troubles when they are close at hand. Surely this applies to design and manufacture too.

You will notice that, although this conference is entitled *Product Development and Manufacturing Technology*, I have put much emphasis upon design. I believe those concerned with manufacture are not brought in early enough. They should have a great influence upon design, and if my comments bring the two a little closer together, they will have been worth while.

The conference is stimulating because it deals with many developments of old activities as well as facing us with new things. It is typical of engineers that one speaker has already seen the effect of equal pay for women and sought to find ways of avoiding the effect of this upon costs.

On behalf of all delegates, I would like to thank the authors, chairmen, conference organisers and hosts, including the warden and his staff, for what has been accomplished. Reward lies not only in the satisfaction of a job well done but also in customers well satisfied. I hope that the conference will be of material help in producing an upturn in some of the U.K. lines on Mr Maddock's charts.

SESSION V

Manufacturing Systems I

Chairman: Professor D. S. Ross
University of Strathclyde

THE MANUFACTURING SYSTEM CONCEPT

P. H. Stephenson
Birniehill Institute

SUMMARY

The completely integrated manufacturing system involving computer control and numerically controlled machine tools poses technical and economic problems, some of which have still to be solved. Operating experience of systems of less sophistication than the ideal can however provide some of the answers. Three advanced, mechanically integrated, manufacturing systems are examined, followed by a comparison of three other systems which are provided with direct computer control of machine tools. Technical developments required for the fully integrated manufacturing systems of the future are stated.

1.0 INTRODUCTION

That much desired goal, the complete integration of machine tools into a system-engineered manufacturing complex, becomes a possibility only with the harnessing of the versatile computer to numerical control. But, although on-line computer control has already been accomplished with great success in such process industries as petroleum and chemicals, the problem is a simpler one in these industries because the processes involved tend to be somewhat static and non-varying.

The use of the computer in metalworking manufacture is likely to proceed more slowly, especially when it is used in conjunction with numerical control (n.c.). Nevertheless, many schemes are under development, especially in the United States. They differ primarily in the use made of the computer. The main problem in selling computer n.c. is that it can only become economic when it involves more than two or three machines, so n.c. manufacturing capacity must be greatly enlarged at the same time as the computer is provided, and how many companies can afford to take such steps at one time? This does not mean that a more gradual approach to integrated manufacturing is not possible. Several approaches are being made at the present time.

Below, a survey of schemes for direct computer control begins with a discussion of three of these less all-embracing projects in increasing order of sophistication.

2.0 INTEGRATED MANUFACTURING SYSTEMS

2.1 *The Herbert-Ingersoll Daventry factory*

A new factory recently completed at Daventry for Herbert-Ingersoll* is itself a good example of a creative approach to the problem of obtaining maximum efficiency in one-off and small-quantity production of precision components ranging from small to large and heavy. It is

---

* The layout of the light machining area is shown in Fig. 10 of the paper by D. F. H. Rushton entitled 'Productivity and Profitability through the Manufacturing System Concept', elsewhere in this book.

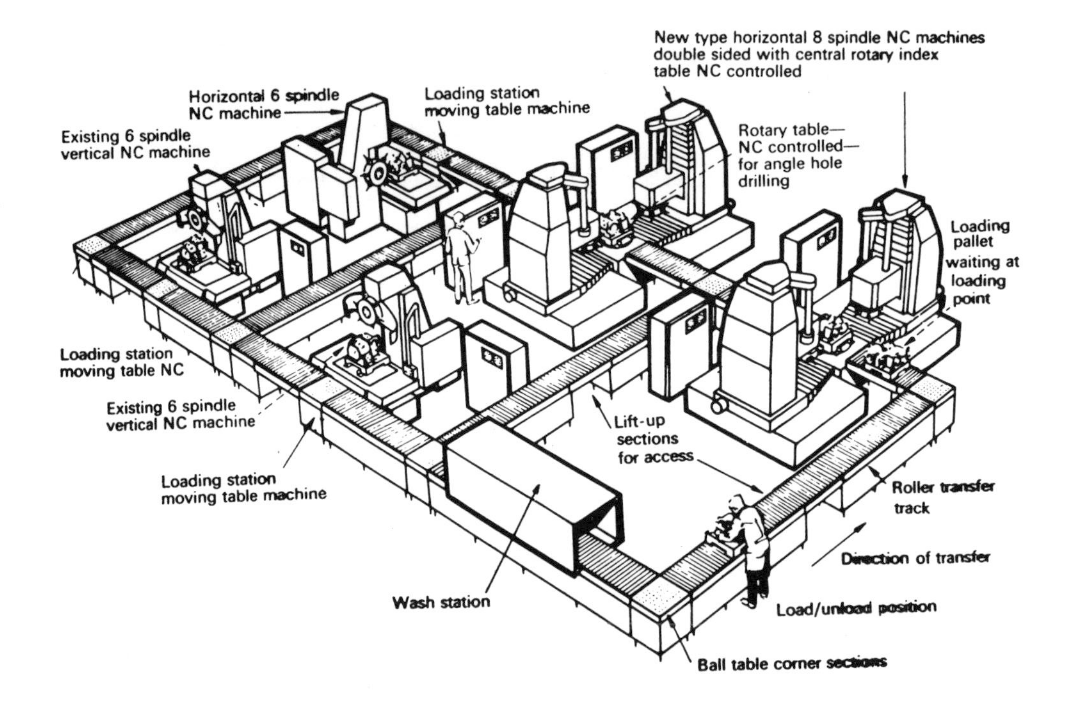

Fig. 1. Above – Borg-Warner system, Letchworth. Below – double-sided eight-spindle n.c. machine with n.c. rotary index table. (Courtesy of *Metalworking Production,* 7 Feb. 1968.)

estimated that the new production techniques being used will achieve an annual output of £10 000 per man per year as against the industry's average of £2500.

The light machining area is of special interest since it comprises functional groups of machines connected by a central work transportation system. Well-established conveyor techniques are used to route work-distribution trolleys from the control centre to individual machines or machine groups. The control centre is equipped with a wide range of cutting tools, holders and fixtures, and it is at this point that workpiece blanks are married to the complete set of tooling which will be required to carry out each operation. The tooling, together with the drawing or control tape, is sent by means of the trolley to the selected station along the line. There it is discharged automatically to the buffer store at the appropriate machine tool. Constant two-way communication is provided between the controller and the machine operators. The machines used in this arrangement are a combination of conventional and numerical control and at this stage no attempt has been made to provide computer control of the flow of work to and from individual machines.

Care was taken in the design of the building to provide the environment required for high productivity and quality of work. The windowless manufacturing area has a high ambient level of lighting, and the temperature is controlled to $\pm 2\,^{\circ}C$. A coolant distribution and swarf removal system is built into the factory floor, providing direct connection between individual machines and the outside of the building. This Herbert-Ingersoll arrangement shows far-sightedness in the use of conventional techniques.

2.2 *The Borg-Warner system*

The new system at present being installed in Borg-Warner's factory at Letchworth (Fig. 1) has gone one stage further. It incorporates standard pallets for transfer of workpieces from machine to machine, and an addressing system which stores the complete routing for each component and utilises all-numerically-controlled equipment.

This 'variable mission' system is based on the use of a new horizontal-spindle numerically-controlled turret machine which handles workpiece and pallet completely automatically in the work station (Fig. 1). The pallet is received, located bi-axially, indexed if necessary, and clamped for machining. Single- or twin-turret designs are possible. Because the system relies primarily on relatively simple turret machines, the number of units possible for a given investment is higher than if more complicated equipment were selected. Hence, more spindles are available to work simultaneously to increase production rate. The line is not dependent on any particular machine, and down-time for maintenance or tool-changing becomes practical. There is again no need for a computer for scheduling or control.

2.3 *The Molins System 24*

The system of manufacture designed and manufactured by the Molins Machine Co. Ltd (Fig. 2) offers integration far beyond anything at present available and is probably the ultimate that will be achieved without on-line computer control of the machine tools themselves. This metalworking plant is at present undergoing full trials, though individual components have been operating successfully for some years. Economic studies indicate that System 24 will be able to reduce the cost of components by a factor of between five and ten as compared with conventional methods. It will bring major reductions in requirements for floor space and personnel, and, surprisingly, Molins anticipate no increase in capital investment for any given level of output.

The system has been designed with the capability of being completely loaded during the day

Fig. 2. System 24 layout. (Courtesy of Molins Machine Co. Ltd.)

shift and continuing to manufacture substantially unattended throughout the night. This is a worth-while advantage under present-day conditions but will become overwhelmingly so during the next ten years because of increasing difficulty in persuading people to work night shifts. Since much of the workpiece setting can be done by girls, there is clear advantage in having no requirement for night-shift labour.

Briefly, a System 24 installation consists mainly of:

- A row of modular numerically-controlled machine tools with contouring capabilities designed for the highest possible metal-removal rate. Although based on a common concept, there are specialised versions designed for optimum performance, for example, drilling machines, three-axis milling machines, a six-axis machine and a numerically-controlled inspection unit.
- An automatic transfer mechanism that will deliver pallet-mounted workpieces from the setters to a buffer store and thence to as many of the machine tools as are required.
- An on-line computer that will control the overall operation, including scheduling. This will perform such functions as seeing that the correct workpieces are delivered to the proper machines in the right sequence and that the desired machining tape and tool magazine are automatically loaded.

The prototype plant is designed specifically for machining aluminium alloy within a size of 30 × 30 × 15 cm. The high-powered machines must be capable of high spindle speeds to take full advantage of the excellent machinability of aluminium.

These machines have identical vertical worktables on which a transferable pallet carrying the component can be located accurately and automatically in position. Thus, each workpiece can be transferred to the machines appropriate to the operations required, and each operation is carried out with maximum possible efficiency. The principle of the system contrasts with that of the manufacturing centre, which keeps the workpiece in one place so that it is operated on with much lower utilisation of capital.

The machines display many novel and advanced features, for example:

- Hydraulically powered spindle and slides (central supply)
- Automatic changing of tool magazines
- Automatic tool-changing and tool-setting on the machine
- Hydrostatic slideways and bearings
- Under-floor swarf removal
- Ferranti magnetic-tape control system (tapes selected from a magazine)

The automatic conveyor provides a pallet storage rack fed from the work-setting station with a storage capacity of 18 h of continuous operation. The pallets are individually coded.

The throughput and flexibility of a six-machine System 24 installation is such that computer control is mandatory. It is provided by an on-line IBM 1130 installation which is responsible for all movements of workpieces, pallets, tool magazines and tape casettes.

This whole concept of Molins takes so many steps forward at the same time that it is difficult to predict the extent of its advantages. However, results from prototype machines that have been in use for over three years have given the designers every encouragement.

3.0 ON-LINE COMPUTER CONTROL OF MANUFACTURE

And now, moving on from the highly sophisticated, unified approach of Molins, let us take a look at some systems where the computer *does* take an active role in the direct control of the machine tool. One of the simplest of these systems is designed around the concept of controlling a complex of machine tools from a central location by time-sharing a computer and part-program library.

3.1 *Bunker Ramo System 70*

In the Bunker Ramo System 70 (Fig. 3) a small, general-purpose computer, equipped with a disc storage unit and functioning as a data supply centre and time-sharing interpolator, is committed to machine tool control.

The execution of a program with System 70 progresses under the control of the machine tool itself. The machine tool is capable of processing incremental commands executed in a fixed period. The execution is on a cyclic basis, much as in a conventional n.c. system. Each

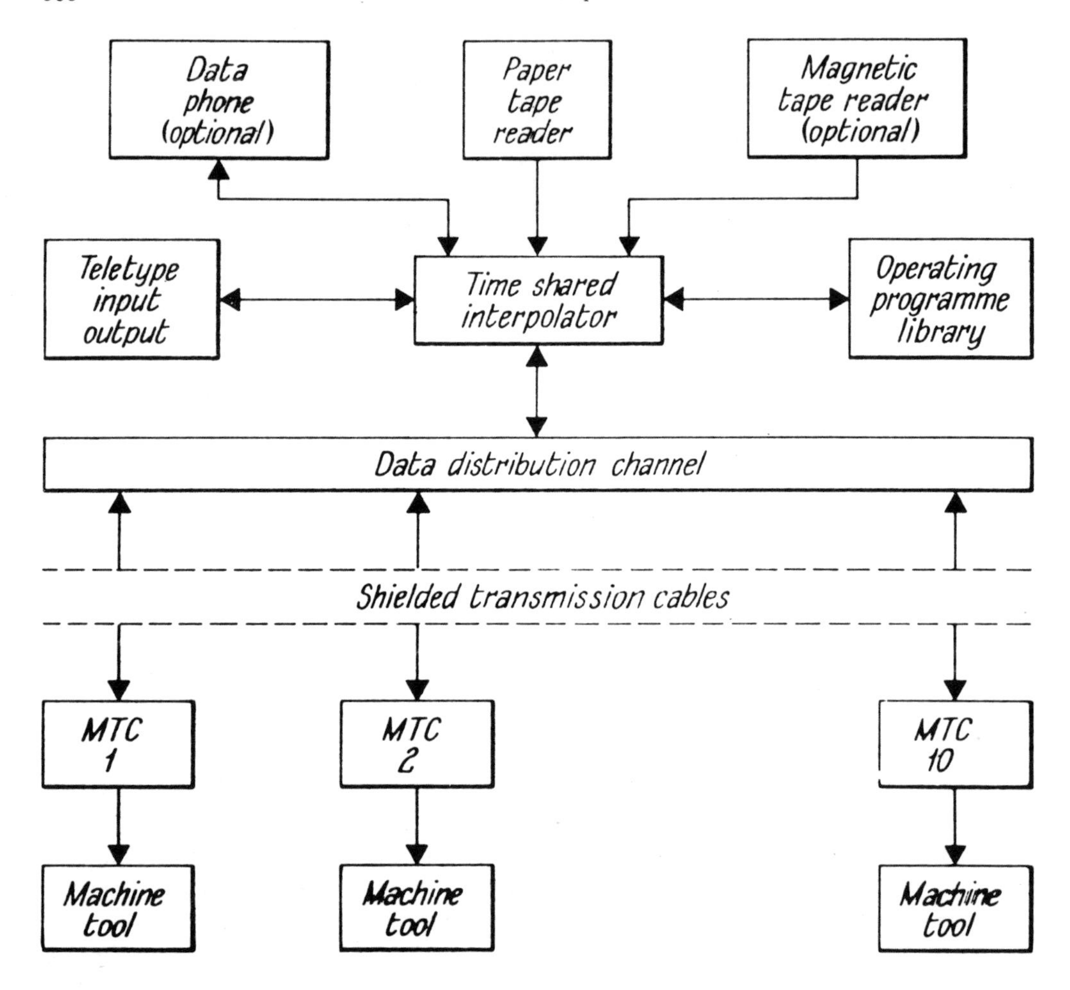

Fig. 3. Diagrammatic representation of Bunker-Ramo System 70. (Courtesy of *Machinery & Production Engineering,* 20 Dec. 1967.)

time a cycle is initiated, a new incremental command is requested by the machine tool control from the central computer. The necessary computations are done in the interpolator (time-sharing with other machines) and the required data are transmitted back to the machine *via* a data distribution channel. This channel also contains a logic section for each machine tool so that it can store transmissions from each machine tool until a sufficient and logical amount of data is gathered to make interrogation of the central interpolator efficient.

A complete set of programs for current production on all the machines in the system is stored in a medium-speed, random-access, high-capacity memory linked with the interpolator. New programs are normally entered on an off-line basis and several alternative methods are available which allow for the transfer of existing tapes or program libraries as well as the use of conventional part programming. Data input from these sources is decoded and stored in a fixed format in a disc store.

This Bunker Ramo system still requires considerable investment without the possibility of a trial period beforehand. The small computer required is specific to the system and in most installations is probably under-utilised. Alternative schemes are aimed at improving this position by allowing the use of in-house or rented on-line large computers on a time-shared basis.

3.2 *General Electric Data Controller*

The simplest approach has recently been made by General Electric, who have designed and are now marketing an interface unit designed to work with most real-time computers and practically any modern n.c. system which can accept high-speed data input.

This Data Controller is a packaged unit which controls the transfer of part program data directly from a computer memory to an n.c. machine control unit. Information is fed in where the system tape reader would normally pick up the data from the punched tape. This leaves the operator with all the possibilities that he would have had with conventional n.c. – sequence number search, block-by-block operation, etc.

Provision has also been made for a two-way communication channel which can handle manufacturing control information. Coded messages concerning the status of each machine may be transmitted directly to the computer for further recognition or action and instructions can be passed to the operator as required. The intention here is clearly to provide users with an opportunity of evaluating the performance and economics of computer-directed systems at comparatively modest cost.

A separate controller is required for each machine tool, but the total number that can be controlled in one system is limited only by the availability of computer memory and time. This is likely to be a very economic approach for a system which involves only a limited number of machines, but, as the installation costs rise in direct proportion to the number of machines involved, there must be a maximum size of installation above which a more fully integrated on-line system should be considered.

3.3 *The Sundstrand Omnicontrol system*

A more sophisticated method of applying direct computer control has been developed by Sundstrand (Fig. 4). Although this also employs a large, centrally located, general-purpose computer which is not solely committed to the machine tool system, a special-purpose language, called Split, has been written to minimise the data-storage capacity required.

The Split language is designed to separate machine-descriptive data from part-descriptive data. Initially a Split machine program, describing each specific machine to be employed, is written and placed in disc-file storage. This program is clearly a form of the conventional post-processor and it remains on the disc file permanently for use in programming all parts for each particular machine tool. A part program is also written in this language for each part and a facility is provided to feed it to the computer for diagnostic comparison with the machine program on file, with consequent reduction in the number of program errors which eventually reach the machine tool itself. The part programs are also placed in disc-file storage.

When the operator calls for a program at the machine by identifying the part number (as well as the quantity of parts to be run), the computer takes out of storage the appropriate part and machine programs and produces an expanded n.c. machine control program. This is used to control the machine tool throughout the planned run of parts, and, unless there is frequent repetition, is then erased in order to release storage capacity.

A conversational facility is provided as required in the machine shop area. It is used to display instructions to operators and provides two-way communication. The display is on a cathode ray tube. A keyboard makes program corrections or modifications possible at the machine tool, for instance during a proving run.

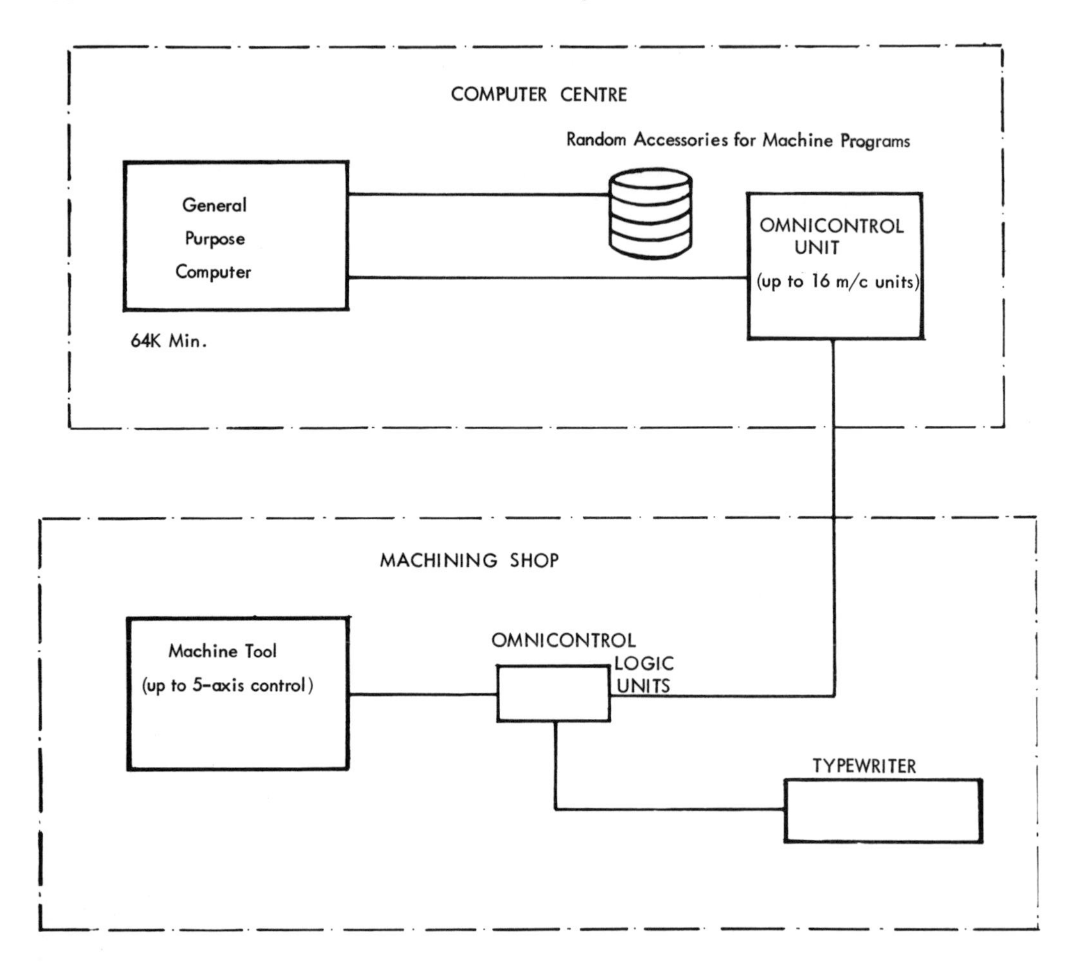

Fig. 4. Diagrammatic representation of Sundstrand Corporation Omnicontrol system. (Courtesy of *Metal-working Production,* 14 Aug. 1968.)

Operational control of the whole system is exercised by a master unit which can handle up to sixteen five-axis machines simultaneously. Up to sixteen master units can be operated within one Omnicontrol system, given adequate capacity in the computer (Fig. 5).

4.0 FUTURE DEVELOPMENTS

These six examples have been chosen in an attempt to cover each level of sophistication of both mechanically integrated systems and computer-integrated numerical control. At present no one development seeks to combine them in one system, although the Molins approach goes a long way towards it. It may be that Mr Williamson of Molins is right in deciding against on-line control of the machine tool itself, and only experience in production operations can produce an answer. On the other hand, it is absolutely certain that any benefit to be achieved from on-line computer control at present will be far less than the prospective gain from mechanical integration if computer control and integration are adopted independently.

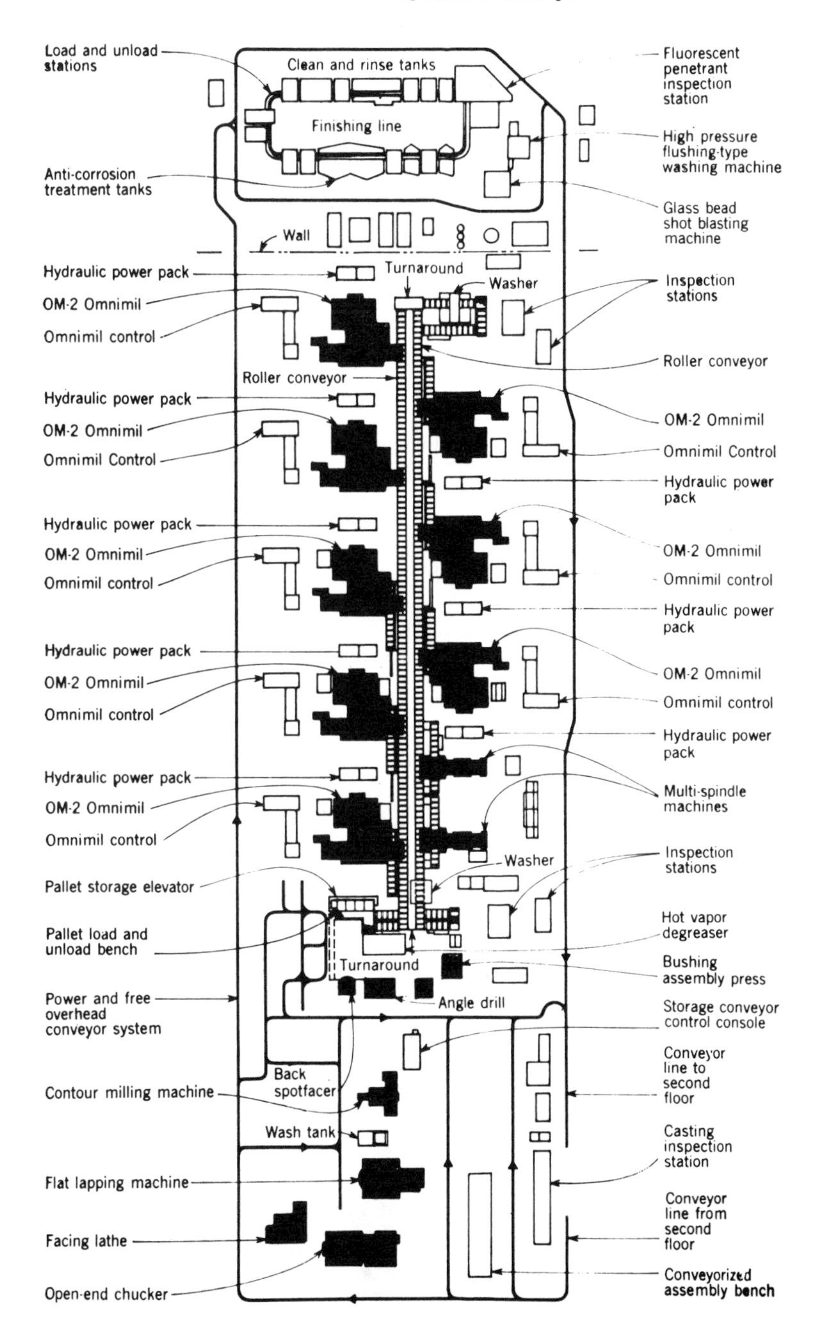

Fig. 5. Sundstrand Aviation programmed machining facility. (Courtesy of *Metalworking Production,* 24 July 1968.)

The potential benefits from a fully integrated manufacturing system will be obvious to an imaginative production engineer, and it is not proposed to list them here, but there are three aspects of computer control which will require careful consideration:

- In a system where there is time sharing of the computer the data handling rates are critical when controlling a machine tool, especially where there are rapid traverse rates in excess of 200 in/min. coupled with resolutions of 0·0001 in.
- In any control system containing shared elements a failure will affect all the circuits involved, and this could mean all the machine tools in the system. The present failure rate of a modern n.c. installation is probably as low as that of a computer.
- Machine control from a distance requires reliable, high-frequency transmission lines. Theoretically this is no problem, but practical and economical solutions may limit transmission distances.

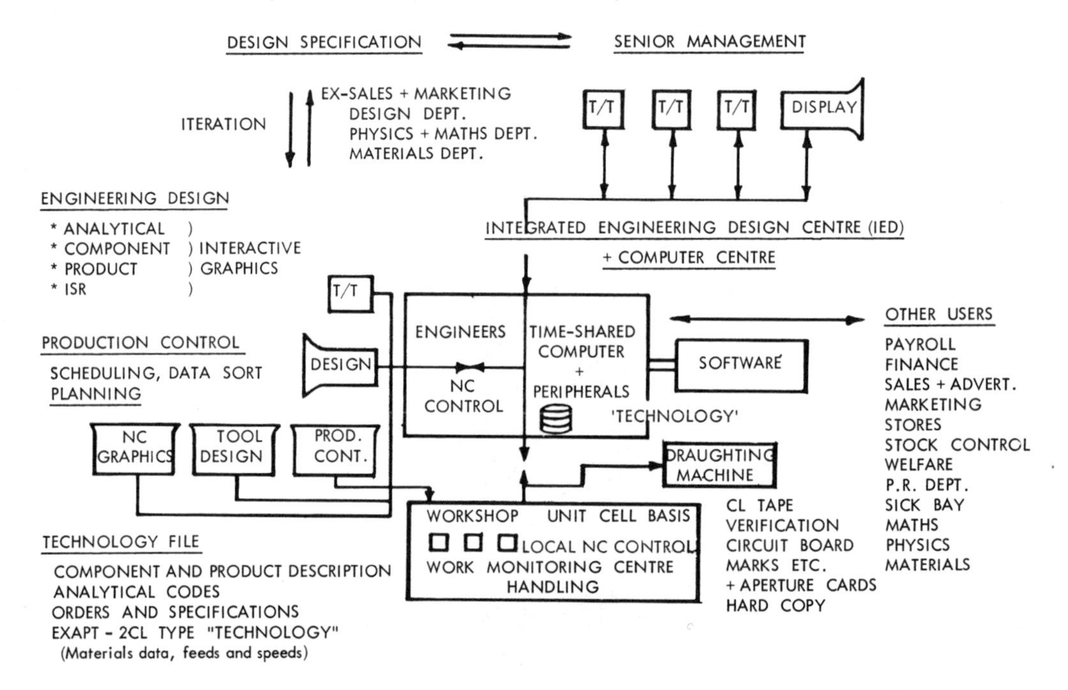

Fig. 6. The overall manufacturing system concept.

That progress in this field will continue to be made cannot be doubted (Fig. 6 and list below). The concept of a manufacturing system, developed as a unified, co-ordinated and automated whole, will bring about a revolution in manufacturing as it is known today. As such it is the most significant area of present research and development. It sets a tremendous challenge, not only to those engineers and scientists who are engaged in it, but also to those responsible for engineering production. They must have the courage and foresight to provide the operating experience that is so vital to the acceptance of any new concept.

FEATURES OF OVERALL MANUFACTURING SYSTEM

- Inherent simplicity of elemental blocks, e.g. Cincinnati Variable Mission
- Flexibility of n.c. machine tool – inherent flexibility overall
- Growth of intelligence within firm. Permanency. Technology is open-ended
- Multiple purpose of time-shared computers. Large central processor can serve several small firms.
- Treatment individualistic. No attempt to 'force' a firm along restrictive, unfamiliar paths.
- Management control on-line and real-time, e.g. Sundstrand Omnicontrol system
- In-process control and inspection reduce overheads and scrap

- Growth proceeds from small beginnings. Fundamental to work within budget. Total system attached in phased stops, starting if necessary from most elementary phases
- Overall manufacturing system not just alternative to mass production system but intended to envelop all automated production systems

VARIABLE-MISSION MANUFACTURING SYSTEMS

Carl B. Perry
Cincinnati Milling Machine Co., Cincinnati

SUMMARY

The next major evolutionary step in automatic manufacturing is to multiple-station programmable systems. Such systems can combine the attributes of high station efficiency, low operation cost, long productive life, and the versatility of continuous, random-order manufacturing. The attainment of these goals calls for significant departures from today's state of the art in areas such as: workpiece registration, work station control, machine configuration, and system management. Problems and opportunities are viewed from the perspective of both system developer and user.

1.0 INTRODUCTION

This document describes some aspects of a new manufacturing philosophy. The goal is a fully automatic system, high work-station efficiency, broad versatility and programmable mission variability. Such a system would provide truly variable mission manufacturing but significant departures from today's state of the art will be necessary to fully develop such a system.

The scope of this paper is limited to consideration of a variable-mission manufacturing system for performing machining operations on parts generally of box-like configuration at production rates above the tool room classification yet below those compatible with mechanized automation (see Fig. 1).

It should be noted, however, that the variable-mission manufacturing (v.m.m.) system concept encompasses a far broader range of applications than the above defined scope. Some of the expanded potentials of the concept will be the subject of future papers.

Variable-mission is a trade mark of the Cincinnati Milling Machine Co.

2.0 TECHNOLOGY INTERACTS WITH MANUFACTURING

Historically, major advances in manufacturing have been triggered by the emergence of new technology. Before the middle of the twentieth century, determining appropriate manufacturing response to a new technology was relatively easy. Since the emergence of numerical control from the laboratory in 1953 this determination has become increasingly complex, and today represents a formidable challenge to those of us concerned with advancing the art and science of manufacturing.

2.1 *Self-evident interactions*

Energy external to man was first harnessed to a machine tool some 400 years ago. The water

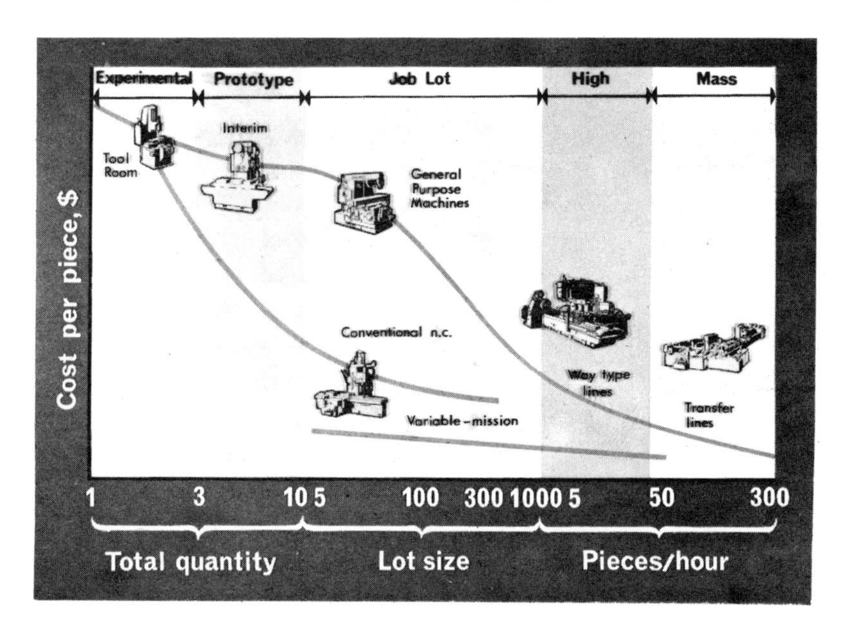

Fig. 1 Production quantity spectrum.

wheel gave way to the steam engine and to the electric motor just 85 years ago. The development of the electric motor, a most significant technological step, resulted in the availability of small, efficient and low-cost energy sources.

No complex analysis was required to recognise that small electric motors, mounted for each machine, should supersede largely stationary engines and a bizarre system of jack-shaft and belts. The appropriate interaction between the electric motor and manufacturing was self-evident.

2.2 *Then came numerical control*

The technical feasibility of numerical control (n.c.) was decisively demonstrated in 1953. From that day forward it has been apparent that this technology has the potential to manage, *via* externally prepared intelligence, all aspects of work-station operation, including sophisticated multi-axis cutter path, position and velocity controls. Sixteen years later industry is still struggling to determine appropriate responses to n.c. potential and stake out its boundaries. The appropriate interactions of this new technology with the manufacturing domain are far from self-evident.

What was so different about n.c.? Was it that the number of optional responses had grown a thousandfold? Or that the basic historical relationship between man and his machine was threatened? Maybe it was that wholly new capabilities could now be assigned to work stations. Or could it be that machines and accessories of entirely different configuration became possible (one thinks of, for example, automatic tool changing, shuttling pallets, adaptive optimisation)? Whatever the differences, numerical control opened a Pandora's box of possibilities for industry, and has left us floundering in our search for a critical path that exploits it to the full.

2.3 *Setting the stage for the electronics age*

As a direct result of our struggles to realise at least some of the potentials of n.c., much has been learned. Most significantly, we have mastered the basic problems of bringing together the previously isolated worlds of mechanisms and electronics.

Sophisticated interfacing devices, transducers and servo-mechanisms have come into being. Through these devices, and the knowledge and understanding behind them, the groundwork has been laid for still another technology to interact with manufacturing. The Electronic Age is about to make its impact upon the domain of manufacturing.

3.0 GROWING COMPLEXITY OF TECHNOLOGICAL INTERACTION

The origin of the electronics age would be difficult to relate to a particular invention or date. Certainly the invention of the transistor 21 years ago contributed significantly to the ascendancy of electronics. The star performer in the electronics domain is the digital computer with its awesome power to contribute to and interact on virtually all technologies[2].

In recent years we have witnessed dramatic improvement in the operating speed, reliability, and versatility of digital computing systems. The advances have been on a broad front. There have been equally impressive improvements in the efficiency and reliability of input and output equipment, and growing sophistication in the software area.

3.1 *Computers move ever closer to the factory floor*

Digital computers have been associated with manufacturing for some twenty years. Early contributions were in the processing of scientific and engineering data leading to improved product designs and lowered engineering cost. Early in the development of n.c. the computer was put to work to reduce the human effort required to prepare part programs. More recently the computer has been applied to a host of other manufacturing-oriented tasks, i.e. production planning, production control, cost control, inventory control and so forth.

3.2 *Digital computer in real-time command*

The examples cited probably all involved a computer remote from the factory floor, processing data in batches at times not in phase with events in the real world. A dramatic extension of the capability of the computer follows when it is applied directly to manufacturing processes in a 'real time' mode, i.e. as events occur.

During the past ten years the number of real-time-dedicated process-control computer installations has grown. More recently, the computer has been applied to the control of such functions as the dynamometer testing of automobile engines, adjusting and testing of automobile carburettors, and the operation of transfer lines. All these events might be viewed as setting the stage for the direct computer control of programmable work stations (d.n.c. – direct numerical control). Indeed, computer suppliers are highlighting d.n.c. as a next major evolutionary step. Several machine-tool builders now offer machines conceived to exploit it.

3.3 *Complexity of goal setting*

The massive array of options available *via* hardwired numerical control are now available through direct use of a computer and appropriate software. Also, the computer can monitor and optimise a work station's response to the execution of its assignment, thereby substantially increasing efficiency.

The concept of work station management can be broadened to encompass control of the movement of workpieces to and from the station, the management of a large inventory of cutting tools required for a variety of different workpieces, and the identification of different workpieces. By emphasising conceptualisation one makes the capacity of the digital computer in manufacturing almost limitless.

By still further broadening of our vision, by taking a fish-eye look at manufacturing, we see the integration of a group of work stations into a total manufacturing system. Such a system, operating under computer control, appears in sharp contrast to n.c., with its isolated man-dependent work stations. And beyond that, the computer can be used to oversee the staging of raw material, production tooling, and perishable tools and to manage these functions in a 'system' sense. It is apparent that the interaction of the computer with the world of manufacturing may well be constrained by the minds of men rather than limitations inherent in the technology.

The digital computer, in conjunction with a vast host of highly developed interfacing devices, transducers and servo-mechanisms, stands ready, like a giant genie, to take command of tomorrow's manufacturing system. But the design, nature, and character of the mechanical system that will, under the genie's command, convert raw materials into finished goods is not apparent. What is apparent is that today's work stations, conceived around an intimate man-machine relationship, are obsolete.

It is equally apparent that preserving today's numerically controlled work stations but modifying the means by which they are controlled, i.e. replacing hardwired n.c. units with a direct computer interface, is self-evidently wrong as a generalised response to the digital computer.

4.0 PHILOSOPHY AND BROAD OBJECTIVES

Early in 1965 the Cincinnati Milling Machine Co. initiated a study to find a better way of manufacturing parts at rates too high for conventional n.c. and too low to justify transfer line methods. The primary motivation came from growing awareness of expansion in this awkward zone of the production quantity spectrum (see Fig. 1).

There was also awareness that new technology was developing rapidly in areas offering to improve manufacturing efficiency. The study group was chartered to see whether we could ride the tidal wave of advancing technology rather than be inundated by it. High on our lists of identified new technologies capable of interacting significantly with manufacturing was the digital computer.

Those of us concerned with advancing the art and science of manufacturing are well advised to re-evaluate the phrase, 'Necessity is the mother of invention'. For in a world dominated by exploding technologies the process is perhaps better stated in the reverse. That is to say, 'new technologies are generating hosts of solutions seeking problems'.

The plan of attack initiated by the study group was as follows:

a. Identify deficiencies in present manufacturing systems.
b. Assess the magnitude of the deficiency and the various levels of improvement.
c. Assess the probability of success in eliminating the deficiency by creative innovation within the framework of new technology.
d. Attempt to develop a new manufacturing philosophy to overcome many of the deficiencies.
e. Subject any new philosophy to rigorous technical and economic feasibility analysis.

From this study emerged the concept of *variable-mission manufacturing* ('v.m.m.').

4.1 *Establishing objectives*

A basic objective of v.m.m. is to break away from many of the constraints imposed by mechanisation. In today's world of manufacturing systems, things happen automatically only by virtue of mechanisation. A notable exception is the functioning of a machine tool under n.c., although even here the work station functions only semi-automatically since a man is required as an operator. In the entire remaining arena of manufacturing, events cannot be made to happen automatically except by mechanisation. The very term *automation* has, in many manufacturing circles, become synonymous with *mechanisation.* A basic v.m.m. objective is to achieve the highest practical level of automatic operation in conjunction with programmable mission-changing.

Another major objective is to achieve new levels of versatility without sacrificing efficiency. The options available in today's manufacturing world do not at present provide this happy combination. The modern tool-changing n.c. machining centre is an outstanding example of versatility, but such machines are versatile at the expense of metal-cutting efficiency. Conventional, general-purpose machine tools, used for job-lot manufacturing, have high metal-cutting efficiency at the expense of machine tool utilisation, labour content and production tool investment. Even the transfer line, thought by many to be an epitome of efficiency, is found to be inefficient when individual work-station output is compared with theoretical potential. This is because all work stations in the system are 'time locked' to the slowest station.

Still another system objective is the attainment of three levels of variability: in the design of individual products being manufactured, in the production rate of a given part, and in the in-field expansion of manufacturing capability (a) vertically by addition of like machines, and (b) horizontally by addition of new types of specialised work station.

4.2 *Generalised description of concept*

A basic principle of the v.m.m. philosophy is that mechanical and electronic hardware, on-line and off-line software support, must all present a good general solution to a wide range of manufacturing problems. This is the very opposite of a system conceived around the needs of a specific product, in a specific material, to be produced in a limited range of production quantities. The concept is especially suitable for box-like parts and may be adapted to meet the special requirements of a very wide range of materials and production rates, (see Fig. 2). System efficiency would be high over a very broad range of production quantities. In addition, commonality would exist between the major system elements for installations ranging from only one machine to an automatic factory in which hundreds of machines are integrated into a complete v.m.m. system. We prefer to call such a factory *cybermatic** rather than automatic, since the mission of the v.m.m. factory may be changed by means of manipulating intelligence. This is a capability not implicit in the term *automatic factory.*

In the v.m.m. concept the high versatility of a modern n.c. tool-changer would be exceeded by performing operations such as milling on a specialised milling module, small-hole processing on a single-spindle tool-changing module, pattern-hole drilling on a special module, and precision boring on a specialised boring module. Because of the very high station specialisation, each machine could perform its assigned task at a very high efficiency. By the mix of such stations any level of versatility may be achieved (See Figs 3, 4 and 5).

*The term *automation* is almost universally associated with the automatic manufacture of identical items in mass quantities. Numerical control makes possible *variable-capability* automation, whereby a variety of *different* items can be automatically manufactured in small quantities. The author has proposed a new term, *cybermation,* to encompass the newly emerging science and technology of variable-capability systems operating under the control of externally stored intelligence.

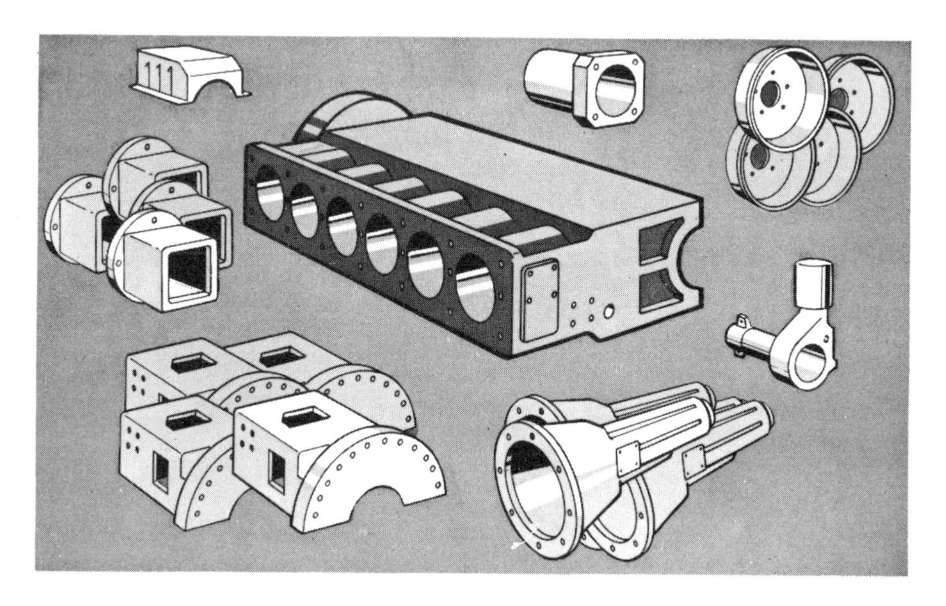

Fig. 2. Parts X quantity = mission.

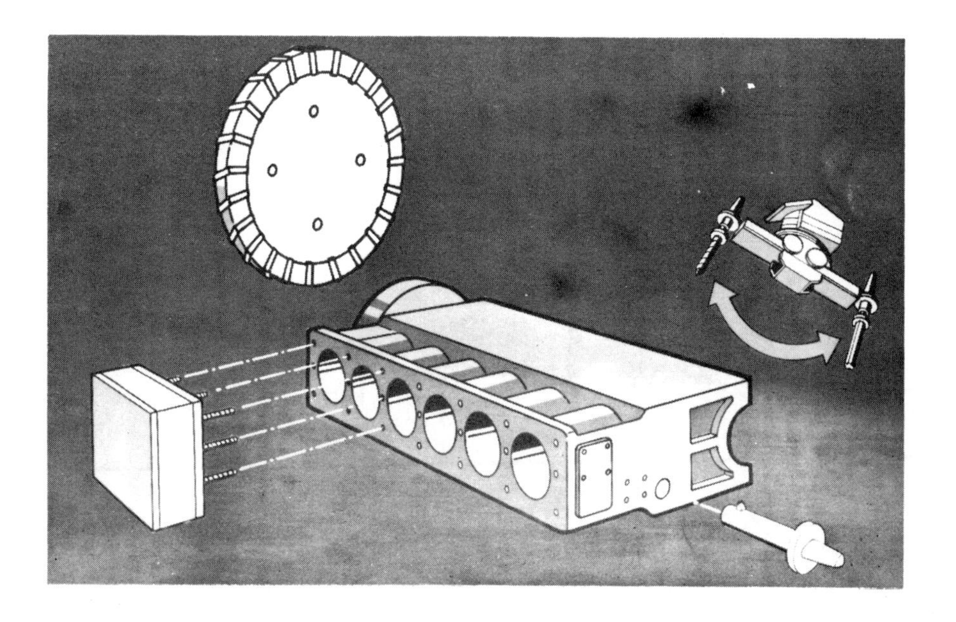

Fig. 3. Operations *dictate* cutters.

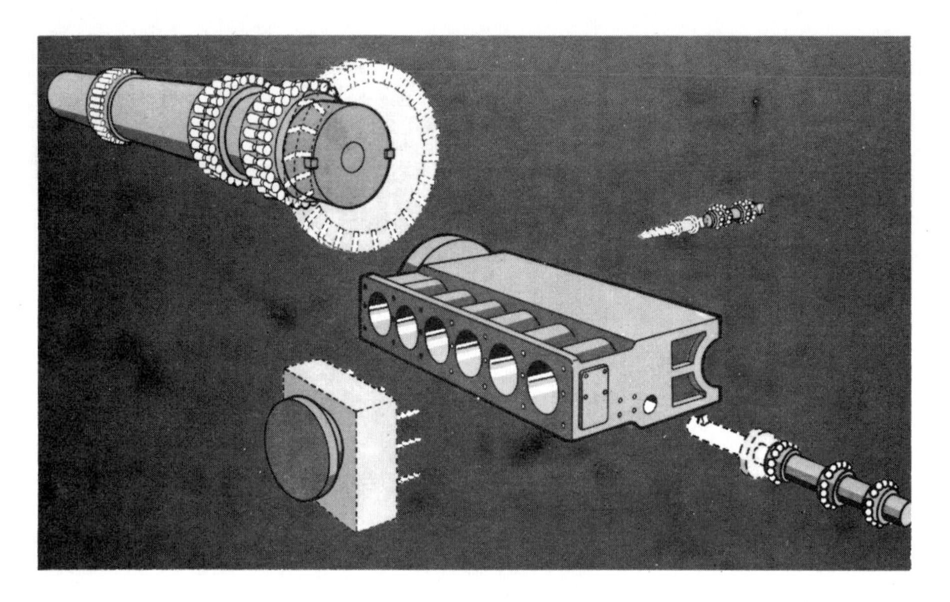

Fig. 4. Cutters *define* spindle design.

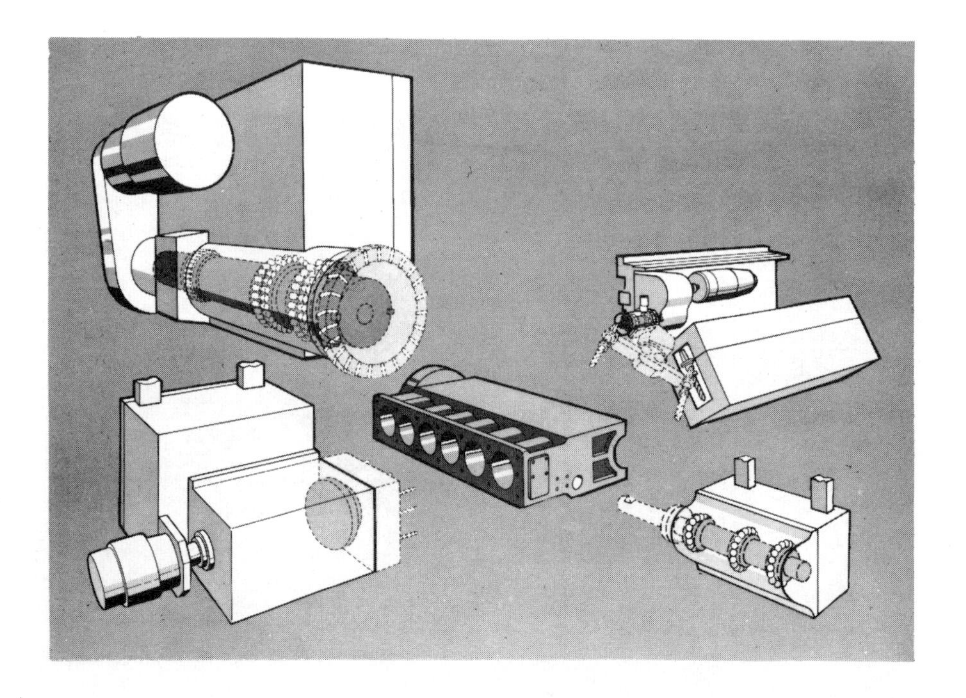

Fig. 5. Specialised carriers.

Another basic principle of the v.m.m. philosophy is that the work station must function without operators and hence be completely automatic. In addition to automatic operation of the individual work stations, the v.m.m. concept requires automatic movement of material throughout the system. Work loaded onto pallets in a staging area would be transported into the system, moving on distribution loops and into specific queues feeding individual work stations. The material handling system would have to be designed so that workpieces could move between work stations in any order. With such a design the constraints (fixed sequence and time-locked movement) imposed by mechanised material handling on transfer lines would be circumvented.

Still another basic objective of the v.m.m. concept is to exploit the capabilities of modern computers on multiple levels:

a Extensive use of a large off-line computer installation to assist in part programming, advance planning of production assignments, and management information reporting on system operation.
b Real-time system operation and management (in v.m.m. terminology, the *central data source*).
c At each work station (in v.m.m. terminology, *station controllers*).

5.0 VARIABLE-MISSION MANUFACTURING OBJECTIVES

5.1 *Assessing technical feasibility*

Now that we have described the broad objectives of v.m.m. let us consider the technical feasibility of attaining them. First of all a study of the concept indicates there are some formidable problems. Some of the more significant are:

1 Full exploitation of the principle of high work-station specialisation requires a new form of registering pallet or fixture at work stations. Existing methods are deficient in accuracy, mechanical stiffness, and maintenance costs. This problem is complicated if the workpiece is to be rotated about a beta axis after registration. An ideal solution would be one in which the initial registration inaccuracy were not altered by workpiece rotation.
2 The problem of workpiece identification calls for a new solution that would have high reliability in the hostile environment occasioned by cutting tools, coolant, chips, etc.
3 Protection of the workpiece registration system from contamination by chips, dirt, and fluids.
4 The requirement for efficient hole-processing at high production rate identifies the need for a work station that would automatically exchange cluster drill assemblies.
5 A new generation of single-spindle tool-changing machines would be needed to assure a very short metal-to-metal tool change time.
6 It would be necessary to develop a mechanical capability, and associated sub-system logic for (a) rapid movement of workpieces from any point in the system to any other, (b) the formation of queues ahead of each work station, and (c) rapid automatic interchanging at work stations.
7 And finally a fully developed v.m.m. system would require solution of many technical problems of electronic hardware and software. These would result from the need to meet the system operating requirements, work station management requirements and off-line system reporting.

5.2 *Establishing specific objectives*

The identification of the above-mentioned problem areas helps to establish specific objectives for v.m.m.

1 Develop a means of coupling workpieces to machines with an accuracy improved by an order of magnitude over that of any present method.
2 Develop a new generation of process-specialised work stations for effective interfacing with automatic material delivery and discharge. The stations should perform without an operator present and should exploit the full potential of the digital computer.
3 Achieve high application versatility through the mix of process-specialised stations.
4 All elements of system to be such that systems ranging in size from one station only up to a cybermatic factory would use the same mechanical hardware, electronic hardware, and support software. This commonality should be such that, in the field, system expansion and modification would be simple and economically attractive.

6.0 WORK STATIONS

Work stations are the basic building blocks of all manufacturing systems. In the world of metalworking we have two basic classes of work station: those which are man-'operated' or - 'tended' and those which are elements in a mechanical system such as a transfer line. None of the machines in either class is suitable for even partial exploitation of the potentials of the electronic age.

General-purpose man-operated machine tools have been evolving for well over a century. Basically these machines represent an extension of man, and more specifically an extension of man's hands. From the floor up they are designed to interface efficiently with their human 'operator'. The basic configuration of the machines and the assignment of linear and angular axes of movement to workpiece or spindle carrier must be re-evaluated in terms of suitability for automatic operation under electronic control.

Mechanised, electronically controlled, means may now be used to replace man in the tasks of loading and unloading machines and changing cutters. These new capabilities sharply interact with the basic configuration of the machine tool element of a system work station.

It becomes evident that there is little about the design of work stations for transfer-line application which would make them suitable for the electronic age. Such stations are conceived within a framework of constraints imposed by mechanisation, basically to perform the operation required for a particular part. The optimum efficiency for such stations is in the performance of their assigned tasks in the time alloted between work-transfer cycles. Thus few stations cut metal at rates close to those theoretically attainable.

6.1 *Configuration and axis assignment*

Work station configuration studies indicate that the spindle carrier should be moved on three axes of translation, X, Y and Z, whilst the rotary axis, β, is assigned to the workpiece support system (see Figs 6, 7 and 8). Studies indicate this to be the best arrangement for interfacing with automatic workpiece delivery and discharge systems while still permitting standardisation of carrier support system designs. This is true whether or not a particular work station has angular orientation capability or the full, high-resolution β capabilities.

6.2 *Capabilities*

The function of work stations in a v.m.m. system differs in major ways from that of

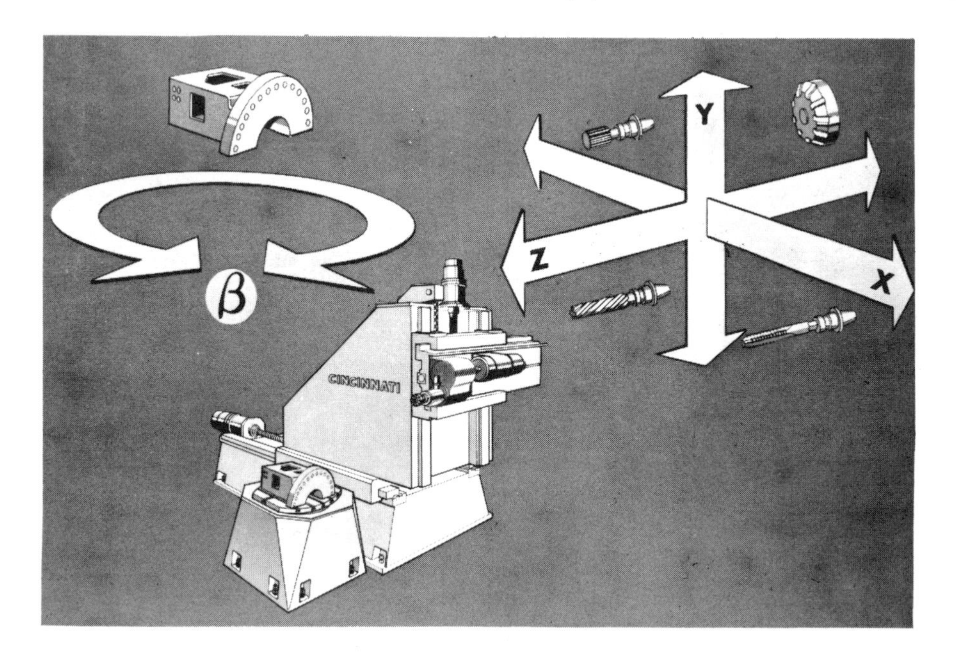

Fig. 6. Positioning axes.

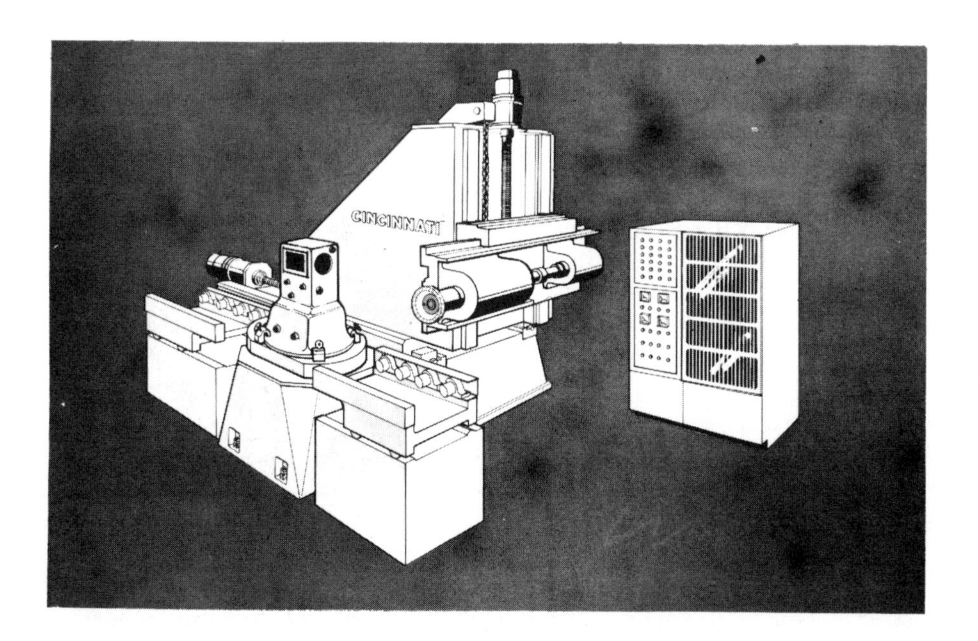

Fig. 7. Work station.

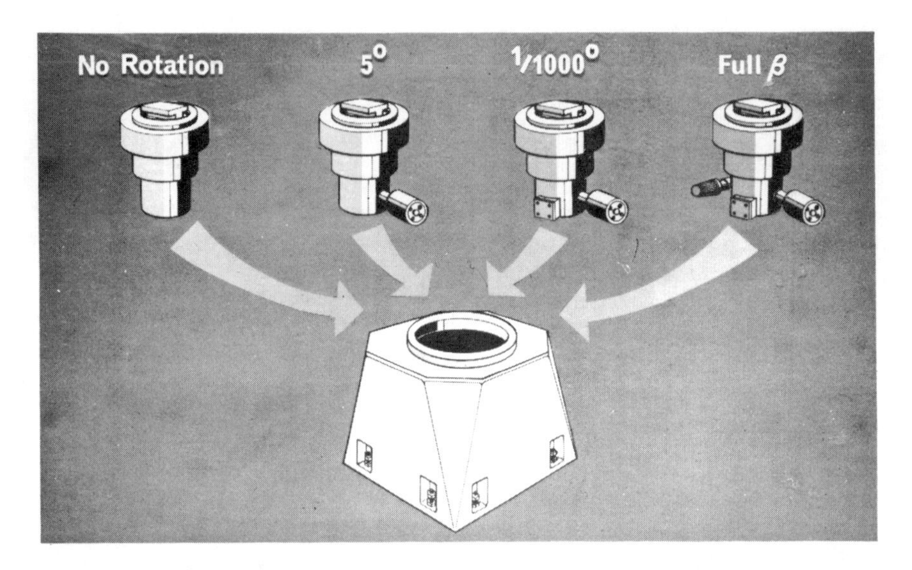

Fig. 8. Work support system.

machines used in a conventional job-lot situation in a transfer line. The principle of process specialisation, combined with the capabilities required of v.m.m. station controllers, sets the stage for the development of a host of new-generation work stations, many of which would have capabilities not available in today's machinery.

The technique used to develop specifications for specialised modules is as follows:

1 Analysis of parts to be manufactured and their associated production quantities per year (see Fig. 2).
2 Selection of the optimum cutting tool for each operation required, consistent with material, production quantity, surface finish, accuracy etc. At this point it should be emphasised that the selection of cutters should not be according to preconceived machine specifications of rev/min. feed rate, etc. Selection should be governed solely by the requirements of the workpiece in conjunction with the latest cutting-tool technology (see Fig. 3).
3 For each cutting tool dictated by the above process, determination of the optimum rev/min, feed rates and coolant application condition.
4 The ideal cutter application generates statistics for spindle horsepower, torsional stiffness of spindle, amplitude and vector of cutter reaction forces (see Fig. 4).
5 At this point the specification of the spindle shaft, its diameter, bearing type, and location, speed ranges, torsional stiffness and so forth can be defined.

From this analysis the precise specification of an optimum spindle-carrier can be developed (see Fig. 5).

Many different cutting tools applied to a given range of material will be compatible with a single-spindle carrier system. The optimum solution comes from a balancing of gains from still higher levels of specialisation against the economic and application versatility associated with higher standardisation. The choice is fortunately not difficult, since sensitivity to specialisation *versus* standardisation is limited to the spindle carriers. The specialised carriers are mounted on highly standardised carrier support systems.

As the size of the system grows the degree of specialisation of the carriers can be increased. Suppose a user starts off with a ten-station system and then needs to double the system output. Instead of just acquiring twice the number of stations with identical capabilities, he would consider the advantages of furthering the degree of specialisation. The probability is doubled productivity with less than twice the number of work stations, because of added efficiency with higher specialisation.

The variety of specialised carriers available as off-the-shelf items will be large. Therefore, it will be practical to solve most production assignments with standard-specialised carriers.

A major objective of v.m.m. is economically superior production of parts at rates much higher than are suitable for today's n.c. (see Fig. 1). This necessitates a work station that would automatically exchange multiple-spindle drill and tap heads. Small-hole processing represents such a large portion of the operations performed on box-like parts that a new capability is required.

The basic concept is to apply automatic tool-changing principles to a multiple-spindle head instead of a single-spindle tool-holder. This presents formidable challenges, the biggest of which is to permit high-speed interchanging of heads in conjunction with high storage density.

6.3 *Management of cutting tools*

The management of cutting tools in a multiple-station, programmable, manufacturing system presents some formidable problems to the system developer. This is particularly true when a desired capability of the system is to manufacture a large variety of complex parts concurrently. Such an application results in individual work stations seeing a large variety of different parts., each of which may require many cutting tools. By the v.m.m. concept the solution to this problem would be to provide stations with a broad range of capabilities for tool management. Some stations might see only one type of tool during their entire operating life while others could be equipped with an automatic tool-changing system. The latter type would interchange tools between its spindle and a storage matrix. It is envisaged that station controllers would manage the entire inventory of tools assigned to the station. This management encompasses removal of tools from the storage matrix in the sequence: requirement, interchange at spindle nose, and finally return of tools to storage matrix.

6.4 *Work support system*

Part of a v.m.m. work station is the work support system. The concept is that of a single, standardised, floor-mounted housing to accommodate a variety of optional β axis indexing sub-systems. The alternatives are: no rotational capabilities; rotation with 5° resolution; rotation with 1/1000° resolution; and a full β cutting axis on which metal can be cut by rotation of the work (see Fig. 8).

The entire work support system is conceived as functioning at optional levels. The lowest level would be manual load and unload. The next level would be automatic interchange of two pallets or fixtures, with manually operated conveyers feeding the automatic workpiece-exchanging system. Finally there would be a level of completely automatic material handling, obtained by interfacing with a distribution conveyor loop under the control of the central data source.

6.5 *Optimising versus controlling*

Ideally, v.m.m. station controllers should be capable of optimisation logic functions. The philosophy of v.m.m. station controllers is that the *assignment* to be executed by a station is transmitted to the controller. The station controller is advised of the end objective and given jurisdiction over the *management of the station during the attainment of that objective.* Thus the speeds, feeds, cutting tool replacement, and etc. would be processed in a real-time mode and the response optimised by the station controller.

A v.m.m. work station under the control of the station controller could progressively increase its efficiency and reliability. Additional transducers and their associated signal-processing interfaces, enabling them to 'talk' to the station controller, might be incorporated. Thus, without substantial hardware modifications it would be theoretically possible to progressively upgrade the capability of the station by development of appropriate function-specific software packages.

6.6 *Specialisation versus standardisation*

A basic assumption in v.m.m. is that work stations would attain very high metal-cutting efficiency through rigid process specialisation. However, in spite of heavy emphasis on process specialisation, a high degree of standardisation, with all its associated economic advantages, is eminently practical. Success depends upon the ability to develop work stations having the proper balance between standardised and specialised elements. The analysis technique described earlier in this section showed how process-specialised spindle-carriers are developed. Such carriers can be analysed in terms of the structure and servo-systems required to support them and drive their respective family of cutters. This analysis could allow standardisation of the carrier support systems.

7.0 SYSTEM DESCRIPTION

On the v.m.m. concept a system consists of a group of work stations serviced by a material-handling system all operating under the control of a central data source. This section discusses some of the hardware which would be necessary to integrate individual work stations into a functioning system. The emphasis is on material handling.

7.1 *Work fixturing options*

Three optional means of preparing workpieces for introduction to the system are possible. The three accommodate the various part types, gemetries and production rates (see Fig. 9).

The first option is to mount the workpiece directly upon the deck of a reusable pallet. This pallet would have precision location, rigid clamping and be compatible with fixture building and clamping components. Such a solution is particularly suited to cases where a pre-machined face exists and where production quantities are relatively low.

The second option would be to mount a part in a conventional fixture previously located and clamped to a standard pallet,

The third option is for a single part produced at very high rates, or groups of compatible parts produced at modest rates, where multiple-part fixtures are normally required. In this last option the normal fixture base would be designed to accommodate the proprietary, Cincinnati-developed, coupling means. This solution offers an opportunity to maximise accuracy, minimise weight and lower the unit costs of the traditional fixture plus pallet.

7.2 *Staging area*

The staging area of a v.m.m. system is the area through which raw material enters the system and finished work departs. Here, too, fixtures and pallets flow in and out of both system and storage areas. The staging area for each system would of course have been tailored to meet the

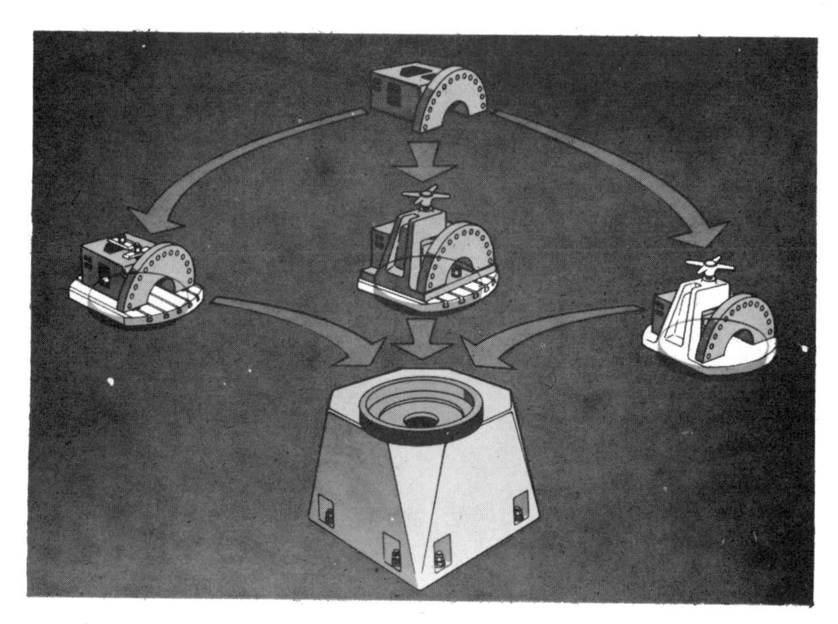

Fig. 9. Work support system.

special requirements of particular workpieces and production quantities etc. All such staging areas would be composed exclusively of standardised v.m.m. sub-system elements. A typical staging area might consist of a series of parallel conveyor units which may optionally be manpower-fed, gravity-fed, or power-fed. Production runs of individual workpieces would be prepared in advance of commitment to the system. This preparation would include the mounting of the first part in a queue to a pallet by one of the methods just described. Part/pallets in queues would then move toward a load and unload section of the staging area for commitment to the system. At the load and unload station the data link to the central data source would permit bilateral communication between the system operator and the central data source. Before commitment of the part to the system, the load station operator would request permission of the central data source to commit the part. The central data source would then consult a series of data files to determine whether:

1 the part was authorised for manufacture at that time
2 the quantity of parts corresponded to management-approved plan
3 modules required to produce that part were on line.
4 all cutting tools were at relevant work stations.

Should everything be acceptable, commitment to the system would follow.

7.3 *Work handling system*

In developing the v.m.m. concept, considerable thought has been given to the work-handling system. All of following requirements are mandatory.

1 To function completely automatically, from the load/unload station to the system and back to a designated sub-zone of the staging area for unloading.
2 To permit movement from any point in the system to any other without need for loading and unloading of individual stations to be 'time-locked' to each other.
3 To permit formation of queues ahead of the machine tools of each work station.

4 The total work-handling system to be laid out for ready accessibility to work stations.
5 To centralise the area occupied by conveying hardware, so permitting efficient control of coolant and efficient collection and processing of chips.

The work-handling system may be composed of the sub-systems for the conveying, distributing, delivery and discharge of pallets at work stations.

8.0 OPERATION AND CONTROL

'A *tool* is but the extension of man's hand and a *machine* is but a complex tool.' So said Henry Ward Beecher. This was the enlightened and prevailing view of the man/machine relationship up to the middle of this century. In a similar context, a v.m.m. manufacturing system may be described as an extension of the mind of man, his neural system, and the digital computer is the communication link between man's mind and the domain of manufacturing. It is therefore impossible to overstate the significance of the role of the digital computer and associated support software.

The contribution made by the digital computer to the v.m.m. programme started when the concept was little more than an assortment of tingling sensations in the neural systems of a few of us assigned to the project. Early work on the basic architecture of the system was evaluated by computer simulation techniques. Many problems associated with the architecture of individual work stations were uncovered and solutions optimised by computer simulation of the operation of the work stations. In many of these areas the solutions arrived at with the assistance of the computer were neither self-evident nor obtainable by other analytical techniques.

For example, the problems associated with the best configuration of a system to produce a particular mix of parts at varied but specified production rates represents an exercise in analysis well beyond the human mind. Picture the analysis involved for even a modest assortment of different part numbers. Take fifty parts and assume an average cutting tool requirement of sixteen tools per part. Produce them at rates per year varying from twenty to 5000. The problem is to find which part numbers in what combination should be committed simultaneously to the system, and the time duration for each part and the quantities that would give the best system load balance. All of these determinations must be made within a framework of system constraints in terms of cutting-tool storage capacity available at the various modules, the pallet saturation level of the various sections of the work-handling system, and so forth. The problem so stated is over-simplified, for in addition to these questions there are others: e.g. how many fixtures are required for the best balance between investment in production tooling and system characteristics?

In short, adequate support software packages are an essential part of the v.m.m. concept since they would be necessary to simplify and make practical the day-to-day solutions of such problems.

So far we have only mentioned the digital computer in the performance of off-line duties. An even more significant role is played in real-time-system operation, control and optimisation at the central data source and the station controllers of the system.

In this section we will describe three application areas where digital computers form cornerstones of the v.m.m. concept.

8.1 *Off-line use of computer*

The v.m.m. concept leans heavily on the existing in-house computer capability of a proposed user. Extensive use of the installation is required to efficiently exploit v.m.m. system potential. Four basic categories of work would be performed by the off-line computer: long range application planning, short-range application planning, part programming, and the generation of management data-system reports. Special v.m.m. software packages would be required for each of these areas.

Other software packages would be needed to inform management for decision on committing work to the v.m.m. system and on planning system extensions and modification. These duties would be executed by establishing:

1 The v.m.m. part-to-system profile for each candidate part being considered for commitment to the system. The 'part-profile' identifies the work content for each module in the system.
2 The date that each new part number is required and the quantities necessary per year.
3 Determination of the composite, per-year, long-term, work-load impact on an individual work station's capacity. Other system constraints would also have to be evaluated with respect to proposed work.
4 Long-term planning might involve the transfer of work between plants, minor or major modifications of the v.m.m. system, and modification of product programmes and related industrial engineering decisions.

The software strategy required for short-range planning has some commonality with that for long-range planning. However, there are major differences, in particular additional system constraints such as maximum storage density of cutting tools at various modules, saturation of the distribution loop of the conveyor system, availability of raw stock required for the part mix, availability of fixtures and/or pallets in the quantities required, etc. Upon approval of the plan by management, the computer would generate the print-outs required to implement the plan. These would include a list of part numbers to be introduced into the system and the sequence of introducing, manufacturing authorisation cards that will move fixtures and raw stock to the staging area, and cutting-tool identification cards to activate the tool crib to prepare cutting tools and install them in the appropriate tool-storage matrices at designated work stations.

The v.m.m. approach to part programming is not radically different from that used in conventional n.c. A primary difference is that individual machine tool modules are identified and machining operations are always related to specific work stations. Optimisation criteria would be included in the part program. Initially criteria would be such relatively simple ones as the maximum hours of usage for a particular cutter before replacement. As time passed optimisation would become progressively more sophisticated. The ultimate objective would be to give intelligence to the station controller to permit local optimisation logic to achieve the specified objective in the most efficient possible manner.

Another long-range objective in the part programming area involves development of contingency decisions at the time of part programming. The philosophy here is that, at the time of programming, the programmer poses the questions: *What is the preferred module in the system to perform this particular operation?*, and *If that module is not available, what is the next most efficient module, and if the second preference is not available, what would be the third?* The part programmer would then program these contingency solutions, which would automatically be applied by the system when the preferred module was not available owing to short-term overload, maintenance or some emergency requirement for a high-priority run.

Still another use of the off-line computer centre would be generation of management data-system reports. These would advise management of the actual performance of the v.m.m. system in relation to its planned performance. The reports would include a print-out of the parts produced and the percentage of available capacity utilised by individual modules or by other sub-elements of the system. The amount of available capacity lost would be included, and the assignable cause, i.e. down time for maintenance, raw material, tooling, want of cutter, etc.

8.2 *On-line use of computer*

The central data source of the v.m.m. system is conceived as managing real-time systems and controlling operation. This implies the receipt and processing of the short-term plan for system commitment, receipt and storage of part programmes, interfacing with the tool crib, and management of the entire perishable tool inventory in the system. The source would interface with the staging area, manage traffic flow in the system distribution conveyor loop, and relay part-program instructions and system management instructions to station controllers. In addition, the source would interface with the off-line computer for system status reporting (see Fig. 10).

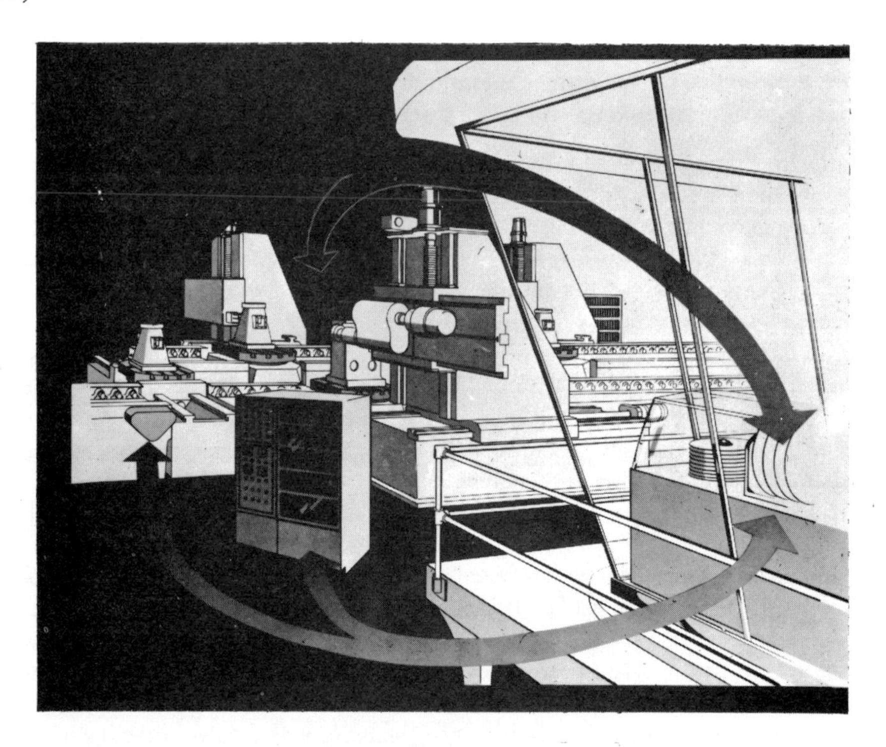

Fig. 10. System control.

The basic architecture and capabilities of the v.m.m. central data source, (c.d.s.) are conceived as follows.

1 Bilateral communication with the off-line computer, provided in optional ways depending on customer facilities and preferences. Part-programme data input by magnetic tape or by automatic interfacing with a high-density, direct-access, memory unit.
2 Input data required for a particular period of system operation transferred to a direct-access storage device, such as a disk or drum, within the c.d.s.
3 A high-speed, modern-architecture, digital computer as the functional centre on the c.d.s.

This computer would manage the transfer of data from a direct-access storage device into core storage, and subsequent transmission to the station controller, staging area, conveyor sub-sections, tool crib, off-line computer, print-out units, etc.

The v.m.m. concept also envisions a c.d.s. room equipped with a system status display panel, a typewriter for bi-directional communication with the computer, a read/write magnetic tape unit and a card reader. The precise make-up of the c.d.s. would vary to some extent, depending upon system size and the character of its production work.

8.3 *Station controller*

V.M.M. station controllers would have to have a high degree of electronic capability, with four input options:

1 Through a manual data input panel with or without a cathode ray tube display unit.
2 Through a tool management panel.
3 By a local tape transport and reader sub-system.
4 *Via* a duplexed communication link with the c.d.s.

9.0 SYSTEM EXPANSIBILITY

In developing the v.m.m. system concept, heavy emphasis has been placed on the real needs of manufacturing and the realities of the market place. This section describes some of the more significant system characteristics that relate to usefulness.

9.1 *In-field expansibility*

It was recognised early in the programme that the potential of the digital computer in its interaction with manufacturing was such that the final evolution would lead to a cybermatic factory. In such a facility the entire process of converting raw materials into saleable goods would be automatic under the direct, real-time control of central and satellite computers. This awareness led to the conclusion that all mechanical, electronic, and software designs must be able to grow from a single stand-alone work station (see Fig. 7) into a complete factory without any hardware or software obsolescence.

Also, this conclusion is closely related to our objective that v.m.m. systems offer a generalised solution to a very broad range of manufacturing problems. Involved is the requirement to produce a variety of part types made from different materials at many production rates. Such capability dictates a virtually unlimited series of optional work-station capabilities.

9.2 *Multi-mode offerings*

In-field expansibility would permit potential users to acquire systems consisting initially of only one work station with a station controller equipped with a conventional tape reader. As this first installation earns money for the user, the acquisition of additional like or unique modules may be considered. These early additions would function as independent stations, or be interfaced with sections of manual or power conveyor. As the system grew, and at a time dependent upon his application requirement, the user might add the c.d.s., automate the entire material handling system, and directly interface with the station controllers. Still further growth might call for multiple c.d.s. units and their associated work stations. At this growth stage several c.d.s. units would be interconnected and operated under the control of a central computer.

The process could continue until virtually the entire manufacturing cycle was being performed with v.m.m. systems.

9.3 *Software expansibility*

The principle of in-field expansibility in the hardware domain would also be applied to the software packages, both in the off-line computer area, the c.d.s. and the station controllers.

10.0 FINANCIAL CONSIDERATIONS

Financial considerations have played a dominant role throughout development of the v.m.m. concept. Some interactions with financial considerations are somewhat different than with conventional methods of manufacturing. A few of the more significant are discussed in this section.

10.1 *Long-term return on invested capital*

The fact that the v.m.m. system is designed for versatility in application and in-field expansibility provides a high level of assurance of long-term return on invested capital. This is unlike the investment in a fixed-mission, mechanised, manufacturing installation whose life is limited to the design life of a particular product. V.M.M. systems could produce an almost unending variety of parts at many production rates, and their useful life will be limited only by technological obsolescence.

10.2 *Predictable return on investment*

System simulation programs for v.m.m. are being developed to predict with high accuracy the return on invested capital. Through these programs it will be possible to take into consideration virtually all elements of cost as well as the special conditions of a particular environment.

System architecture is such that uninterrupted operations would be possible with individual work stations, or even sub-sections, taken off-line for servicing or repair. As a result, a v.m.m. system could be operated economically on a continuous basis. Large installations might use mutually supporting central data sources, so malfunction of a particular computer would not result in significant loss of productivity.

11.0 TOMORROW AND BEYOND

The basic philosophy is unstrained growth. This potential for growth is inherent throughout the system.

Virtually all known metalworking manufacturing processes, including those around tomorrow's corner, could be accommodated. It is even conceivable that completed parts could be inspected, sent to an assembly area, and automatically introduced to a cybermatic assembly system.

12.0 CONCLUSION

Since the middle of this century it has become increasingly difficult to determine the appropriate manufacturing response to new technologies. The advent of the electronic age and the digital computer dictates a fresh analytical approach. The concept of v.m.m. came into being when the deficiencies of today's manufacturing capabilities were shown up by the high-speed digital computer.

The progressive intrusion of the digital computer into the domain of manufacturing is well advanced, but harnessing this versatile genie to today's machine tools is not a forward and may well be a backward step. The vast potential of the computer challenges all concerned with the advancement of manufacturing arts and sciences to see beyond such applications of transitory and questionable benefits.

The digital computer is capable of planning, managing, and optimising the execution of all aspects of manufacturing. We know how to harness this capability to perform new tasks, to manage a new generation of work stations, and to integrate these into automatically operated systems.

The cybermatic factory does not strain the capabilities of the digital computer. Why settle for less?

REFERENCES

1 C. B. PERRY Variable-Mission Manufacturing System *32nd Anual Machine Tool Electrification Forum,* sponsored by Westinghouse Electric Corporation, Buffalo, New York, U.S.A. Paper No. 304-106N. p.2–4, 5-6 June 1968

2 M. McLUHAN. *Understanding Media.* New American Library. New York, U.S.A. pp.300–311 (1966).

3 C. B. PERRY 'Numerically Controlled Automation *American Society of Tool and Manufacturing Engineers Technical Paper No 468* Vol. 36. Book 1, pp. 3–5. 1963.

PRODUCTIVITY AND PROFITABILITY THROUGH THE MANUFACTURING SYSTEM CONCEPT

D. F. H. Rushton
Herbert-Ingersoll Ltd, Daventry

SUMMARY

The manufacturing system concept is explained as the logical approach to maximum profitability and productivity. It is necessary to define clearly what is expected of a manufacturing system in terms of productivity and profitability before the system can be described. The fundamental requirement is for balance between a responsive reaction to market situations and a demand for production efficiency. The balance can be precarious. Optimum solutions can be achieved only by studies in depth. The use of the professional system study reduces risk in investment decisions. Rapid advances make it desirable for many companies to supplement their own expertise with contributions from outside specialists in manufacturing technology. Examples of systems resulting from this approach are described, including the light machining system at Herbert-Ingersoll's own plant at Daventry.

1.0 INTRODUCTION

Most manufacturing businesses started and developed into healthy commercial ventures through the innovative and entrepreneurial abilities of the founder, and perhaps of his successors. From this background there has evolved over the last two hundred years a pattern of manufacturing facilities which are frequently less than adequately matched to the task they are required to perform. This paper describes the total system concept, which must necessarily be applied in the planning of new or updated manufacturing facilities in order to meet the requirements of profitability in today's economic and technological climate.

In the early years of manufacturing industry machine tools were purchased usually because the manufacturer had a production requirement which he could not meet with his existing facilities. Because most small firms existed by offering a general service to the local community (the narrow specialisation common today came much later), the manufacturer, when purchasing, would insist on many extra facilities in his machine tools. For example, until relatively recently most purchasers would insist on screw-cutting means in their lathes, though their actual requirement for this operation was low.

With the more rapid change in the value of money since the last war, as shown in Fig. 1, managements insist on more detailed justification of new purchases before order placement. Managers and production engineers in many firms have therefore concentrated on maximising the returns – usually interpreted in the limited sense of 'savings' – from each new investment. They have been under pressure to obtain the best performance, sometimes with ingenious modifications at low cost, from existing machine tools.

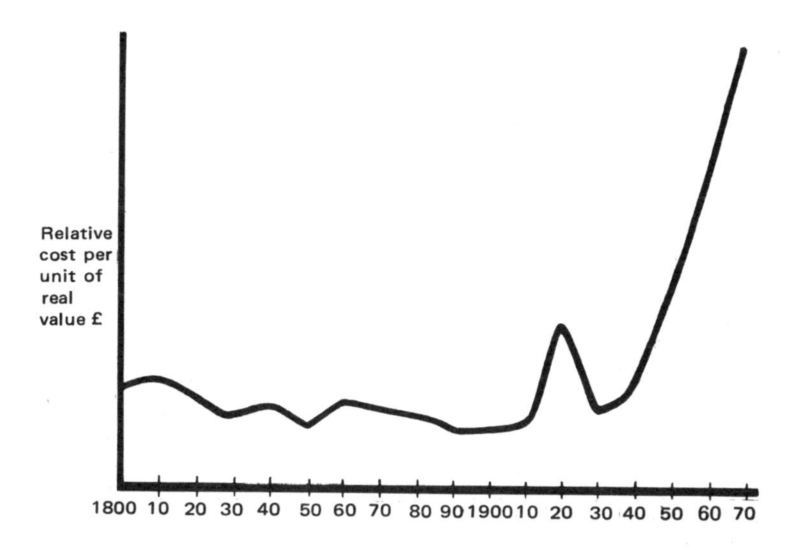

Fig. 1. Relative cost per unit of real value from 1800 to present time.

There is one example of the opposite situation – the automotive engine industry. The demand for motor-car engines is such that a reasonable 'life' can normally be expected. Allowing for revisions to accommodate model changes, and for manufacture of spares after the model ceases normal production, machinery can generally have a working life of perhaps ten years. Thus, each time a new engine has been introduced, it has become customary to install new equipment to make the crank-case, cylinder head or other transmission parts in the best way for the required quantities. Such equipment is normally of the kind known as a transfer line, and is limited in its application to the part for which it was designed.

The greater part of engineering production is not, however, in the mass-production automotive industry. It is in the thousands of factories that supply a wide variety of products, in ever-changing quantities, to an ever-changing and fickle market place. It is interesting how often, during early discussions with a manufacturer about his production problems, he says, 'Of course we are in the jobbing business' – even in industries where one would expect the quantities to approach mass production! With the average age of existing machine tools rising each year, and with money becoming ever less available, drastic steps must be taken to remain competitive and profitable. It is difficult to take these steps when one's eyes are focused on the image of the traditional jobbing shop.

Even in situations where the product is varied, and the quantities vary, careful planning of the entire manufacturing system can shorten the path to profitability.

2.0 THE MANUFACTURING SYSTEM CONCEPT

The fundamental requirement for profitability in each manufacturing situation is balance between the need for responsive reaction to market situations and the demand for production efficiency.

Fig. 2. Parts of ships' blocks produced by Brunel's system early last century. The first panel shows **the shell,** the centre panel shows the sheave, and the third shows the assembly.

We shall consider an early example of a manufacturing system before proceeding to a more detailed examination of the planning of a manufacturing system and the factors which affect this critical balance. This part of the paper will conclude with the practical steps necessary to achieve profitability from a manufacturing system.

2.1 *Portsmouth block-making machinery*

I am indebted to K. R. Gilbert and the Science Museum for the following information[1].

> The machinery for manufacturing ships' blocks which was set up in the Royal Dockyard at Portsmouth at the beginning of the 19th century is of historic importance as the first instance of the use of machine tools for mass production.

By 1808 the Portsmouth plant had a yearly output of 130 000 blocks. The complexity of the system that was required can be appreciated when the nature of the parts is considered. As Fig. 2 shows, and again in the words of Gilbert:

> A ship's block consists of at least three parts: a sheave or pulley, turning on a pin, in a shell. The shell is a shaped piece of elm, scored on the surface to hold a rope strap. The sheave is of lignum vitae and in the case of naval blocks was fitted with a bell-metal bearing called a coak. The pin formerly made of lignum vitae or other hardwood was usually since the mid 18th Century made of iron.

Marc Isambard Brunel – father of the famous railway engineer – conceived the then-novel system for total manufacture of the blocks. Through his brother-in-law, Kingdom, he offered it to the Taylors of Southampton, who since 1759 had been the principal suppliers to the Admiralty. Selling such an idea, however, was not an easy matter. Samuel Taylor replied to Brunel's offer by reciting the virtues of the current methods of manufacture and concluding in his letter:

> My father has spent many hundreds a year to get the best mode, and most accurate, of making the blocks, and he certainly succeeded; and so much so, that I have no hope of anything ever better being discovered, and I am convinced there cannot. At the present time, were we ever so inclined, we would not attempt any alteration. We are, as you know, so much pressed, and especially as the machine your brother-in-law has invented is wholly yet untried. Inventions of this kind are always so different in a model and in actual work.
>
> Believe me, dear Kingdom,
> Yours in great truth
> SAMUEL TAYLOR

In 1801, therefore, Brunel approached The Inspector General of Naval Works. He arranged for an order to be placed with Brunel by the Admiralty for the block-making machinery. Gilbert says, with some understanding:

> Taylor's complacency must have been rudely shattered when in 1803 because of the adoption of Brunel's proposals his contract was cancelled and renewed only on a short-term basis. By 24th March 1805 production by the machinery had reached a level at which it was possible for the Admiralty to discontinue the supply by the contractors.

Brunel devised the system to meet the required quantity of production, and overcame limitations by duplicating critical machines. The total system is believed to have comprised 45 machines of 22 varieties. Examples are illustrated in Figs. 3 and 4.

> The building of the machinery was the first large undertaking of the distinguished engineer Henry Maudslay and must have influenced machine-tool engineering through his own firm, Maudslay, Sons & Field, and through his employees who later became leading engineers and included such eminent figures as Richard Roberts, James Nasmyth, and Joseph Whitworth.

Clearly this manufacturing system was closely matched to the real need, which was to produce specific parts cheaply and in large quantities, and was so successful that it defeated the existing suppliers of blocks. That it was economic is indicated by the long useful life served by the machinery, and it is an interesting comment on its original quality that much of the system

Fig. 3. Brunel's mortising machine.

Fig. 4. Brunel's shaping engine.

is in tolerably good condition today. It must have made an exceptional return on the investment for its owners.

With the passage of time others introduced specialised manufacturing equipment, leading towards the high-production equipment of today. It would be less than realistic to claim that all have met the desired levels of productivity and profitability which their progenitors claimed. It is easier to be wise afterwards, but we almost always discover that the system was not precisely matched to the requirement – was designed without a sufficiently deep understanding of economic as well as technical aspects of the problem. A system can only be successful if its planners have a very deep understanding of all aspects of the manufacturing task, both technical and economic.

2.2 *Planning a manufacturing system*

To *understand* the real needs for a manufacturing system is a prerequisite to their satisfaction. One must be able to answer some key questions.

What is the final object of the exercise? To:

- produce a return on a new investment?
- increase the return on present investment?
- eliminate losses?
- improve and keep delivery promises?
- make a new product?
- increase production?

and so on. When the object has been attained what will be the values of:

- return per annum on new capital?
- production level?
- work in progress?
- delivery promises?
- selling price?

and so on.

What obstacles stand in the way of achieving these conditions? Examples could be:

- lack of adequate production control, lack of control of tools, fixtures etc.
- excessive lead times in the shop
- inadequate space to perform efficiently
- inadequate handling facilities

and so on. What must be done to overcome the obstacles?

In addition, of course, detailed knowledge is required of the parts to be made, production quantities, accuracies required, and probable future capacity requirements.

To obtain such deep understanding of the manufacturers' needs requires that the machinery builder and the manufacturer work together in a manner altogether different from that which results from the issue of purchase enquiries to a selection of potential suppliers. When preparing such enquiries a prospective purchaser thinks in terms of machine specifications, of preconceived solutions. An objective approach to a manufacturing system must be directed to the task.

We must be TASK-oriented – *not* MACHINE-oriented.

Many companies delay planning new or additional facilities until their sales curves rise. They are not prepared to face the 'risk' of such forward thinking, or any expenditure for the future.

when sales are low. This however is the very time when forward planning is best done. In the absence of previous planning a quick reaction to a sharp rise in sales leads to the purchase of equipment, on short delivery, which may not have been adequately matched to the real requirement, and tends to perpetuate traditional manufacturing methods. Such investments can rarely provide the returns which can be gained from innovative solutions making best practical use of the latest technology – these need time to plan and procure. It is essential that the planning stage be completed before the critical need to order machinery is reached. Some expenditure, whether internal or external, must be made on planning ahead of the traditional business cycle. The best solutions can only be devised when there is time to think the problem through.

Having understood the objectives and nature of the problem we can now proceed to the weighing of the various interactive factors.

2.3 *The critical balance*

Consideration of plans for new manufacturing plant normally falls within the professsional duties of the production engineer. He makes recommendations to management, at least when major expenditure is involved. Something of an idealist, the production engineer knows what he would like. He would:

1 choose as few models as possible, preferably only one
2 seek the co-operation of the design department to get maximum notice of proposed changes or new models
3 like accurate market forecasts from the sales department so that the capacity of the plant could be matched to the anticipated requirement at a constant level of output
4 recommend highly productive machinery (if the quantities were sufficient, of transfer-line type) to maximise output with minimum labour and part handling.
5 liaise with the purchasing manager to ensure planned receipt of e.g. castings or other raw material, to minimise investment in inventory

At this point practical considerations weigh heavily and many production engineers enter, like Pilgrim, the Slough of Despond. They cannot imagine their industry behaving thus ideally.

Why is it that such ideal conditions frequently do not, or cannot, exist? Could it be because continued profitability ultimately depends on the ability of a company to make the RIGHT goods at the RIGHT price at the RIGHT time, and SELL them to someone who has a need?

Consider the entrepreneurial aspects of the same business. What factors would assist the company to respond correctly and rapidly to changing market requirements? To each of the production engineer's desires there is a marketing counter-claim:

1 Many models or designs satisfy more potential customers
2 Flexibility permits rapid design changes at short notice
3 A 'flexible' labour force enables the manufacturer to raise or lower production to suit the current market level
4 Minimum investment in equipment and tooling aids flexibility and eases new design
5 High stocks of material and work in process to facilitate rapid response to a wide variety of orders for different models or products.

We can now see the problem in its true perspective. There is only one current level of investment which the manufacturer can make for his business – that investment which will produce, when properly applied, the maximum continuing profitability for his company.

To achieve the desired solution to the problem management must correctly balance, not only the individual items discussed, but the total effects allowing for interaction between the factors involved, and at the correct level of investment. This balance, illustrated in Fig. 5, is fundamental to the success of any system.

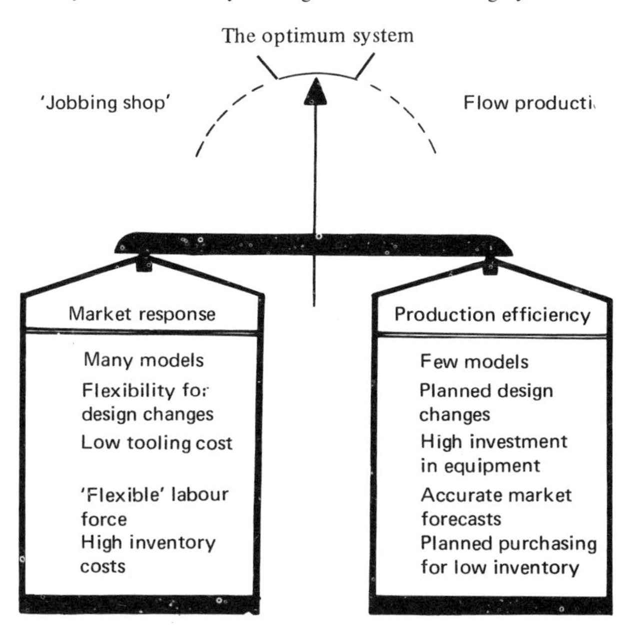

Fig. 5. The optimum system is obtained at balance. Achievement of balance requires a *bold step,* not piecemeal improvements.

3.0 EXAMPLES OF MANUFACTURING SYSTEMS

If we consider the differences between high-volume production as in a transfer line, and low-volume production of different parts, we see how the balance changes.

In a transfer line the movement of parts is controlled automatically, and, because the cutting tools have been designed as part of the machine, they are both efficient and long-lived. There is thus a high investment in productive metal-cutting time, quality control is built into the system, and the problems of control of work are minimal.

On the other hand, the flexible, numerically controlled, machining centre is capable of performing many operations on one workpiece, again at relatively high capital cost. In this instance, however, there is only one spindle, cutting (with standard tools) for a smaller proportion of the shift hours. Certainly the sequencing of operations on one part has eliminated problems of production control or work flow, but a relatively low proportion of the capital has been invested in productive metal-cutting – the remainder has gone on supporting services built into the machine. The question of the level of investment and the balance between the conflicting demands is thus more critical, since a smaller part of the capital is being used to get effective chip-making capacity.

In the traditional jobbing shop, with groups of similar machines, and work patterns involving movement between each operation, the major problems of management are again not in metal-cutting. They are in controlling the flow of work to minimise inventories, in providing the services to machines to enable them to produce, and in providing inspection to control quality. The utilisation of spindles on machines is normally low, and large numbers of machines are required to achieve required production levels. Clearly, if the flow of work could be controlled, and at the same time the level of inventories, not only would production in shorter lead times be possible, but more capital could be invested in meeting this improved situation.

In the early days of production engineering nearly all problems centred on metal cutting – so the technologies of cutting advanced rapidly. But the techniques of handling, work flow, knowing the exact location of work, providing the tools and services to the machines to permit higher cutting times per machine, and of controlling inventories have advanced rapidly in the last decade. This is due to the computer, which has helped not only when directly applied, but also because systematic definition of problems and analysis of results have accompanied its introduction.

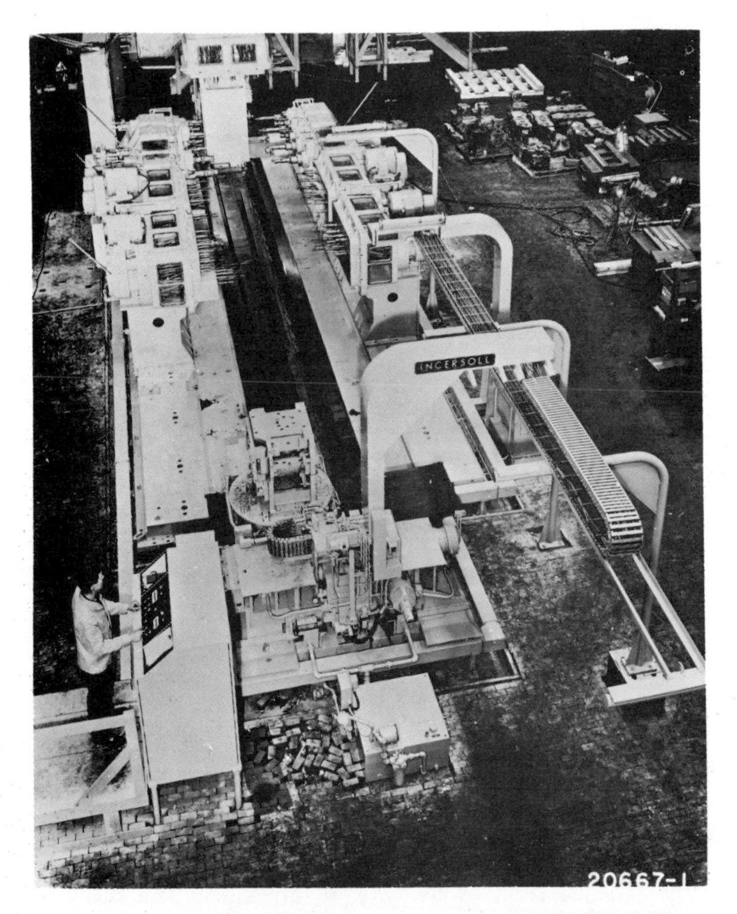

Fig. 6. Flexible system for production of a variety of tractor transmission parts.

Fig. 6 shows an early example of a machining system involving numerical control (n.c.) and incorporating many such principles. It is the X.30 line, built by Ingersoll for a well known manufacturer of earth-moving equipment. One of a number of transmission parts can be placed on the pallet, and the machine will carry out a full sequence of operations under numerical control. When the tape is changed other parts can be machined by the same system. There is provision for stations to be added in the future.

A second example, also in low-volume production, is shown in Fig. 7. It is part of the cylinder-block line built for a Continental manufacturer of truck engines. The production rate is

Fig. 7. Portion of a flexible cylinder-block line capable of handling families of cylinder-blocks, both in-line and vee, with different numbers of cylinders.

low – four to eight blocks per hour depending on type – but the line is capable of handling thirteen families of cylinder blocks (in-line and vee formations) with different numbers of cylinders. Several of the machines in this line are numerically controlled. Further examples of this type of approach are indicated in Figs. 8 and 9. Note that there is a common location on the pan rail or sump face, and common alignment of the crankshaft bore[2].

In another system, more recently designed to handle ten families of parts, or a total of about 180 different parts at a volume of 100 000 parts per year, it was decided that eighteen machines provided the optimum system. However, when the logistics of work flow and the provision of n.c. tapes were studied, it was found that an on-line process computer was required to handle the information and direct the eighteen individual machine tools. Financial justification for this could be found if it only acted as a giant tape reader and eliminated the filing and handling of some 2500 tapes. But more detailed investigation showed that it was capable of assisting much more in other ways. I shall return to this subject later (see 5.5.1).

In the grouping of parts into families requiring similar operations we see the application of what has come to be known as *group technology*. The principles of group technology have long been practised by Ingersoll in making systems for manufacturing related groups of parts such as have been described in this paper.

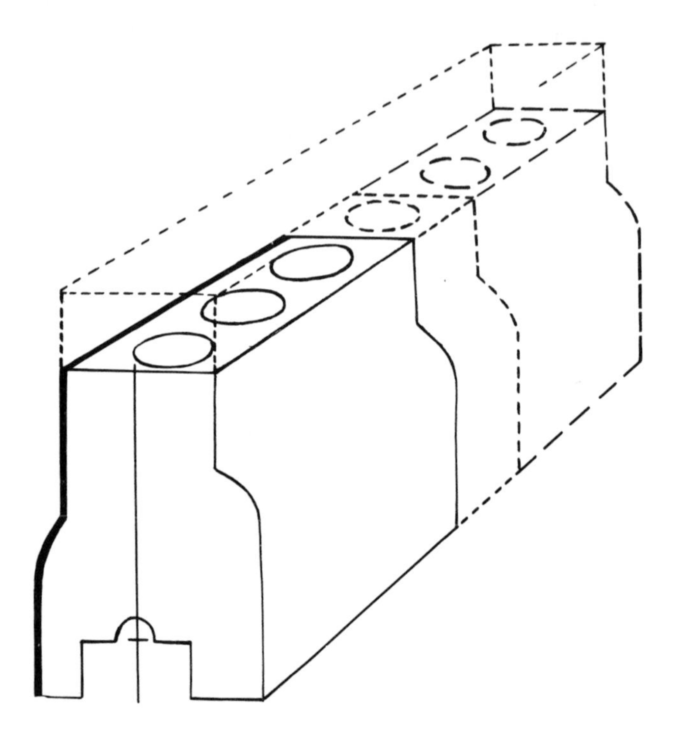

Fig. 8. One transfer line can make cylinder blocks of similar configuration in three different lengths and two different heights for a total of six different blocks.

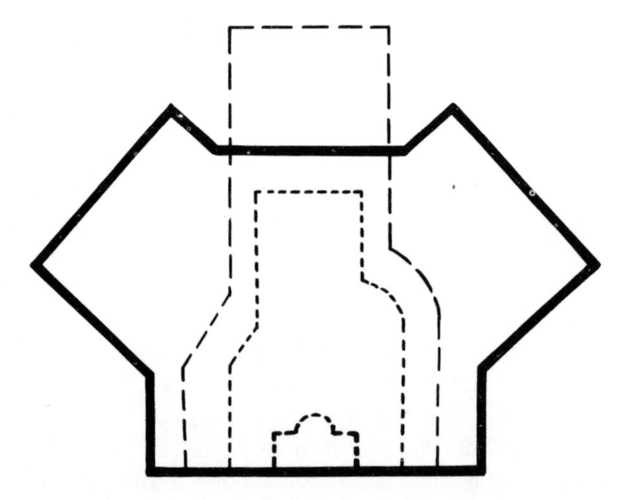

Fig. 9. An advanced transfer line can turn out cylinder blocks of dissimilar configuration. In this case in-line blocks, V-blocks, and slanted-top blocks of varying sizes can be turned out on one line.

4.0 SEVEN STEPS TO AN ADVANCED MANUFACTURING SYSTEM

I have referred to the new type of relationship between supplier and purchaser that is necessary to plan what Herbert-Ingersoll call an *advanced manufacturing system,* i.e. a system matched to the precise needs of the task. Such a detailed co-operative 'partnership in planning' may require special attention, particularly if the problem is complex, the purchaser has limited production engineering staff, or he wishes to obtain a time advantage. A new approach will be discussed in the next section.

To keep the total task in perspective Herbert-Ingersoll list seven steps to the optimum performance of a manufacturing system.

1 Planning the system
2 Engineering the system
3 Building the system
4 Testing the system
5 Installing the system
6 Starting up the system
7 Managing the system

The partnership which commences at step 1 – the planning phase – should continue until the objectives are achieved at step 7.

Ingersoll have had this approach to manufacturing problems, informally, for nearly eighty years. In the last few years, through the professional system-study subsidiary Ingersoll Incorporated, they have conducted over eighty studies of manufacturing systems.

5.0 THE PROFESSIONAL SYSTEM STUDY

We have seen the need to find optimum solutions to complex problems, solutions which are vital to the long-term health of any company – and we have also seen that such solutions can only be arrived at by a study in depth of the problems concerned. We refer to the organised, *systematic approach* to a manufacturing problem as a *system study.* It is conducted in a highly professional, totally objective manner. It begins with the TASK, continues with consideration of alternative SOLUTIONS, and ends with comparison of RESULTS.

5.1 *Problem definition*

The first phase is to obtain a thorough understanding of the specific task facing the manufacturer. During this phase a small team works in the client's plant, co-operating closely with the resident staff, who have a deep knowledge of their products, their current methods and their problems. The result of this joint work is a deep, penetrating 'problem definition' which is accepted by all concerned as the best representation of the facts. This understanding is reviewed with the client company executives at all levels, and agreement on the ground work for the study is obtained.

5.2 *Development of alternative solutions*

The second phase, in which alternative solutions are devised, involves creative work by specialists in many fields, combined with the wide experience of 'generalists' in manufacturing problems.

Technology is advancing very rapidly – in cutting tool techniques, in raw materials, of which metals are only one group, in new control methods, in computer applications, in electrical, electronic and electrochemical techniques. It is only with a widely spread, widely experienced team that the latest appropriate developments in technology in all fields can be made available to each manufacturer, through the medium of the system study. This is a difficult task for a company concerned with its own day-to-day problems, and in the longer term with the successful development of its own product group in the competitive field. It is work which requires specialists in a team whose expertise is in manufacturing technology, and who are up to date with the latest technological developments in their own field.

5.3 *Measurement of results*

The alternative solutions have to be judged against the technical requirements and economic factors, so that the optimum system may be planned while giving full weight to all relevant factors.

Further, when various solutions are considered at different investment levels, it is possible to identify which system will give the best return on investment – in fact to decide the optimum *level of investment.*

The detailed proposals in the alternative solutions are fully discussed at all stages with the client's executives, both those who are profit-oriented and those who are production-orienated. This is characteristic of system study in combining two types of knowledge – that of the client and the professional adviser – to achieve the overall best result.

5.4 *Timing of a study*

At this point it is relevant to consider the timing of a system study.

If the investment decision is to be *right,* the study should be completed before any commitment is entered into for the new project. The frequent practice of ordering major equipment on long delivery at the preliminary planning stage is clearly not right, for a study in depth may reveal solutions of a radically different nature which could offer attractive investment possibilities.

When a major investment in plant is under consideration the decision sought is probably among the most important to be taken by the client in a decade. Clearly it is desirable to take sufficient time to permit the planning of the optimum solution. A few months of time well spent at this stage can result in vastly different returns on the ultimate investment.

5.5 *Examples of systems resulting from studies*

5.5.1 *High-output transfer line*

Turning to examples of systems which have resulted from systematic study of specific problems, it is interesting to consider one of the most recent. The case was that of a high-output automotive transfer line.

The objective was defined as: *To manage a transfer line efficiently by making available meaningful data and good communications.*

Observations on the existing transfer line revealed two major factors:

- The large proportion of stoppages of short duration, when the line would be running again before the cause could be established by the supervisor
- The loss of production from some machines owing to inadequate flow of blocks caused by other hold-ups in the line

Analysis of these and many minor problems showed that action was required to:

- minimise downtime, but inform the superintendent immediately of the causes
- provide performance data permitting the right managerial decision to be taken

After much more precise analysis of the requirements in each of these areas a 'production control centre' was designed. This consists essentially of an on-line process computer with two television screens built into the control console. There is a typewriter facility for interrogation purposes. The console constantly shows current performance data and other relevant information, enabling the superintendent to minimise downtime and get the best production and accuracy.

Lights show when predetermined functions on the line operate late or incorrectly. The superintendent can, by pressing a button, have the cause displayed on a screen. Decision may be taken and the legend discarded, or the image may be transferred to a second screen for retention and later decision or action. Items of planned maintenance can be brought to the screen before they are due so that the optimum use may be made of any unplanned downtime. Any information on either screen can be printed out by the typewriter for retention.

What has this achieved?

Basically it has removed the decision point from one of a number of operators on the line, each unaware of current happenings elsewhere, and placed total information in the hands of the superintendent. He is then enabled to take optimum decisions to maximise production and minimise downtime of the *whole* line.

5.5.2 *Manufacturing system for large components*

It is more unusual to contemplate the idea of a manufacturing system in a heavy general engineering shop, but one system study was completed in a well known British company with this objective.

Precisely, the objectives were defined as: *To reduce manufacturing costs, reduce cycle times, reduce part handling and set-up, and to improve management control of the flow of work.*

Careful study in the shop, handling parts over 20 ft long, 15 ft wide and 8 ft high, revealed that the real problem areas were:

- The need to eliminate post-machining handwork
- The loss of production time owing to single-station loading
- Excessive work-handling necessitated by multiple machining operations
- The amount of marking out for drilling and similar operations

The system had three basic requirements:

- FLEXIBILITY to cater for even larger parts in the future, and a largely unknown part mix but with definite trends in product policy.
- TECHNICAL ACCURACY which, on such large parts, could be achieved without subsequent handwork only by adopting the portal type of machining centre for precision combination boring and milling.
- PROFITABILITY

Five alternative 'total systems' were considered. They were appraised financially with the client. The system finally chosen included three large machines with double tables to replace thirteen previous machines. Numerical control was introduced for drilling, which was separated from milling and boring. Digital readout facilities were recommended for the latter. The total system is planned to cut set-up and handling times by 50%, reduce man hours by 74% for machining, and certain other benefits.

The attack on the total system was of prime importance.

5.6 *What system study does*

In sum, a system study is objective – it is pursued to find the best way to make parts in the right production volume. Participants in the study consider impartially the best ways, irrespective of the source of the needed equipment, and make objective recommendations based on practical knowledge, recommendations which can be applied in practice.

A system study provides deep understanding for management of the implications of investments – and reduces the risk in the decisions which have to be taken. It involves a deep knowledge of matters which are of the highest commercial importance to the client company. It can only work successfully when there is a clear acceptance of the commitment by both parties, and complete confidentiality is maintained.

The system study is the first or planning phase of the seven steps to an advanced manufacturing system. A good deal of information resulting from the study can be used in preparation for production and in setting standards for management in step 7 (see 4.0). The achievement of these planned standards is essential if the user is to reap full benefits from his investment at the earliest time. At Herbert-Ingersoll we believe that the partnership in planning which commences with the system study is not complete until builder and user have combined to show achievement of the planned returns.

6.0 MANUFACTURING SYSTEM AT HERBERT-INGERSOLL, DAVENTRY

The system built into the new plant at Daventry in 1967 was devised to meet a special need – after a study in depth of the problems involved. Targets were set for productivity and profitability well in advance of the stage traditional in the British machine tool industry.

6.1 *Problem definition*

The business of the company closely follows that of its American parent, Ingersoll Milling Machine Co. – building special machines.

Most of these form parts of total manufacturing systems devised after methodical study of the manufacturing task. The machine parts have therefore to be produced in one-off or very-small-batch (2-6 off) quantities. Experience showed that sequential loading of large parts in carefully planned positions on the tables of the larger machines enabled Ingersoll to control the flow of large parts in their shop. Small parts, requiring light machining, set a very different problem.

The wide variety of small parts required in complex machine tools, and the inability to predict part movement on a set sequence of operations, called for a system with inherent flexibility. The Ingersoll shop at Rockford was largely traditional in grouping similar machines by function. This resulted in the traditionally common problems, namely how to:

- ensure availability of small parts to meet assembly requirements
- know where any part was at any time
- provide the right tools at the right place at the right time
- maximise output from a given number of machine tools and men

In the new plant for Daventry the company sought to:

- achieve a high output per man employed – two or three times the U.K. national average for the industry
- control the flow of work to ensure availability for assembly and permit achievement of guaranteed delivery dates
- minimise work-in-process inventory
- minimise handling of work

6.2 *Analysis and solution*

Because of the general similarity of work in the new shop to that at Rockford it was possible to analyse one year's volume of the machining load by function. This was done from examin-iation of the routing cards.

A movement diagram showed that certain machine groupings could advantageously reduce part movement. An experimental group of machines was selected, and the problem of handling 'job packages' (comprising workpieces, routing sheets, drawing job tickets, tools, gauges) was defined.

An outside firm of handling engineers, Rapistan, devised the system of conveyors and pallets, and an experimental installation was made with the group of machines in Rockford as shown in Fig. 10.

Basically, a tool control centre, staffed by a superior type of setter/operator, was linked by bench-level conveyors to each machine. A lower-level conveyor provided for return of finished work to the control centre. Experience with this prototype system showed the need for a direct communication link between controller and machine operator. A two-way microphone/ loudspeaker system was installed.

The need for a machine operator to leave his machine, except for personal reasons, had now been eliminated. Provided with an adequate flow of complete 'job packages' he could concentrate his efforts on 'producing chips'.

6.3 *Implementation*

The Daventry handling system was designed and constructed by handling engineers. Complementary handling systems were provided. Thus, incoming material, stored and cut to size in an efficiently equipped material-handling area, is carried to the work stations by a driverless tractor train. The trailers have roller tops at the same level as the Rapistan conveyors, so work lifting is minimised. In the light machine shop each operative has a pendant-controlled pillar crane to assist in machine loading. Off-line setting on sub-tables has increased the utilisation of knee-type milling machines and DeVleig borers.

Most of the machine tools are connected directly to an underground flume system which removes all swarf to a central separation plant. Lubricating oil is also piped to the machines, which have automatic lubrication systems. All plant services are built into the roof space so that their maintenance does not involve the production area. A heat-treatment department at the middle of the machine shop has an air curtain so that, although access is not hampered, the shop temperature is not altered when furnaces are opened.

6.4 *The human element*

Having described the technical aspect of this advanced manufacturing system, I think it important to state that considerable efforts have been made to improve the human climate so that production can proceed efficiently.

The company's employee relations policy, not only expressed but also demonstrated, is that all employees will be treated fairly and as individuals. The company endeavours to create a climate of co-operation wherein all employees do willingly what is asked and expected of them. Performance is formally reviewed at regular intervals. It is recognised that there will be differences of opinion between individual employees and their supervisors. When these differences arise the company listens carefully to the individual and shows that it is willing to change its view if the

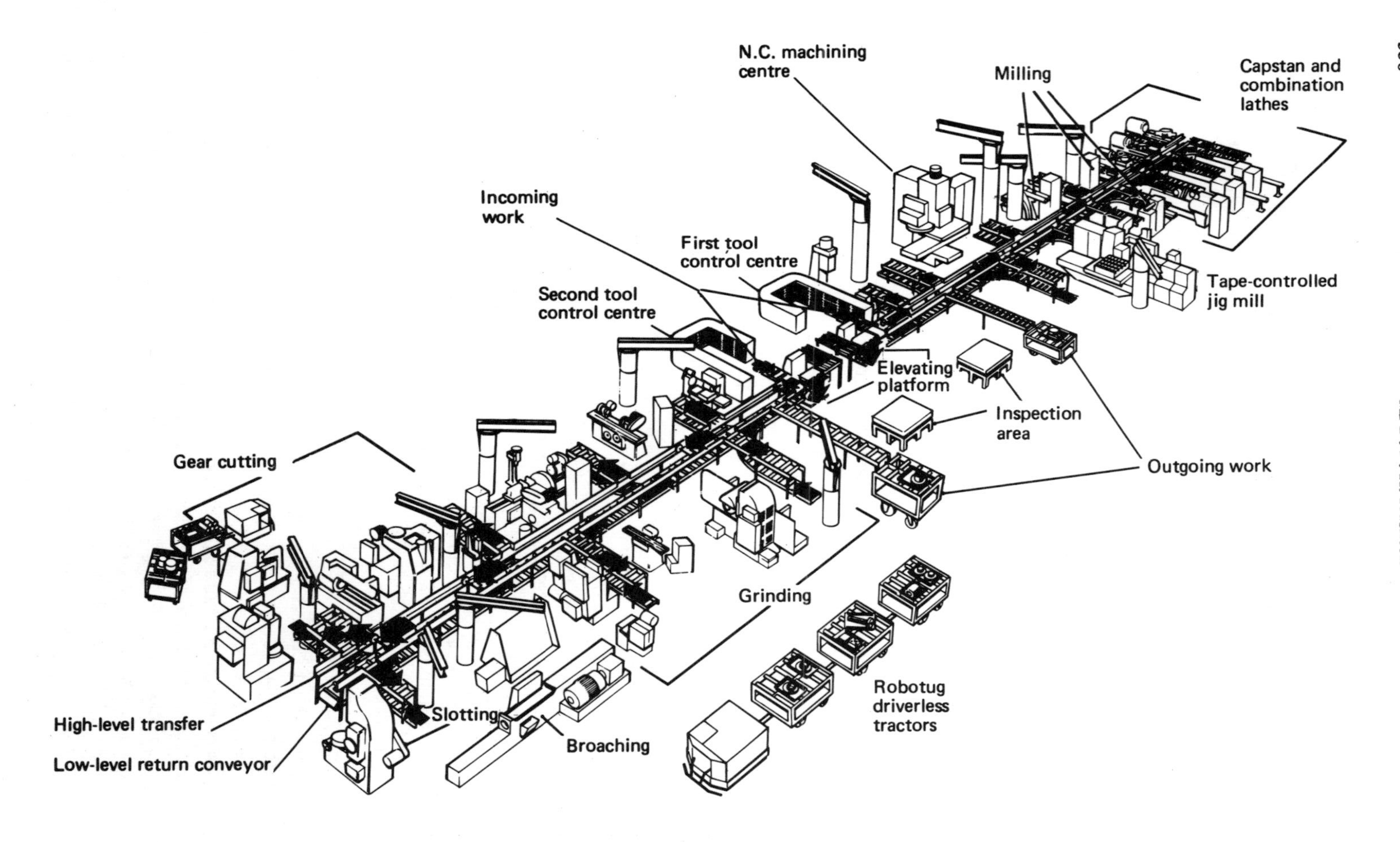

Fig. 10. Integrated light machining area at Herbert-Ingersoll, Daventry. Automatic conveyors move work between control centres and machining stations. Transport between areas is by driverless tractor train.

employee gives new insight into the situation. The company will go as far as it can to explain its position so that the employee understands why a certain decision has been taken.

The company recognises that management will err, and wants its decisions to be reviewed by others when relations between the company and its employees are involved – hence the 24 hour rule. Under the 24 hour rule any employee raising a question with his superior is entitled to an answer in 24 hours. Failing a satisfactory answer he is responsible for progressing the matter to the next higher level. Each level has a 24 hour time span and in this way a query raised on Monday morning can be heard in the Managing Director's office by the following Friday.

The company has consciously tried to break the work-staff barrier that normally exists in industry. From labourer to managing director, all employees are salaried and have individual contracts with the company. Classless car-parks and restaurant demonstrate this philosophy to some extent.

6.5 *Performance*

The aim in setting up this advanced manufacturing facility was an output per man considerably higher than that current in the British machine tool industry. The achievement to date has been stated to be about twice the national average for this industry – and is still rising.

At present the weekly shop load is prepared manually by the routing department. Shortly production control will be computerised. Ultimately the direct linking of machine tools to the computer will be possible. The first necessary step which has been achieved is a manual system which works effectively. In the words of the director of manufacturing, 'it is the best tool we have found to help us control the flow of work in our shop'.

7.0 MANAGEMENT RESPONSIBILITY FOR INVESTMENT DECISIONS

The foregoing examples of total systems, including that at Herbert-Ingersoll, demonstrate that, when the particular managements want the most profitable system for their manufacturing tasks, they are willing to accept responsibilities to make this possible.

The first is the responsibility to see that time is available to plan the desired manufacturing system before the date of order placement is reached.

The second is the responsibility to take the correct investment decision. This involves many more factors than the purely technical or the purely financial – essential though they are. It requires an intimate knowledge of the market, forward trends, product plans and other critical determinants.

Management cannot delegate its real responsibility of decision to a subordinate in any one of the several specialist fields. It must face the responsibility, recognise that it takes time but is vital to the business, and get involved.

8.0 CONCLUSION

The title of this paper is *Productivity and profitability through the manufacturing system concept.* We have considered what that concept is and how a professional system study provides practical means for planning such a system by combining the best local knowledge with outside expert advice. We have given instances of significant advances in productivity and profitability obtained by a radically new approach instead of the linear expansion of present practices.

We know that the advanced system involves extra risk. We know that technology is changing rapidly. We know that the best system available today will not be the leader in five to eight years' time, yet we have to grasp this opportunity firmly if we are to improve our competitive position. We have to find that combination of speed, reliability, lower costs, consistent accuracy and flexibility which we need for our particular manufacturing problem. The total manufacturing system concept is a sure approach to the optimum result.

ACKNOWLEDGEMENTS

Figs. 1, 5, 6, 7, 8, 9 and 10 are reproduced by courtesy of Herbert Ingersoll Ltd, who hold the copyright. Figs. 2, 3 and 4 are reproduced by courtesy of the Science Museum, London, and Crown copyright is reserved.

REFERENCES

1 K. R. GILBERT. *The Portsmouth blockmaking machinery.* H.M.S.O., London, 1965.

2 H. WALTER LEWIS. 'Centralised control of manufacturing systems'. *32nd Ann. Machine Tool Electrification Forum.* Buffalo, N.Y., 1968.

NUMERICAL CONTROL OF MACHINE TOOLS IN AN INTEGRATED MANUFACTURING SYSTEM

B. J. Davies
Staveley Engineering and Research Centre

SUMMARY

The paper describes some of the requirements of integrated manufacturing systems from the production engineering aspect. These considerations form the background to the design of different levels of the Staveley Integrated Manufacturing System (S.I.M.S.) which is being developed. One machine tool in this system is described. Considerations cover n.-c. machine tools, automatic transfer of work between machines, on-line computer control, trials of a new component on an integrated manufacturing system, software, fail safe, self-checking and servicing.

1.0 INTRODUCTION

The ability of a numerically controlled machine tool to accept data produced automatically from a computer, and the increasing capital cost of n.-c. machine tools and their peripheral hardware, are causing an increasing concentration by users and manufacturers on the n.-c. machine tool as part of a manufacturing concept rather than a product complete in its own right. Some of the effects of this trend on production engineers and on machine tool and control equipment manufacturers can already be seen, but in general the effects and problems have not yet made much impact on n.-c. usage in this country. This paper deals with some of the implications of the Manufacturing System concept on manufacturing from the point of view of a machine tool builder. These implications form the background to the development, now under way, of the Staveley Integrated Manufacturing System (S.I.M.S.) which, in its various stages and forms, implements the Manufacturing System concept.

2.0 N.-C. MANUFACTURING SYSTEMS

The configuration of n.-c. manufacturing system selected depends on the type and batch-size of workpiece. Technically, the competence now exists to build very sophisticated n.-c. manufacturing systems.

2.1 *N.-C. machine tools*

N.-C. metal-cutting machine tools are required for all stages up to completely automatic operation. The functions required include multi-axis contouring, automatic tool change, and workpiece change, and automatic control of swarf removal and coolant. An example of this type of machine is shown in Fig. 1. It is a machining centre type of machine, capable of machining a workpiece completely with operator supervision. Operator intervention is necessary for a change in type of component which requires different sets of tools and different tapes.

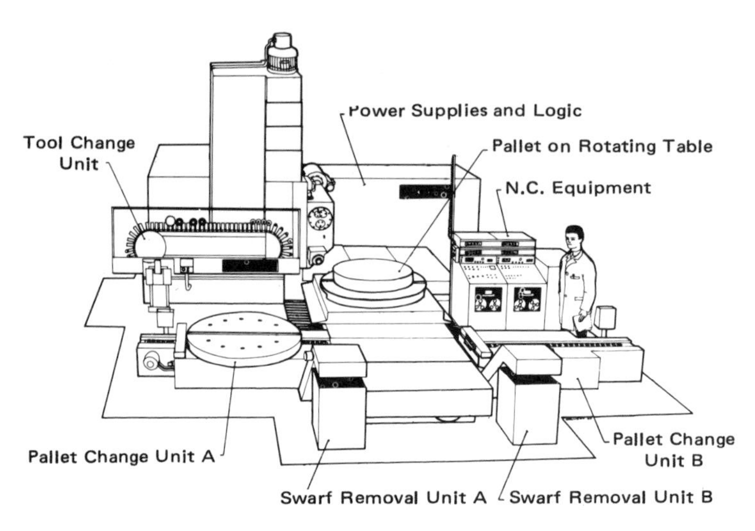

Fig. 1.

Machining centres are n.-c. manufacturing systems in the simplest form and have become established as a most important type of n.-c. machine tool.

3.0 AUTOMATIC WORK TRANSFER BETWEEN MACHINES

In some cases the machining centre type of machine illustrated cannot complete a workpiece because machining is required which is outside its capabilities. For example, turning may be required on the same workpiece. In some cases, for a given family and batch-size of components, it is more costly to use a machining centre with the required range of machining performance (speed range, metal removal, accuracy, etc.), under the production limitation that only one tool may be used at any one time, than it is to use a group of simpler n.-c. machines. In either case work transfer is required. This can be provided at all stages, in form varying from transfer between substantially independent machines to completely automatic and accurate loading, unloading, checking and routing work-transfer.

The machining centre shown in Fig. 1 has a standard pallet which can be transferred to another machine such as a vertical turning lathe.

Separate machining centres such as the one referred to have some provision for minimising the non-productive time in which the type of component being made is changed. An automatic pallet-loading facility permits different workpieces to be loaded in sequence, with no increase in non-productive time.

Pallet location on machine tools in an integrated manufacturing system is more difficult than on machining centres because it has to be accurate enough for the most accurate operation required in the line. Repeatability of pallet location between machines may therefore have to be not worse than a few tenths of a thousandth of an inch. As with all machines capable of presenting different sides of a workpiece to a machine, pallet location errors can double normal machining errors. The machine shown incorporates automatic checking of pallet location.

Many pallets are required in an integrated manufacturing system and the cost can be considerable. Some stations, such as those for rough milling and drilling, do not themselves need high pallet accuracy.

One step which can sometimes be taken to minimise cost is to limit all finish machining to a conventional accurate machining centre which is the last unit in an integrated manufacturing system. In this way the accuracy required for interchangeability becomes unnecessary.

A simple automatic pallet-transfer system between machines, as advocated for example by Pera, is a strictly sequential system in which each pallet goes to each machine in turn. The machines are grouped so that machining operations can be shared – the milling machines can, for example, drill. In this way it can be arranged that the machining time at each unit is approximately the same.

More elaborate systems provide means of routing components to stations in any order and of omitting stations if required. Such systems require additional software and hardware, but are more versatile and can cope better with breakdowns if units are duplicated.

4.0 RETOOLING A MANUFACTURING SYSTEM

Retooling a transfer line is a substantial operation. A similar operation has to be carried out on an integrated manufacturing system with minimum down-time. The machining centre shown in Fig. 1 incorporates an arm by means of which the tool store may be loaded and unloaded with manual intervention while the machining cycle is being carried out. Two tape readers are provided so that tape-changing time is not unproductive. The machining centre is fitted with a conventional n.-c. system.

Provided that the economics are correct for the volume and type of component, the change-over between different workpieces can be completely automated in the S.I.M.S.

The arm provided can load and unload the tool magazine automatically from pallets of tools which are transferred to the machine automatically by a similar, or the same, pallet transfer mechanism which is used to transfer workpieces. Most of the loading and unloading of tool magazines can take place during machining time.

It should be noted that the number of tools required at individual stations of an integrated manufacturing system is normally less than that required on a single machining centre. The introduction of integrated manufacturing systems will give a substantial impetus to the standardisation of tool-holders, preferred sizes of tools and codes for tools.

Most machining centres and integrated manufacturing systems use tools which preset to length and/or diameter. The Molins System 24 uses tools which are automatically set to length.

5.0 ON-LINE COMPUTER CONTROL

It has long been realised that there is considerable control system and computing redundancy if machine tools, all working on the same workpiece, are controlled by independent n.-c. systems. Most n.-c. companies now offer small units which will interface between existing n.-c. control cabinets and a computer of the process control type, which carry out interpolation and computation for several machines in time multiplex mode, and which distribute information to the individual machine n.-c. controllers by data link at the rate required by the machines.

This computer is linked to a larger computer capable of running the main n.-c. processor, and indeed capable, in principle, of controlling the entire manufacturing process from machine level to line loading and optimising level.

This arrangement leaves machines with n.-c. units which can either accept paper tape or work on line to a computer. It is clearly redundant in hardware, but offers the advantage that existing equipment can be used and new programmes can be tried out and corrected off line in the usual fashion from paper tape. In an emergency the machine can operate in the normal way from tape, if available.

The next step is to restrict the electronic control functions on individual machines to that which cannot be performed by a central computer. Thus a memory, some data conversion, and perhaps some interpolation circuits, together with a push-button station, may be all that is left of conventional n.-c. equipment on individual machine tools.

6.0 TRIAL OF NEW COMPONENTS ON AN INTEGRATED MANUFACTURING SYSTEM

All users of n.-c. are familiar with the problems and time involved in first getting a new n.-c. tape to produce a correct workpiece and then optimising the program to minimise cost. Probably introduction of adaptive control will reduce the length of this process, but at the moment one cannot be sure that a program is correct until at least one, and preferably several, components have been produced on a machine.

It is common to spend even longer in proving a transfer line on a new product: and an integrated manufacturing system can be considered as a generalised transfer line. The complete concept of the integrated manufacturing system will pose difficult technical and organisational problems in the equivalent of 'tape proving'.

One helpful feature will be the ability to introduce correcting data at the individual machine tool. Currently the organisation of n.-c. software into a sequential two-pass system of a main processor, followed by a post-processor, makes this difficult because there is no way of up-dating the processor input statements automatically from changes in post-processor's output statements.

N.-C. software with a different organisational structure, such as Conapt, is being developed to overcome this difficulty. Portable video or hard copy terminals on machine tools will help.

7.0 SOFTWARE IN N.-C. MANUFACTURING SYSTEMS

Good software is fundamental to an n.-c. manufacturing system. A collection of n.-c. machine tools and associated hardware, such as that for work transfer, becomes a truly automatic and economic manufacturing system for batch production to an extent which depends very largely on the level in the production processes for which it is economic to produce the software.

Standard computer programs comprising processors and post-processors are well known. One reason has already been examined for modifying this level of software. There are perhaps others. There is, for example, the need to distribute machining functions between different machines in such a way as to balance work load between machines.

One general geometric description of the workpiece is all that should be needed for the complete manufacturing system. The appropriate operations, technology and tools should be selected automatically for individual stations. This implies a change in the present philosophy of a single CL tape which is converted into instructions for one machine. This is a very substantial problem. Fortunately, economic applications of machining systems do not have to wait for its solution.

Software is also needed to deal with machine loading and associated problems. The problems will really become difficult when on-line loading decisions are made which take into account the system irregularities which exist in the present machine shop and which will exist in the n.-c. manufacturing system. Such things as breakdown, lack of materials, modifications and scrap will impose very severe software problems if an attempt is made to automate rescheduling decisions on an optimising basis.

8.0 INSPECTION

Inspection by manual methods of parts produced by a machining centre can now take longer than the manufacture of the parts. The production rate of an integrated manufacturing system is several times higher than that of a single machining centre because several spindles operate simultaneously. The inspection problem is therefore increased, and the need to integrate mechanised or automatic inspection into the manufacturing system becomes evident. Automatic cleaning of workpieces is usually required before inspection.

Tape-controlled automatic inspection machines are available which detect deviations from programmed tool centres, surfaces and contours. Similar machines are not generally available for checking hole diameters and the presence or quality of machining features such as the thread in a tapped hole, or the surface finish of a bored hole. These features can be checked automatically on transfer machines, but the problem there is much easier as special-purpose gauges can be introduced at stations along the line. It is expected that integrated manufacturing systems will lead to further developments in automatic inspection.

9.0 AUTOMATIC MONITORING OF AN INTEGRATED MANUFACTURING SYSTEM

An integrated manufacturing system of the first generation will require manual supervision because ways have not yet been developed for monitoring all its functions economically. Even such a simple thing as tool breakage on a machining centre is very difficult to detect during machining because the size and type of tool used can vary widely. It is therefore to be expected that supervisors will constantly monitor operation of the system.

A natural extension of the use of an on-line computer is to assist in monitoring the performance of the system. Several functions are relatively easy to monitor: for example, those relating to interlocks or the absence of supplies, or the total cutting time of cutters. The computer can check the status of the system to some extent and can output diagnostic messages or instructions for maintenance. It is expected that, with the increasing complexity of integrated manufacturing systems, centralised automatic status checking will become necessary.

Unfortunately, as already pointed out, some basic aspects of the cutting process (such as accuracy, or whether a tool has broken) cannot be checked in general during machining. Adaptive control is likely to assist keeping the process within acceptable limits of cutting force etc. In-process gauging will also help in this respect, but further developments are required in both areas.

10.0 SERVICING

The integrated manufacturing system presents no really new servicing problems, but emphasises the present problems in n.-c. servicing. These arise from the need to get a system running again with minimum delay, and the need to regard the system as a whole in analysing the cause of the symptoms. Centralised automatic status checking will help servicing. It will also be helpful to have some queues of components at stations so that failure of one station does not bring the system to a halt. Automatic loading schedules can be worked out in advance for breakdown of different sections of the system. In elaborate, work-scheduling, optimising systems this can be done, in principle, on line, and a wider range of system malfunctions can be dealt with.

It is clear that serious attention must be given to selection and training of staff for servicing, and indeed all functions of an integrated manufacturing system.

11.0 ROLE OF WORKPIECE STATISTICS

Assuming a given level of automation, to design the appropriate integrated manufacturing system it is necessary to know the range of size, the material, and the distribution of machining operation times and cycle times. As machining centres are inherently versatile and so may be required for a wide variety of parts, it is often very difficult to obtain a clear picture of the range of parts to be made over the life of the system.

A start can be made by deciding on the part size, range and shape and number of faces to be machined. This determines the modular unit sizes of the integrated manufacturing system. Workpiece statistics can then be used to determine the range of likely machining operations and the times of these operations. It is then a matter of making the best compromise assembly of units permitting reasonable time-balancing for the majority of components. This usually involves some duplication of stations and some interchange of functions between stations.

12.0 OPERATIONS OTHER THAN CONVENTIONAL METAL CUTTING

Automatic inspection and cleaning have already been mentioned. Staveley see the need to integrate other operations into the integrated manufacturing system in some cases, rather as in Staveley link lines, which incorporate broaching, heat treatment and automatic assembly.

13.0 CONCLUSION

Some of the background to the design considerations of the Staveley integrated manufacturing system as they will affect the production engineer has been presented. To a large extent the ultimate in current concepts has been presented, but the greatest impact of manufacturing systems will first be with the simpler systems with considerable manual intervention and with software which does not interact between various levels, such as part programming and machine loading. At first systems will usually consist essentially of existing types of n.-c. machine, usually simplified, linked by work transfer equipment (the machines and work transfer probably not being controlled by a central computer). However, as confidence is gained and the economics become clearer, it is expected that the manufacturing system will develop along some of the lines outlined in this paper.

SESSION 5. DISCUSSION ON THE PAPERS BY P. H. STEPHENSON, C. B. PERRY AND D. F. H. RUSHTON

P. P. LOVE (*Glacier Metal Co.*): It seems to me that these integrated manufacturing systems described in Professor Stephenson's paper as presented by Mr Davies are going to pose very much greater social than technological problems. Is the University or the Institute drawing the attention of people who can deal with some of these problems to their existence? Are the people who are doing this work on these highly sophisticated methods of manufacture consulting sociologists?

B. DAVIES: The short answer in terms of the sociological aspect is, 'No, we are not doing anything yet'. Perhaps we should.

M. ZVEGINTZOV (*N.R.D.C.*): I would like to strongly support Mr Love. If we do not start looking at the sociological problems we shall get into a worse mess in union/management relations than we are now. Perhaps the University might take a serious look at this.

W. SCOTT (*University of Strathclyde*): What has worried me greatly is the problem of compatibility. When one sees a system developing of the size which has been depicted on the slide today, one wonders: is there any possibility of the industry trying to ensure a measure of compatibility in the interfaces and in the program languages? This is one of the major problems for any industrial company looking at the use of computers, particularly in complex systems of this type.

Dr S. B. L. WILSON (*Rolls-Royce*): As a computer man I must jump to the defence of all my colleagues in this field following Mr Davies' comments. He tended to place a lot of the blame on the lack of software development and our ability to provide this. We in computing can only provide the software if the designer of the system tells us what he wants it to do and what he is going to pay for it.

A. TACK (*Rolls-Royce*): Would Mr Perry be a little more definitive in his definition of a soft wire control?

C. B. PERRY: I think I used the term 'hard wire controller' as defining the kinds of control now available. These are controls in which the logic functions are limited and governed by the particular wiring that is inherent in performing the logic functions required. The station controller that we are developing for variable missions uses a computer as its central element and its logic functions can be modified simply by programming modification. This gives us the option of performing a host of logic functions, not now economically practical with the hard wire controller. We can metaphorically plaster the works station with sensors, and we can monitor temperature, velocities, reservoir levels, and the interaction of forces generated in the cutting zone.

G. R. FRANKLIN (*W. E. & F. Dobson*): Could Mr Perry please expand on the manufacture of rotational parts? I would imagine that this is to do with the using of the β axis as a powered driving unit.

C. B. PERRY: Yes, precisely. The distinction is that, to produce a part of rotation, we must rotate the workpiece with sufficient torque to overcome the cutting forces generated by a rotating cutter, and even higher forces by a fixed-point cutter. We have that ability with the full β cutting axis. We will normally be doing roughing work with a rotating cutter, while the workpiece is turning and we can optionally finish with a single-point cutter.

D. E. LEWIN (*Rolls-Royce*): Two speakers emphasised reduction in cost of components using numerically controlled machine techniques. Earlier we were told that, in order to innovate, we must get a product on the market as soon as possible. Would Mr Perry like to comment on his system as a means for bringing in a component or a product before a competitor does, in other words reducing the lead time?

C. B. PERRY: One of the major attractions of a programmable manufacturing system is that it permits a great shortening of the time lapse from design concept to first part moving into the market place. Beyond that, during the product's life, the fixing of the production rate which is implicit in mechanisation is quite incompatible with the realities of the market. New products enter the market usually with a product-acceptance time-cycle according to which the rate desired would climb slowly with time until it reached some ceiling. Then, if it is a well-received product, it might enjoy a high level of production for a good many years. As its terminal life approaches the desired rate descends. Finally it is replaced by some new product. Even then, we must maintain an ability to produce parts for replacement. It is this total incompatibility of current manufacturing systems with the real needs of our present society which moved us to think about variable mission.

D. B. LLOYD (*Hoare & Co.*): It has been admitted that the Herbert Ingersoll project has cost an awful lot more than was envisaged and in the first two years of operation will lose something like £2½ m. Could Mr Lindem, who presented Mr Rushton's paper, outline some of the problems met in establishing this plant in the U.K. and tell us when does he expect it to become profitable?

T. LINDEM: If we look at the total system concept, if we look at the seven steps from planning to the managing of a system, we see that this is an extremely large system. It is not something that is planned, developed and managed in a very short period of time. We did not intend to be in profit till the latter part of 1970. We consider that we are not at stage 6 – starting up the system. Productivity per worker is about twice the national average. We hope to increase this to three times the national average.

H. M. LEBRECHT (*Kearney & Trecker*): How will the systems study work in practice? Who pays for the study? Who carries out the work? Is the study truly impartial? Would equipment manufacturers making a study recommend other manufacturers' equipment? Do you consider that one study by one manufacturer is satisfactory from the customer's point of view?

T. LINDEM: The client pays for the study. It becomes his property. He can go to any manufacturer for a solution or for a special machine if it is required. We not only will, but in many cases have, recommended other machinery. We have, as a result of a study, recommended to one customer that he get rid of an Ingersoll machine that he had. We feel that we are impartial in the studies. It is the client's prerogative to go to whoever he feels would be best capable of supplying those machine tools. Now, did I answer all the questions?

H. M. LEBRECHT: Yes. Could I just ask, has it ever happened that you did a study for a customer and he then put it out for tender and placed the order with other people?

T. LINDEM: Yes.

SESSION VI

Manufacturing Systems II

Chairman: Mr J. D. Houston
Managing Director
Higher Productivity Ltd.

OBJECTIVES, LAYOUT AND POSSIBILITIES OF THE OPITZ WORKPIECE CLASSIFICATION SYSTEM

Dr Klaus Brankamp

Machine Tool Laboratory,
Technical University of Aachen, Germany

SUMMARY

Rationalising of single and small-batch production is difficult because of continual changes in production programmes. Investigations have shown that most machine tools in workshops are too large with respect to the parts which they produce. A classification system, which gives a systematic survey of the part spectrum, can therefore be of great help for different departments of a company. The Opitz system is such a technique for bringing together similar parts. It is based on a shape description with five digits and on a supplementary code with four digits. After a description of the system in some detail, examples are given of its use in design and work-planning departments. Two examples, one the selection of a highly automated lathe and the second the setting-up of a flow line for part-groups, are given.

1.0 ASSIGNMENT OF WORKPIECES TO MACHINE TOOLS

What is the Opitz part-classification system and what the basis of its development?

Eight years ago the Machine Tool Laboratory of the University of Aachen investigated the assignment of machine tools and workpieces, with the following terms of reference:

- design of machine tools
- investment-planning
- machine tools existing in the workshop

With the results it should be possible to better adapt machine tools to workpieces.

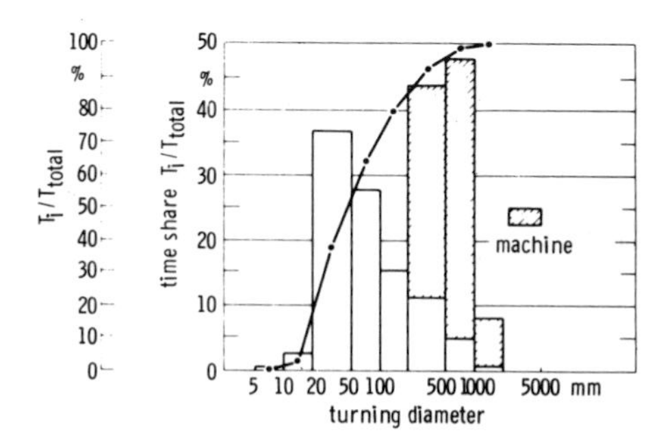

Fig. 1. Maximum workpiece diameter and allowable turning diameter.

Twenty-five firms with different manufacturing programmes were investigated, and about 4500 workpieces requiring about 320 000 machining hours were registered.

Fig. 1 shows the best-known result of these investigations: a comparison of the dimensions of workpieces with the dimensions of machine tools. Thus the dimensional 'exploitation' of lathes is considered. The figure shows the diameter distribution of workpieces to be machined on lathes compared with the distribution of diameters permissible on lathes in the firm. The example is taken from a manufacturer of apparatus. The maximum workpiece diameter is between 20 and 50 mm. About 80% of the workpieces are less than 200 mm in diameter, but the permissible diameter on all machines is greater than 200 mm so the machines are too large with respect to workpiece diameter. At least some of the machines could be smaller and therefore better adapted to the actual machining problems. A similar result was obtained regarding the workpiece length *versus* machine tool capacity. These findings are borne out by many firms and are not based on isolated cases.

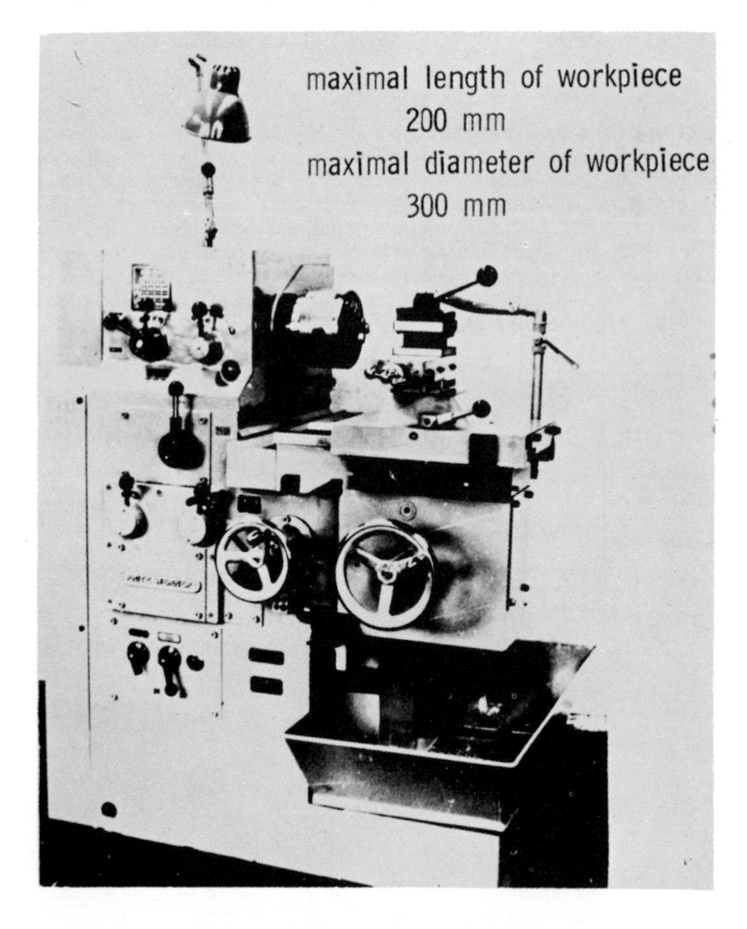

Fig. 2. Short lathe.

The consequence of those results must be a call for adjustment of machine tools to machining requirements. This usually creates opposition by plant management, which fears variations in the product-programme. The fear is unjustified because most production assignments are very similar, as many investigations have shown.

One outcome of the investigations was a proposal for a lathe for workpieces within a certain range of dimensions. Fig. 2 shows an example of such a short lathe. The turning-diameter is up to 300 mm and the length up to 200 mm.

2.0 THE OPITZ PART-CLASSIFICATION SYSTEM

The aim was to state the principles of optimal allocation of workpieces to machine tools, but the analysis also showed that, in spite of all their differences, workpieces follow certain rules. Classes of workpiece have been found which are similar with respect to shape.

This in itself was not new. Similarities had always been used to speed up work: the designer had used similar workpieces or groups as a pattern, the work-planner had used similar workpieces for calculation purposes, and the production manager had tried to combine similar parts to save set-up time. However, the exploitation of similarity had always been dependent on the memory of qualified persons, or even on mere accident. Systematic investigation in design, standardisation, work-planning or manufacturing had been nearly impossible.

The goal was, therefore, to give these departments an aid to the quick and systematic grouping of similar parts. Such an aid is the Opitz Classification System, developed and tested at the Laboratory for Machine Tools, Technical University Aachen, Germany, by Professor H. Opitz and his collaborators.

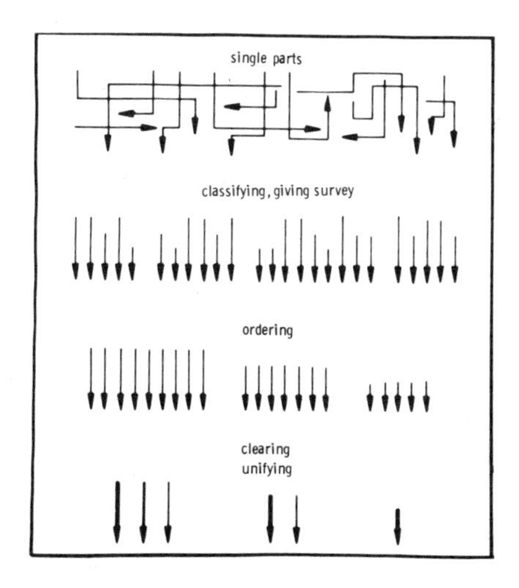

Fig. 3. Workpiece classification.

2.1 *Systematic classification procedure*

The aim of the classification is to give a systematic survey over the part spectrum (Fig. 3), first dealing with the parts, next with groups of similar parts, and finally with clearing and unification.

Systematisation is impossible without the aid of classification. It is known from investiga-

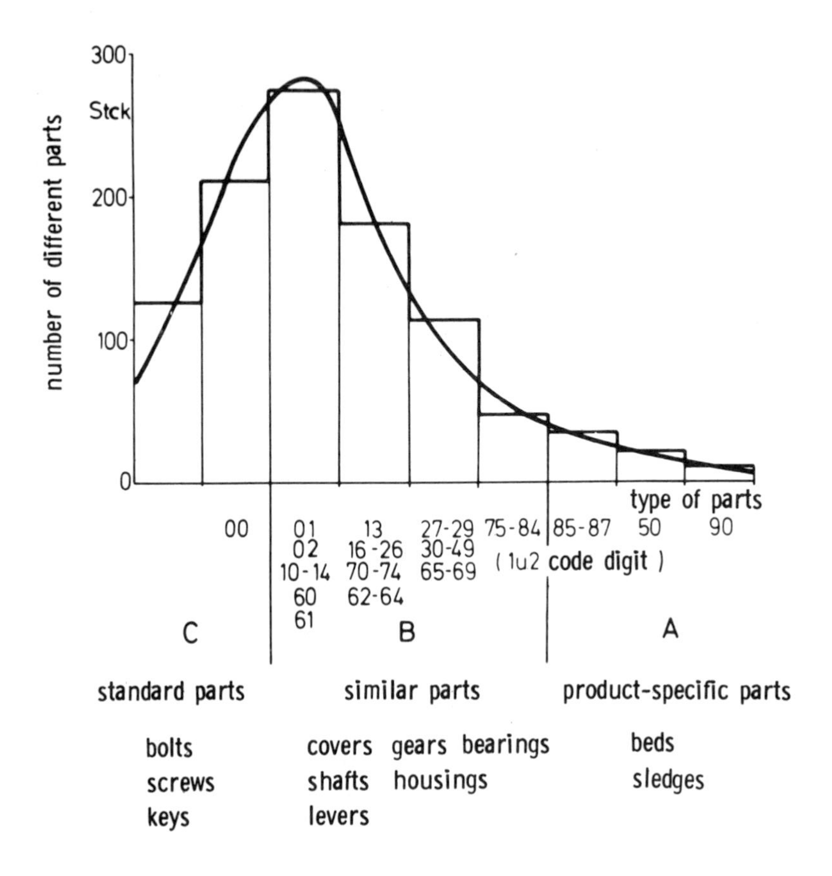

Fig. 4. Distribution of components in a machine tool.

tions in five companies that newly designed parts add about 20% a year to existing parts in the machine building industry, where the stock is about 200 000 to 300 000 drawings.

2.2 *Component grouping in a single product*

A further investigation (Fig. 4) has shown which section of the part spectrum of one machine can embrace similar parts. The figure shows the part variety of a product. The typification of parts takes into account approximately the grade of complexity. On the left of the figure appears the frequency of the *C*-parts, mostly standard parts like screws and keys, and on the right the so called *A*-parts, which can be seen as specific product parts like machine housings. In the middle is the large group of *B*-parts – covers, rings, shafts, levers, etc. The group of *B*-parts is predestined for classification. Generally, one can say that the more complex a part is, the lower is the chance of reuse, and *vice versa.*

2.3 *Generalised classification system*

A product-independent description of parts is possible according to different criteria, for example according to function, shape or manufacturing requirements. A classification system for all requirements in design, work-planning and manufacturing must always be a compromise between the different criteria. In addition, the number of digits should be low enough for

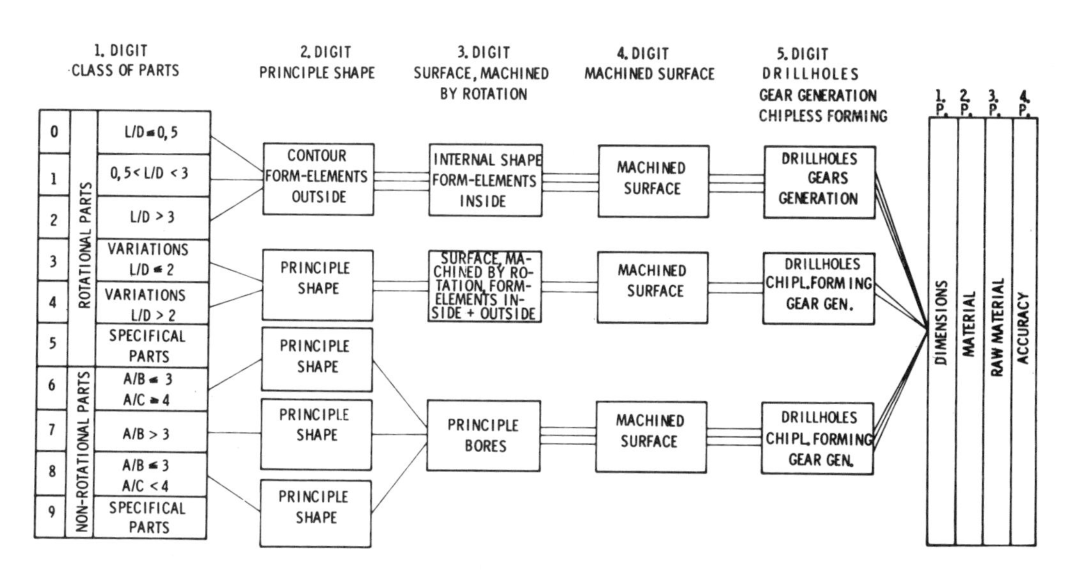

Fig. 5. Opitz Classification System.

economy and high enough for the system to be good to handle. This is mainly a question of learning and memorising.

The solution, found by the Machine Tool Laboratory, Aachen, is such a compromise. It serves as an aid in the different departments of companies.

Fig. 5 shows the layout of the classification system. It consists of two parts, a form code and an additional code.

The form code has five digits. In the first the general shape of workpieces is characterised. In the second the numbers 0 to 2 are for components with external shapes that are 'rotational'. All other second digits cover the main form. The third digit covers the internal shape in terms of elements which are respectively the form and position of the main bores. The fourth describes the plane machining and the fifth the auxiliary holes, gears and forming. Within the part class characterised by the first digit the workpieces are subdivided into *rotational* and *non-rotational* parts.

A few workpieces, special to firms or products, do not fit easily into such a classification unless the system is expanded unreasonably. For these workpieces it is better to use a functional notation. Therefore the fifth position has been reserved for specific rotational and the ninth position for specific non-rotational parts. Within these classes, internally adapted codes should be used.

Rotational pieces have been subdivided according to length-to-diameter ratio, that is into disc-type, medium and shaft-like parts. In part classes 3 and 4 – rotational parts with deviations – there is subdivision into short and long forms.

In a similar fashion, non-rotational parts are divided into flat, long and cubic parts according to the ratio of length and width. Beside the form code, additional information is necessary for

	Diameter D or length of edge A (mm)
0	≤ 20
1	> 20 ≤ 50
2	> 50 ≤ 100
3	> 100 ≤ 160
4	> 160 ≤ 250
5	> 250 ≤ 400
6	> 400 ≤ 600
7	> 600 ≤ 1000
8	> 1000 ≤ 2000
9	> 2000

	Material
0	grey cast iron
1	nodular graphitic cast iron and malleable cast iron
2	steel ≤ 42 kp/mm^2 (St - steel)
3	steel > 42 kp/mm^2 (C and Ck steel)
4	steel 2 + 3 heat -treated
5	alloy steel
6	alloy steel heat - treated
7	non-ferrous metal
8	light alloy
9	other materials

	Initial shape
0	round bar
1	bright drawn round bar
2	triangular, square, hexagonal or other bar
3	tubing
4	angle, U-, T- and similar sections
5	sheet
6	plates and slabs
7	cast or forged component
8	welded group
9	pre-machined component

	Accuracy in coding digit
0	no accuracy specified
1	2
2	3
3	4
4	5
5	2 + 3
6	2 + 4
7	2 + 5
8	3 + 4
9	(2+3) + 4 + 5

Fig. 6. Additional code.

an exact classification. This is collected in the additional code (Fig. 6). The first digit of the additional code covers the diameter or length of workpieces. In the second digit the materials are subdivided according to strength.

The shape of the raw material is denoted by the third digit. The fourth indicates that the workpiece a locally higher accuracy. For example, position three means that in the fourth digit – that is in plane machining – the accuracy is higher. Increased accuracy means an IT-Quality 7 or better. The limit has been set according to statistical investigation and has been proved to be good.

2.4 *Typical example of coding*

In the following example the layout and use of the form code are explained.

The coding for a workpiece is given in Fig. 7. It is a rotational part, progressively stepped, with a slot and axial, indexed, drill holes.

Fig. 8 shows how the code digits 1, 2 and 3 for rotational parts are subdivided. The example (Fig. 7) belongs to part class 1 (first digit) because the ratio of length to diameter (L/D) lies between 0·5 and 3.

In the second digit the external shape and the form elements are described. The external shape of the example is *one side increasing* and has the form element *thread.* Therefore a 2 is given for the second digit.

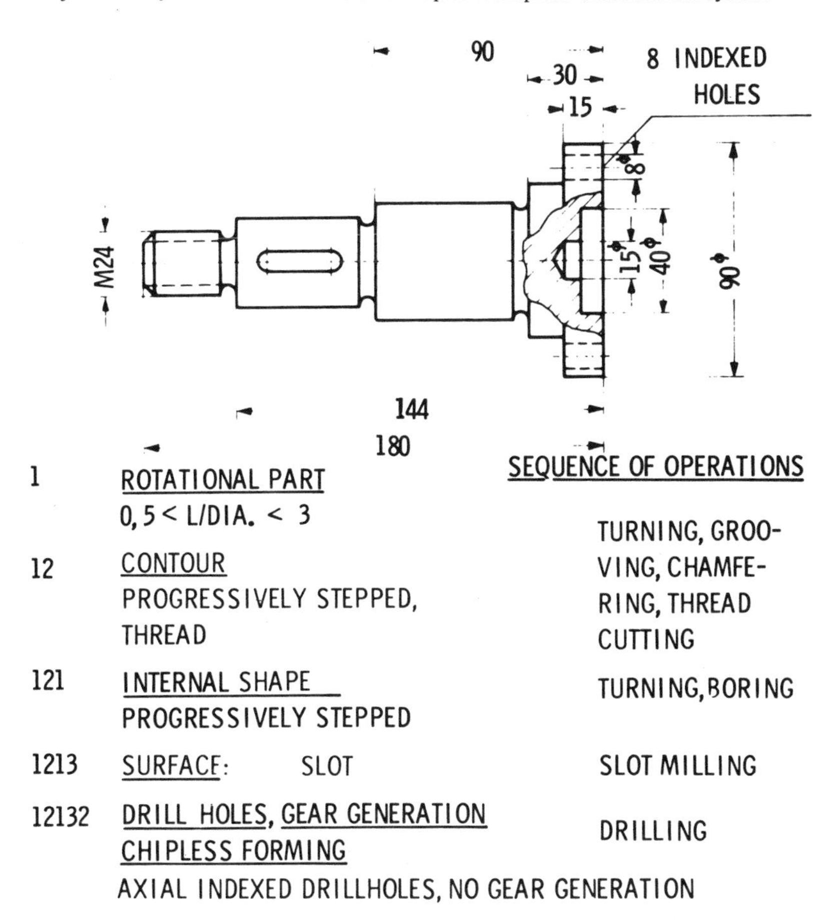

Fig. 7. Coding a rotational part.

For the third digit – internal shape – the same characteristics are provided as for the second digit. The internal shape of the workpiece shown is *single side increasing* without form elements, and therefore a 1 appears in the third digit.

Fig. 9 shows the final two digits of the form code for the part classes 0, 1 and 2. The fourth example has an external key-way, therefore a 3 in the fourth digit. Auxiliary holes and gearing are registered in the fifth digit. Considered here are those holes which cannot be machined on a lathe. Accordingly the four holes, ordered on a pitch diameter, are coded with a 2 for the fifth digit.

The terms used in the classification system are exemplified in the so-called definitions. They contain the coding rules, the application of the system, and definitions.

3.0 USER EXPERIENCE

The system has been tested in recent years on more than 100 000 parts. The results have shown that it is easy to learn and to handle. The training time to code accurately is in the range of two to five days. After this the coding staff can classify between 100 and 150 parts a day.

	1st Digit		2nd Digit		3rd Digit	
		component class		External shape, external shape elements		Internal shape, Internal shape elements
0	rotational parts	L / D ≤ 0,5		smooth, no shape elements		no hole, no breakthrough
1	rotational parts	0,5 < L/D < 3	stepped to one end or smooth	no shape elements	smooth or stepped to one end	no shape elements
2	rotational parts	L / D ≥ 3	stepped to one end or smooth	thread	smooth or stepped to one end	thread
3	rotational parts		stepped to one end or smooth	functional groove	smooth or stepped to one end	functional groove
4	rotational parts		stepped to both ends	no shape elements	stepped to both ends	no shape elements
5	rotational parts		stepped to both ends	thread	stepped to both ends	thread
6	nou rotational parts		stepped to both ends	functional groove	stepped to both ends	functional groove
7	nou rotational parts			functional cone		functional cone
8	nou rotational parts			operating thread		operating thread
9	nou rotational parts			all others		all others

Fig. 8. Formcode: part classes 0, 1 and 2; 1st, 2nd and 3rd digit.

As the system was developed and tested, prerequisites were formulated for its use in different departments such as design, standardisation, work-planning and shop and investment-planning.

3.1 *Design office application*

In the design department the customer's order is translated by the creative work of the designer into drawings and a list of materials. In many cases the designer is bound only to few connecting dimensions and has therefore several possibilities in the shaping of the single work-pieces. This results in a lot of work in the detailing process. A representative investigation showed an average of 35% for this type of work with respect to the whole design-time. (See Fig. 10.)

Here is the starting point for rationalising design by organisational and technical means, because shaping of components is more or less routine work. A prerequisite is the recording, ordering and registering of the relevant data as well as the systematisation, standardisation and typification of the spectrum of parts. After this a drawing file can be built up, which is ordered according to the code number and therefore allows quick retrieval of components. One possibility is to put the drawings on microfilm. Fig. 11 shows a combined punch card. Beside the 35 characters for the data there is an area which contains the film image of the drawing.

Fig. 12 illustrates the information flow from an idea to a sketch and to the final drawing.

4 th Digit

Surface machining	
0	no surface machining
1	surface plane and/or curved in one direction, external
2	external plane surface related by graduation around a circle
3	external groove and/or slot
4	external spline (polygon)
5	external plane surface and/or slot, external spline
6	internal plane surface and/or slot
7	internal spline (polygon)
8	internal and external polygon, groove and/or slot
9	all others

5 th Digit

Auxiliary holes and gear teeth		
0	no gear teeth	no auxiliary hole
1		axial, not on pitch circle diameter
2		axial, on pitch circle diameter
3		radial, not on pitch circle diameter
4		axial and/or radial and/or other direction
5		axial and/or radial on PCD and/or other directions
6	with gear teeth	spur gear teeth
7		bevel gear teeth
8		other gear teeth
9		all others

Fig. 9. Formcode: part classes 0, 1 and 2; 4th and 5th digit.

After the general layout of an assembly and detailing, sketches are coded either by the designer himself or by coding staff. Then the designer searches for similar parts in the drawing files, which are ordered according to the code number.

Depending on the type of part – in this case from a simple washer to a complicated shaft – the designer can refer to *reuse* parts or to *similar* parts. In the case of a reuse part, only the object number may be in the material list. In the case of a similar part the part serves as a pattern and can be used with slight alteration. If neither reuse parts nor similar parts are available, the workpiece has to be designed. If the problem is solved thus, the paperwork runs normally from the drawing store to the work-planning department.

It is obvious that the reuse probability of simple parts with few degrees of freedom is much higher than of other parts. Because these parts are often needed the use of a central file is too expensive. Therefore so-called similar-part-catalogues have been developed which are especially easy to build up if punched cards are used. Each designer has such a catalogue at his desk.

Fig. 13 shows as an example a section of such a catalogue which is already used in several alternatives. The head contains a schematic sketch. Under the picture a computer list of all

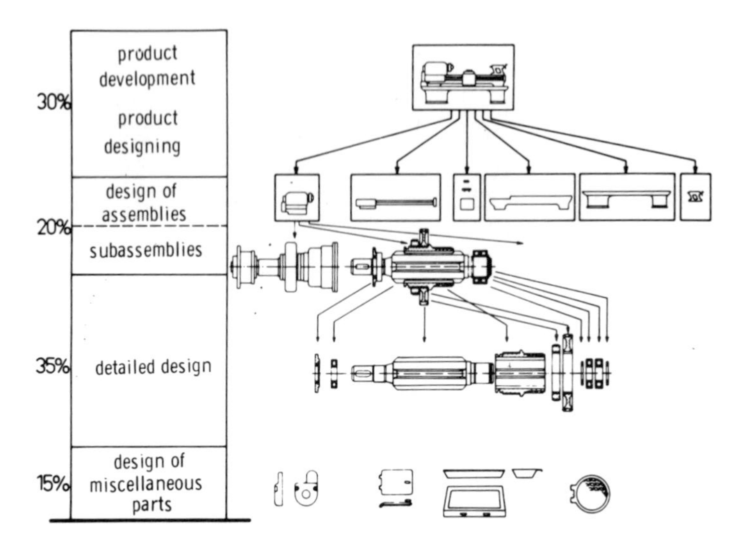

Fig. 10. Distribution of design time of a certain product.

existing parts is added which has the relevant code number. Now the designer can search in the list for the part which best fits his requirements. The list is updated approximately each month.

Applications arising are: (i) short-term, establishing drawings and working plan files, (ii) medium-term, establishing standard times, manufacturing-device-catalogues and standard working plans, and (iii) long-term, preparing the use of electronic data-processing equipment for automatic planning.

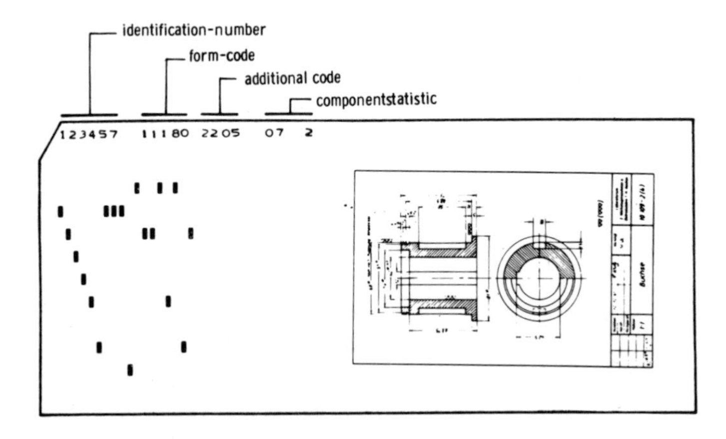

Fig. 11. Microfilm punched card.

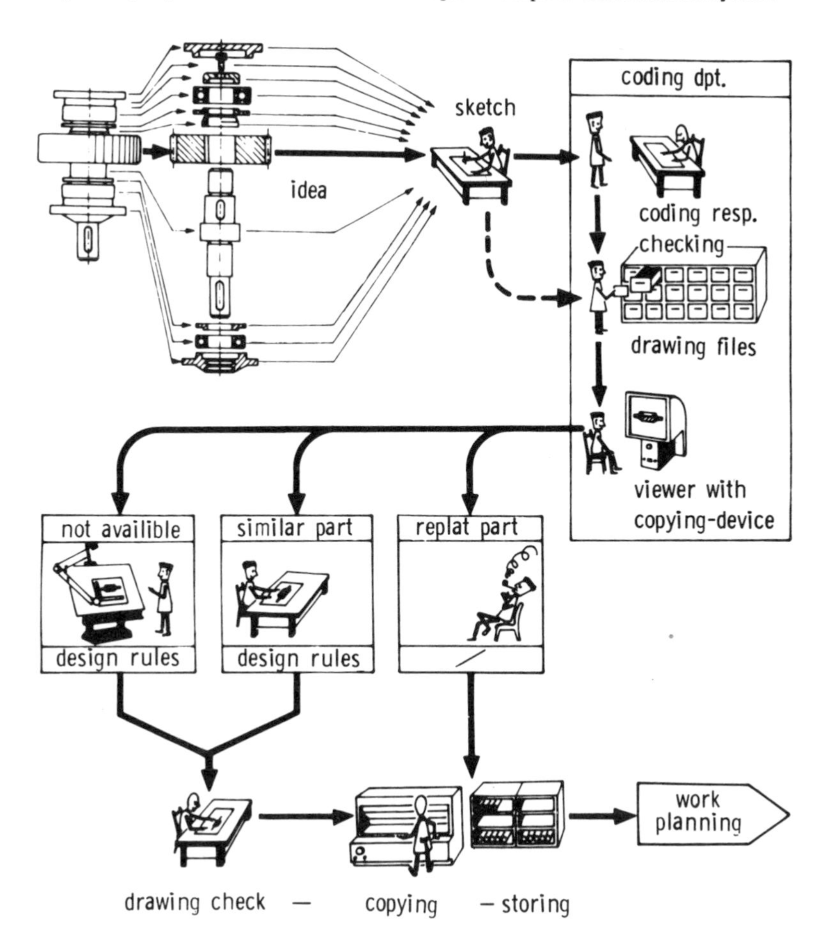

Fig. 12. Execution of a design order.

3.2 *Process planning application*

As an example of the application of the classification system in the work-planning department, Fig. 14 shows a standard working plan for similar parts. The working steps are put down on a list. Steps with numbers 5, 15, 20 etc. must be made. The other ones, e.g. 26, 27, 31, 32 etc., may be. So variations are possible. From this standard plan is developed the plan for a real case.

One of the main applications of the classification system in the work-planning department is the grouping of parts.

Plates, rings, washers | 00102 code number | 3 sub group

Inner dia d_i	Outer dia d_a	total length	Material	pitch circle d_{Tk}	fastening holes	other dia d'	d_2	other length l_1	l_2	drawing number	F
5,50	54,00	5,0	C35	9,0	1X4H7					25-000.382-0	4
11,00	80,00	6,0	C60	16,0	1X6H7					25-000.381-0	4
13,50	100,00	14,0	C35	50,0	1XM12	070		004		25-000.456-0	4
17,00	56,00	13,0	C35	44,0	3XM 5	037	022	007	11	43-000.188-0	4
17,00	115,00	17,0	C35	50,0	1XM16	080		005		25-000.451-0	4
17,50	70,00	11,0	C35	36,0	1XM16	048		004		25-000.612-0	4
17,50	70,00	11,0	C35	32,0	1XM16	045		003		25-000.701-0	4
22,00	80,00	11,0	C35	44,0	1XM20	055		003		25-000.598-0	4
22,00	90,00	14,0	C35	46,0	1XM20	060		004		25-000.700-0	4
30,00	110,E8	11,0	C35	94,0	4XM 6	076		003		17-002.118-0	4
32,00	110,E8	11,0	C35	94,0	4XM 8	078	051	003	007	17-001.443-0	4
34,00	110,00	11,0	C35	94,0	4XM 8	078		003		17-002.119-0	4
38,00	110,E8	11,0	C35	94,0	4XM 8	078	051	003	007	17-001.448-0	4
45,00	110,E8	11,0	C35	94,0	4XM 8	078		003		17-002.120-0	4
46,00	110,E8	11,0	C35	94,0	4XM 8	079		001		17-002.296-0	4
50,00	110,E8	11,0	C35	94,0	4XM 8	078		001		17-001.976-0	4
54,00	92,00	15,0	ST37	80,0	3XM 5	072	068	003	012	43-000.376-0	3
54,00	125,H6	11,0	C35	108,0	4XM 8	092		003		17-001.745-0	3
80,00	125,H6	11,0	C35	108,0	4XM 8	092		003		17-001.743-0	3
122,00	160,H6	11,0	MRST37-2	143,0	8XM 8	132		003		17-001.548-0	3
205,00	310,00	20,0	ST37	225,0	8XM 8	300		015		30-000.109-0	3
220,00	299,00	14,0	MRST37-2	250,0	6XM12	270		004		14-002.604-0	4
228,00	289,00	15,0	MRST37-2	252,0	6XM12	270		005		14-002.152-0	4
340,00	408,00	8,0	MRST37-2	360,0	6XM 6	402		005		30-000.110-0	3
380,00	478,00	15,0	MRST37-2	410,0	6XM10	440		003		14-002.953-0	3

Fig. 13. Excerpt from a reuse part catalogue.

The classification aids preselection of parts for a part family. It has been found that not all information of the form and additional code are required, but only the so called characteristic data (Fig. 15). In the chosen example these are the part class (digit 1), the external shape (digit 2), the diameter (digit 6), and the material (digit 7).

The main advantages of group technology in manufacture are smaller set-up times, more highly automated machine tools, fewer batches in the shop, and less planning work. Grouping of additive batches has as an additional result – decrease in stock. Because the necessary batch size is reached by collecting different parts, the optimal batch size for each single part is reduced. The mean stock size therefore decreases.

3.3 *Investment planning application*

Beside the grouping of parts the manufacturing devices and the flow of material have to be adapted to the part spectrum (Fig. 16).

Management has to fix the number of different products, including those which have still to be developed by estimation and market analysis. The workpieces, coded according to the classification system, can then be merged independent of product, into the so-called machining profile. The machining profile is determined by the size, working accuracy, output capacity and number of machines. The existing capacity, determined from the existing machines, and the nominal capacity, determined from the products to be manufactured, are compared.

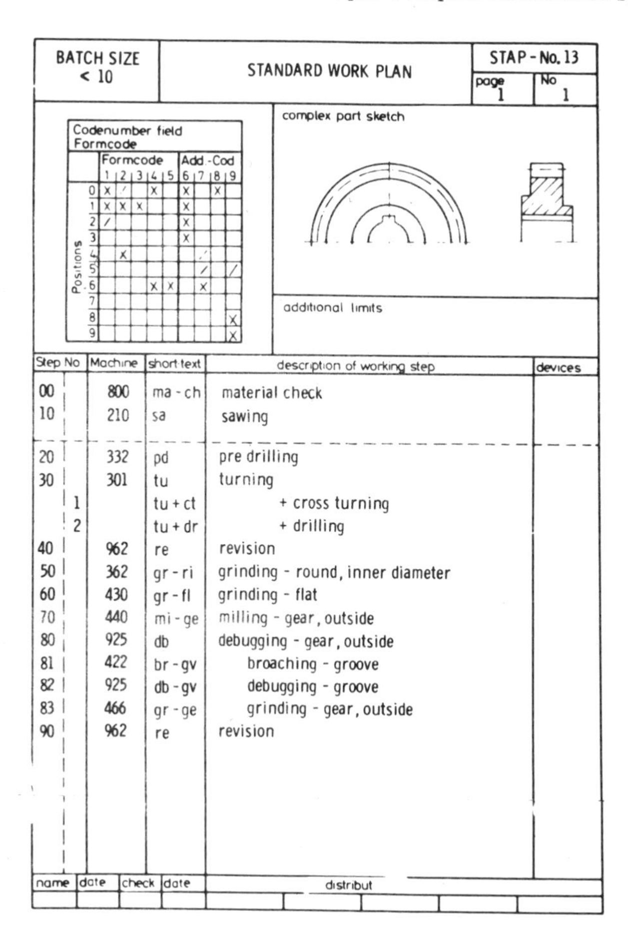

BATCH SIZE < 10	STANDARD WORK PLAN	STAP - No. 13, page 1, No 1

Codenumber field Formcode

complex part sketch

additional limits

Step No		Machine	short text	description of working step	devices
00		800	ma - ch	material check	
10		210	sa	sawing	
20		332	pd	pre drilling	
30		301	tu	turning	
	1		tu + ct	+ cross turning	
	2		tu + dr	+ drilling	
40		962	re	revision	
50		362	gr - ri	grinding - round, inner diameter	
60		430	gr - fl	grinding - flat	
70		440	mi - ge	milling - gear, outside	
80		925	db	debugging - gear, outside	
81		422	br - gv	broaching - groove	
82		925	db - gv	debugging - groove	
83		466	gr - ge	grinding - gear, outside	
90		962	re	revision	

name	date	check	date	distribut

Fig. 14. Standard working plan.

4.0 INDUSTRIAL CASE STUDIES

Beside the grouping of parts and investment planning there are other applications. Two case studies from companies in Germany may serve as examples.

4.1 *Machine tool selection*

In the first case a machine-tool-producing company had the problem: would it be more economic to buy several turret lathes or one multi-spindle automatic lathe? The lot sizes of shop jobs were such that the multi-spindle lathe would not have been fully loaded. Even experts in that field could not decide whether the multi-spindle lathe would be economic or not. The advantages of the multi-spindle lathe compared with the turret lathe were:

1. Higher productivity, because the machining time is only about an eighth of that of the turret lathe.
2. Because of the shorter machining times several turret lathes could be replaced, therefore saving floor space for machines and stock, transportation distances, and eventually manpower.
3. The company, as producer of the multi-spindle lathe, could utilise the machine in its own production and thereby test and improve it.

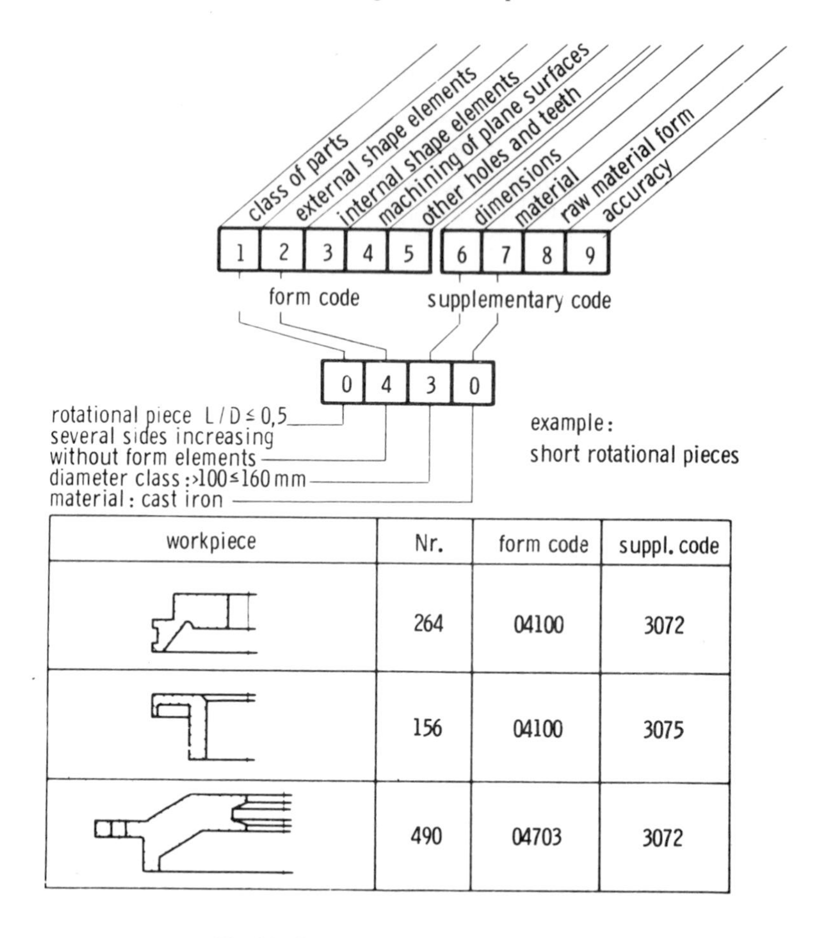

workpiece	Nr.	form code	suppl. code
	264	04100	3072
	156	04100	3075
	490	04703	3072

Fig. 15. Part group and characteristic data.

The disadvantages of the multi-spindle lathe are mainly set-up time, which is about 2·5 times that of a turret lathe, and higher tool expenses.

For the investigation all the company's workpieces were considered. Each was recorded on punched cards, one card being recorded for each working step. From these cards, with the aid of the classification system, were selected those parts which suited the requirements for machining on a multi-spindle lathe.

The machining profile of the multi-spindle machine was transformed for that purpose into a code number field, which considered the size, the shape, the material and the raw material form of the workpieces. A code number field [Fig. 17(a)] aids selection of parts with certain common features. It has the form of a matrix and contains all digits which arise in the code numbers of the parts considered. In Fig. 17(a) therefore a 2 appears in the first row, 5 and 6 in the second and 0, 3 and 0 in the third, fourth and fifth digit respectively. Also, for a machine tool, a code number field can be set up. The field preselects the part to be machined on that machine. This was done for the multi-spindle automatic lathe, and from the thousands of parts those which fitted the requirements of the code number field of the automatic lathe were selected.

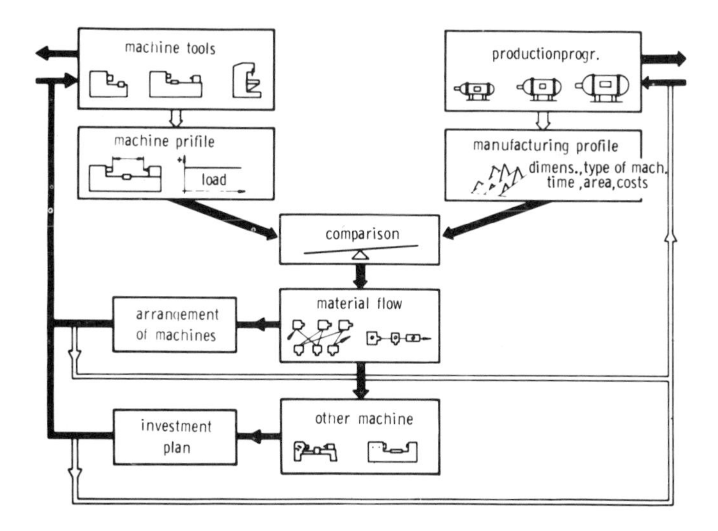

Fig. 16. Long-range adaptation of shop to production programme.

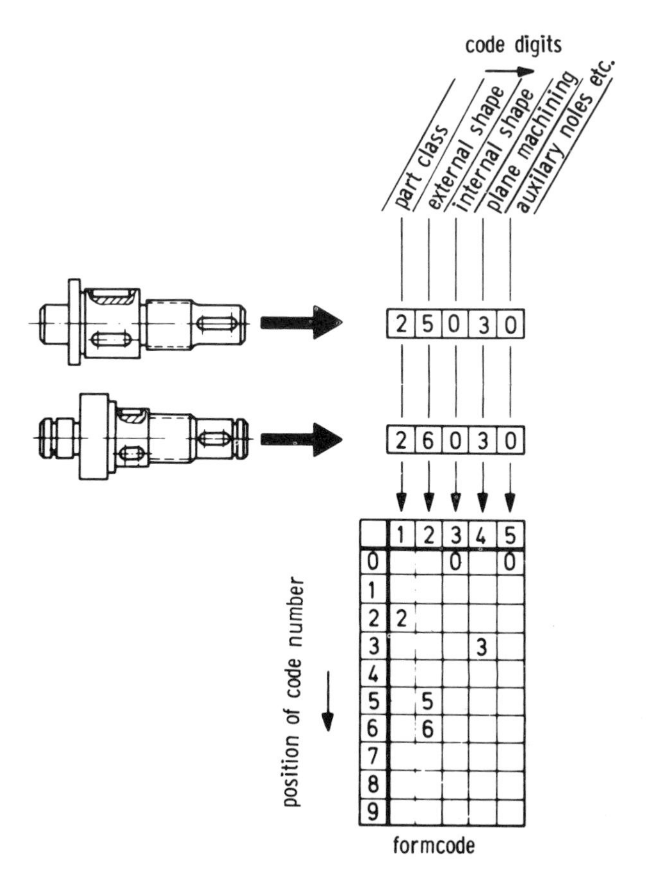

Fig. 17(a). Generation of a code number field.

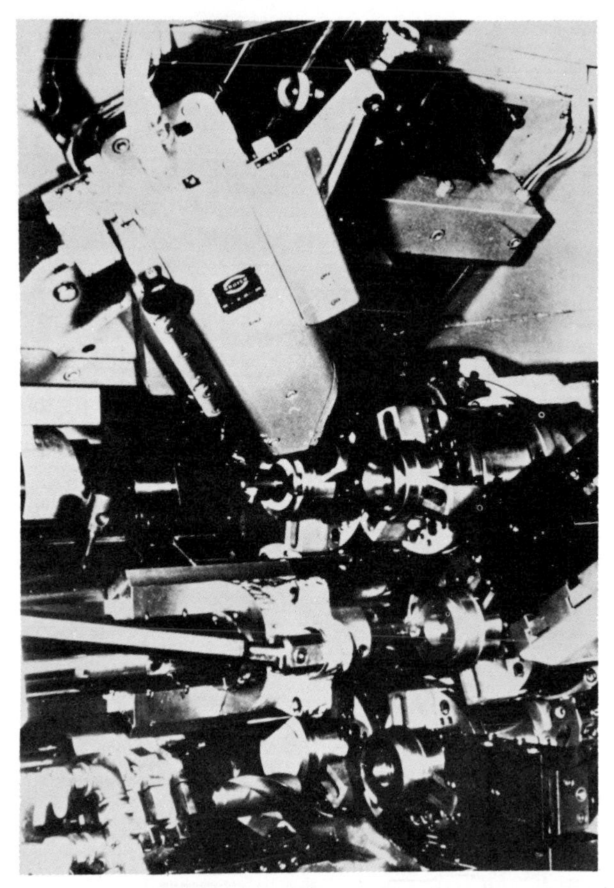

Fig. 17(b). Tooling for a part group on a multi-spindle automatic lathe.

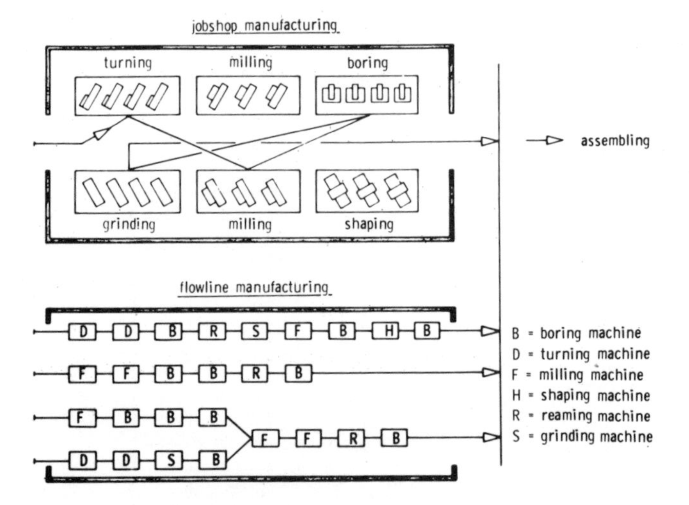

Fig. 18. Job shop manufacturing and flow line manufacturing.

For those parts the capacity required was determined. The investigations showed that a six-spindle automatic lathe would best fit the technical and economic requirements.

The tooling layout of the automatic [Fig. 17(b)] is done according to the workpiece with the most complicated shape within one part group. The machining proceeds from the most complicated to the simplest workpiece, so that the changing of the set-up becomes minimal.

Because of the utilisation of the multi-spindle automatic, four turret lathes and three places of employment could be saved in the cited case.

Before rearranging, savings of 30% of the manufacturing costs were expected, that means 60 000 DM/year. After one year of running the new machine a check revealed that really 50 000 DM had been saved. The investigations and the rearrangement had cost about 25 000 DM, so they had paid for themselves after six months.

4.2 *Arrangement of production flow line*

Finally, an example will illustrate the use of the system for the layout of a production flow line.

Machining on flow lines (Fig. 18) becomes obviously advantageous if different parts have the same working sequence. In single- and small-batch production those parts can be found among spindles, gears, rings, levers etc. The requirements for building a flow line are: (1) product-independent manufacture, (2) grouping of parts which are similar with respect to manufacture, and (3) full employment of the line.

With the aid of the classification system these requirements can be fulfilled and checked. The advantages of the flow line are so much higher, as the workpieces are more nearly similar. These conditions must be considered in the design and work-planning department.

For investigations before building a flow line, the whole workpiece profile was divided into code number fields of similar groups with respect to machining. Because the probability of full employment was highest in the biggest group, the investigation was first done for short rotational pieces.

Altogether 4000 parts were selected. Because most of them had to pass the turret lathe, a certain type of machine tool was determined as the so-called main machine.

To avoid blocking of the line, a maximum time limit of 15h was set according to statistical evaluations, and jobs set aside which had a greater operation time.

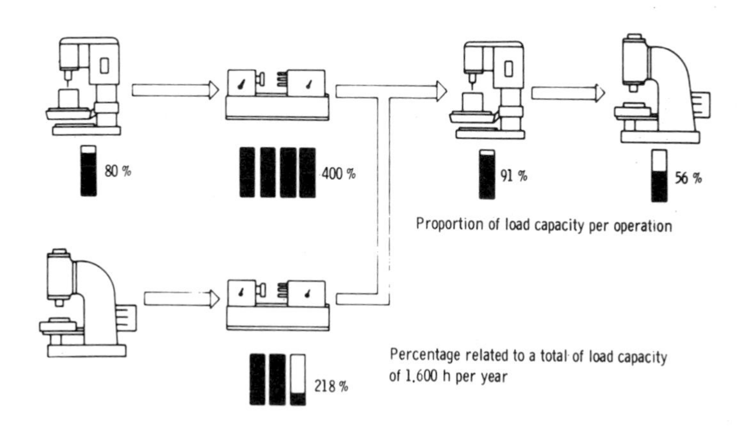

Fig. 19. Flow line according to typical working sequences.

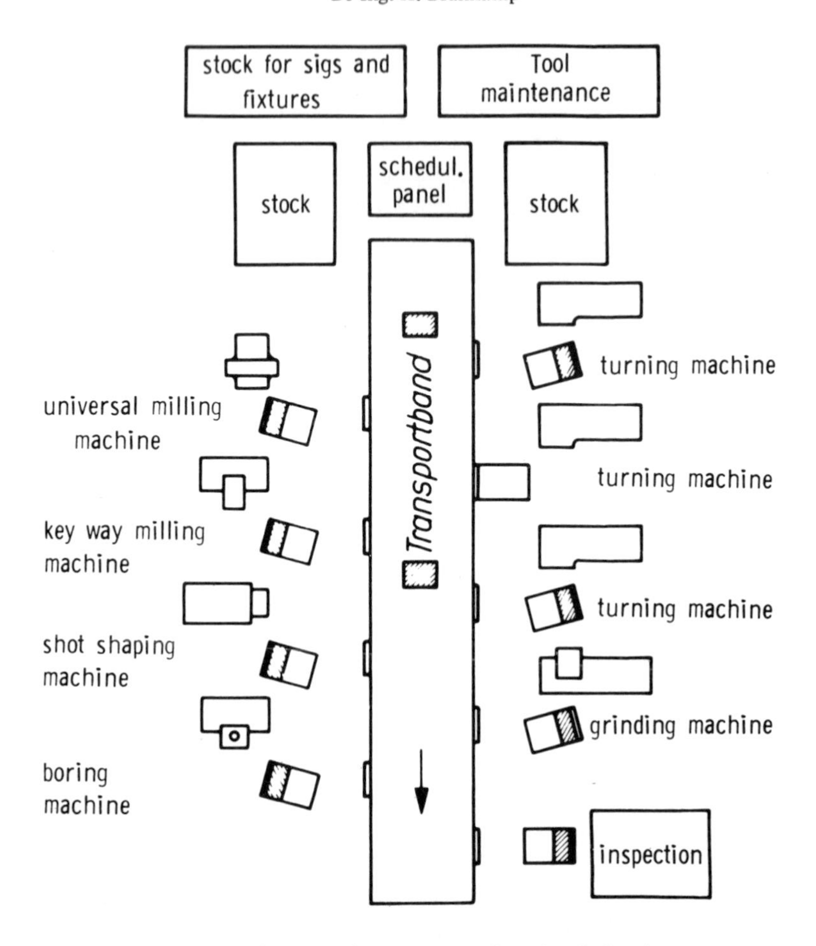

Fig. 20. Flow line for part groups (rotational pieces).

As a result of the investigations a flow line according to Fig. 19 was recommended to the company.

Ordering of a machine within a flow line gives opportunity to arrange machine tools along a conveyor line (Fig. 20). Jobs are inserted into the line from a control panel at the head of the conveyor. Retransportation is also done on the conveyor. Workpieces are stored between operations on each side of the control panel. According to the date and load situation, the job is transferred to the next place of operation.

The conveyor line described has been in use for several years in a German company and has proved a great success. Other firms have picked up this model and are now in the realisation phase.

5.0 EXTENT OF USE OF THE OPITZ SYSTEM

As has been shown, the classification system can increase the efficiency of the production department.

Especially by long-range adaptation of the production devices to the production programme, considerable savings are possible. It is important not to lose flexibility. An exact knowledge of the workpieces to be machined is therefore the basic condition for rationalising provisions.

To what extent is the system used in practice? This question is difficult to answer for two reasons.

On the one hand the system is not used in all departments of companies at one time. So one company puts the effort on design, another on the shop, the third on special investigations. About thirty companies are known to work partially with the system. These companies are not only in Germany, but also in the Netherlands, Belgium, Switzerland, France, Great Britain, Japan and the U.S.A.

On the other hand the question is difficult to answer because the system is available without any licence agreement or any other restrictions. Many applications came to our knowledge accidentally. The real number of companies using the system is therefore much higher. A certain measure may be the sale of the system book, which is now about 1200 altogether.

Use of the system in a certain company is finally decided when the question, 'What are the possibilities of rationalisation when identical and similar parts can be brought together by the classification?', is answered.

BIBLIOGRAPHY

1 H. OPITZ *Werkstuckbescreibendes Klassifizierungssystem.*
2 H. OPITZ 3. *Tagung Werkstucksystematik und Teilefamilienfertigung.* Essen, Girardet, 1967.
3 H. TULLY 'Einsatz eines Mehrspindelautomaten in der Einzel- und Kleinserienfertigung'. *Werkstatt und Betrieb,* 100, H3, S. 117–185, 1967.
4 E. A. HAWORTH 'Group technology – using the Opitz system'. *The Production Engineer*
5 R. HAHN, W. KUHNERT and K. ROSCHMANN. 'Die Nummerung im Fertigungsbetrieb Systeme der Teileklassifizierung Werkstattstechnik', 58, H. 7, S. 324–326; H. 7, 362–365 1968.

COMPUTER CONTROL OF MATERIALS HANDLING

K. B. Warwick
Geo. W. King Ltd, Stevenage

SUMMARY

A brief historical review of automatic control of assembly line conveyors is followed by a survey of applications of computer control in the fields of container handling, car assembly and steel rolling.

1.0 HISTORY OF AUTOMATIC CONTROL OF MECHANICAL HANDLING PLANT

The author's first connection with any organised method of automatic control of mechanical handling was in 1949/50, when the Austin Motor Co. decided to erect a new car assembly building on the old flying field at Longbridge, Birmingham. The four new assembly lines, capable of producing 5000 cars in an 80h week, were to be fed by a system of dual-duty overhead conveyors supplying chassis, axles, engines and bodies from three or four factories, some ¾ – 1 mile distant and around 100 to 150 ft below the new building.

The factories operated different hours and the scheme was to be capable of running for half an hour should any supply conveyor stop for repair work, each assembly track running on an approximately 2 min cycle.

The selection system was operated mechanically from the main supply body conveyor and consisted of a Hollerith punched-card tabulator. At the time the manufacture of a motor-car in quantity production took approximately 24h, the body (trimmed) was required 2h before the car was complete on the end of the assembly line, the engine 3h and the axles some 3½h. This was for a car or a van with a chassis which was current at the time.

Sequencing lines of conveyors were installed for completed main units, i.e. axles, power units and bodies, the appropriate units being automatically transferred to these lines when pegs on the suspension units of the slings operated the required limit switch or switches. The body, being the unit required at the latest time and having the greatest variation in paint colours, trim colours, left- or right-hand drive, etc., was made the master. As the body arrived at the actuating point on the conveyor line, the appropriate punched card was selected, fed to the 'reader', and the correct axle and engine were selected and started on their journey from the sequencing lines to final assembly.

The original planning of this scheme, which eventually featured some 14 miles of conveyors, was conceived by Frank Griffiths, the visionary enthusiast whose undoubted keenness forced it through.

This system was, in a sense, the precursor of computer-controlled mass production and remained serviceable in its initial form for many years.

Around 1956 the Simca Co. in France took a step further with a punched tape control to be linked with a data processing computer in the sales office. This was, unfortunately, only a limited success, owing partly to lack of air conditioning. Dust in the atmosphere affected the punched tape. Also there was not sufficient time to get over teething troubles, owing to production demands. It is also thought by some that too much was attempted by way of automatic operation, which could be, and subsequently was, achieved by simpler and less expensive means.

None the less, the system taught a great deal to those of us who at that time regarded computers of any kind either as a magic box or an electronic brain.

Interest in automatic control of the processing, service, transporting and assembly of motor vehicles seems to have lapsed since that time. The lead in the use of computer control has been taken over by the petrochemical industries.

2.0 WAREHOUSING

In recent years it has been realised that the cost of warehousing an article, which is in part the obvious one of capital locked up in stored articles, is a heavy one. Here again pernaps computer control is more easily welcomed by senior management in industry than was the case a few years back. The modern warehouse, whether handling groceries for supermarkets, power units for production lines, or spare parts in the automotive industry, rarely makes optimum use of the computer.

The number of warehouses operating with on-line control in the world is still counted in tens at most, rather than hundreds.

The expression *on-line* is used of a computer that gives controlling instructions direct to another machine, e.g. stacker cranes. The term *off-line* is used of a computer that gives instructions, whether as print-out or punched card, to an operator on the stacking or picking device.

Control of stacker cranes, retrievers or fork trucks is usually manual. Punched cards or tape readers are used to optimise the method of order picking. Overall control of stock is by data processing.

It would seem that the warehouse can be made fully automatic, but this is rarely the case if unit loads are not handled both inwards and outwards.

If a motor-car engine, or a massive box of detergent packets, is to be placed in and taken out of racking, the problem is relatively simple. If, on the other hand, loads consist of large stillages containing numbers of small parts normally called for individually, or in small numbers, then the operation becomes the more complicated one of 'order picking'.

Stacker cranes with forks travelling on a vertical mast can be considered preferable to the more complicated retriever crane for order picking. Manual operation of cranes under joy-stick control will frequently be required if unusually complicated picking equipment is considered too expensive to justify other savings.

Computers, this time off line, can be used (a) to schedule loading, and (b) to deal with stock control, notify when stocks are at a minimum, and even handle re-ordering.

A year or so ago my company equipped a large warehouse in Canada for the Northern Electric Co. (a subsidiary of Bell Telephones). The warehouse is in the outskirts of Montreal. It has ten bays, each 60 ft wide and from 125 to 250 ft long. Nine bays are equipped with stacker cranes with reversible forks which can stack to the right or left of the aisles. They can handle a maximum load of 3000 lb.

The crane driver's cab, attached to the back of the fork carriage, travels down the aisles at 350 ft/min. He can stow away complete stillages or large palleted units, pick individual loads by hand, and store such loads temporarily on the shelves of his cabin. The aisles are only 4 ft 6 in wide, three to each bay, so that six racks, some 25 ft high, can be dealt with in each bay.

Items stocked range from single mouldings or 2 BA screws to complete telephone kiosks. Pallets or stillages are used, depending on the size of the stock item. Each day the computer, having worked out optimum methods, provides a list of orders to be picked up by the driver. The small items are taken to the end of the bay when the shelves in the cabin are full. Here they are put onto gravity roller tracks at different levels, moving thence to belt conveyors taking them to the repair depot or despatch bay as required.

After the initial difficulties were surmounted, during the first month after handover, the handling equipment of the whole warehouse was reported to be running at over 90% efficiency. To date no difficulties in operation have been reported.

For this type of work, where orders vary from half a dozen complete telephone kiosks to half a dozen strainer bolts, off-line computer direction and manually controlled crane operation seem ideal.

3.0 CONTAINER HANDLING

Container handling at ports is ideally suited to computer control. The loads arrive in single units, or twos, if road transport is involved. They must be stacked according to plan, preferably with heavily laden containers arranged so that they can be loaded on to ships first. Indeed, if details of the ship and the capacity are available, a loading plan can often be worked out in advance (bearing in mind that it will have to meet the approval of Mr Mate!).

Units are normally stacked four or five high for handling into the ship by special-purpose crane. A deal of shuffling is inevitable when loads arrive at the docks, but, once a ship is berthed, a turn-round can be rapid if stacking is planned. Computer-controlled cranes, with feedback and display panels to assist visual checking, help to speed operations.

It would seem easy to use similar methods for making up freight trains in a marshalling yard. A good deal of work has been done on freight handling, much of it by one firm of mechanical handling engineers. The next short step would appear to be computer control. Here even optimising truck selection would surely justify itself by ensuring lower operation costs, and, more important, quicker turn-round of rolling stock and more rapid delivery of goods to users.

4.0 MONITORING

The control computer is ideal for monitoring.

It is one thing to direct a conveyor, crane or truck to a task and proceed to the next, but it is equally important to learn that the first task has been completed. A signal to this effect, often coupled with visual display on a panel, can be given with relative simplicity.

It is also useful to know that a machine is out of service. It is still more important to know that a machine is likely to be out of service before long. The control computer can be used for such information in certain circumstances, for example when monitoring gearbox temperature, motor current consumption, timing of operations being increased, etc. Thus maintenance people can attend to a machine right away, or mount watch and remedy faults between shifts.

During visits to a plant one hears so many apologies about Machine A or Process B not operating today owing to breakdown. I do not suggest that every small constituent operation should be monitored, or that performance checks are permissible on every item of plant, but on key machines monitoring is a *must*. Far too little attention is paid to it in U.K. industry.

5.0 MAINTENANCE

It must be emphasised that the more sophisticated a plant becomes, the more important is maintenance and the more skilled must be the type of mechanic or electrician engaged upon it.

Works engineers have often been heard to say that computers and transistorised controls are a source of anxiety to them. The ordinary electrician has advance warning of troubles on conventional, if complicated, electrical control panels. With computerised panels this is far from the case. 'Don't forget', says the works engineer, 'I've got to keep this plant running. They charge my department £1000 a minute for a conveyor stoppage on an assembly line'. This serious argument is advanced by a fine body of men without whom our export markets would fade away.

What can be done? Surely there is a case for monitoring to *anticipate faults,* and a case for much more *preventive maintenance* on mechanical, electrical and electronic plant. And the high-grade electronics man must become increasingly a leading member of maintenance crews.

6.0 ON-LINE CONTROL FOR MOTOR-CAR PRODUCTION

One must ask, why did we stop auto-control in motor-car production? Why not, for example, put the Frank Griffiths set-up on computer? Why, for that matter, does this not appear to have happened elsewhere?

The answer is, I believe, twofold: (a) capital equipment is expensive, and (b) the top man is inclined to think that, as he has a data-processing computer for stock control, to see that stocks are adequate, he does not need complete on-line computer control of handling.

I gather that, in some U.S. factories producing cars, small computers feed information to final assembly lines. They notify all shortages to the production engineer in charge of assembly, and advise him of the more important rejects. He is left to fill the gaps as best he can.

A program could be written to indicate alternative or even obligatory courses of action. Naturally the programming would be on a vast scale. There are some 400 parts in the modern car, and to provide alternative programs for each would be no mean task. A strike at the supplier's works may be over tomorrow – or it may last for weeks. Programming could cater for few alternatives, but a responsible and experienced executive deals automatically with contingencies.

Thanks to the computer, man has recently succeeded in getting to the moon: but the final landing had to be 'by hand'. The computer is obviously a marvellous tool, and we must use it as such, but there are times when the human brain must take over.

If we know in time that the pink polka dot body does not come up to standard and is rejected, we may be able to insert a van or a shooting brake in its place. A computer will tell us whether we have a van or shooting brake body to fill that space – a space is anathema to all automotive production engineers. Generally it would seem that the small, purpose-made computer, or even a selected standard model of control computer, can supply vital information well in time for the responsible executive to take action, feeding him advance information regarding shortages and rejects, and also telling him what stock levels are available.

6.1 *Automobile manufacture*

It would be less than just to the car industry to suggest that its use of computers is restricted to warehousing. Computer-controlled machine tools have been used for some time. The production control of complete vehicles, as propounded by W. R. Wissner of I.B.M., was stated by Frank Ford (in his article in *Control,* November 1967) to have been developed at B.M.C. (now B.L.M.C.). Ford emphasises that the body is still the key item in the system.

7.0 PRODUCTION CONTROL

On the relative advantages of on-line and off-line computers I quote from some discussion notes by Ferranti's:

> The traditional computer-based production control system involves the off-line application of established data processing techniques. This is an obvious, effective and necessary starting point, but is not in itself sufficient. The success of any control scheme depends on an overall plan in conjunction with a means of implementing it effectively.
>
> In the production control context, the proper implementation of the production schedule required it to be updated by real-time events as they happen. The steady-state 'off-line' system must be brought to life by an 'on line' extension so that the whole integrated system is fully dynamic. The 'off-line' system cannot respond to short-term variations, nor can it react to human errors, plant failures or incorrect assumptions which invalidate the master plan on which the 'off-line' system is based.
>
> Any deviation from planned operation will therefore stabilise the system at a lower level of efficiency, normally by under-utilisation of plant and operators. This condition will persist until positive action results in rectification procedures. An 'on-line' system allows the plan to be either confirmed or modified in the light of the current situation in such a way that the overall aims of the plan are achieved.
>
> In conjunction with an efficient schedule, it can ensure maximum utilisation with consequent gains in productivity and profitability.

8.0 ROLLING MILLS

A computer has been used by the Parkgate Iron and Steel Co. for some time. This takes over, on-line, from the moment of manufacture of an ingot. The weight of the ingot is fed to the computer, which assesses the number of passes 'knowing' the temperature and material of the ingot. There is overriding manual control of the mill should it be required. The computer also decides the lengths into which the eventual rolled section is to be cut to avoid 'short ends' of waste material.

Thus the entire operation, from ingot to cut-off rolled section, is computer-controlled. This would seem an almost ideal application.

9.0 ADVANTAGES AND DISADVANTAGES OF COMPUTER CONTROL

9.1 *Advantages*

The overall control of plant as an integrated machine, and the setting of tempo, is achieved in a link-up of material-handling equipment with the demands of assembly.

Stocks can be kept to an agreed low level, and stock control can, by adequate feedback, be made entirely realistic so far as maxima and minima are concerned.

With monitoring feedback for key items of plant, preventive maintenance can be realistically based.

The on-line control computer can normally be linked with existing data-processing computers already used for stock control, costing etc.

9.2 *Disadvantages*

Capital cost is high.

Time is taken by all concerned, that is users' experts in planning, processing, tooling, manufacture and maintenance as well as costing, in the designing of the system. In addition these people will no doubt be involved in presenting programming data so that the program can subsequently be prepared, and tested, and the mechanical handling and machine tool suppliers' experts will be involved also. This is a vital stage and must be handled by people who really know their particular expertise. The difficulty of this important stage must not be minimised.

Maintenance personnel, including really first-class electronic technicians, are expensive.

ACKNOWLEDGMENTS

The author desires to thank the following for their ready assistance in the preparation of this paper. Geo. W. King Ltd (T.I. Co.). E.M.I. Electronics Ltd. Parkgate Iron and Steel Ltd. I.C.L. Ferranti Automation Systems Division. Frank Griffiths (Consulting Engineer).

SESSION 6. DISCUSSION ON THE PAPER BY K. BRANKAMP

G. R. FRANKLIN (*W. E. & F. Dobson*): I do not wish to detract from anything that has been done at Aachen, which is obviously very impressive, but surely the system of family group machining has been in common use in various countries in Europe for almost twenty years? I believe it was attributed to a Russian engineer called Metrogonov who started in a tractor plant in Russia after the second world war. Full details of the system were published by the Soviet Academy of Sciences in the middle 1950s. Perhaps Dr Brankamp could explain to us what advantages, if any, are credited to the Opitz system over those other commercial systems which have been in use for very many more years: apart from initial cost, of course.

Dr. Ing. K. BRANKAMP (*Aachen*): It is quite right that Professor Metrogonov developed the ideas of the classification of parts. I believe that this was in 1953 (a book on the subject has been published by Lunger and Ross). I do not think it is my job here to compare the different classification systems. I do not think it matters which system you use, but I think it is most important that you do use one.

OPEN FORUM ON MACHINING CENTRES AND MANUFACTURING SYSTEMS

Professor D. S. ROSS (*Strathclyde University*): With the advent of integrated manufacturing systems do machining centres still have a future? Would any of the panel care to comment?

J. P. DRISCOLL (*Molins Machine Co.*): I am sure the machining centre still has its place since it can be made specifically to suit particular requirements in any one product group.

B. J. DAVIES (*Staveley Engineering*): I agree. The machining centre is particularly suited to lower-volume production than the integrated manufacturing system, which is essentially a multi-spindle operation. If spindles are going to be kept in operation for the same amount of time as the single spindle on a machining centre, then the product rate will clearly be higher. Not all applications warrant this. There are problems in changing too rapidly from one workpiece to another in an integrated manufacturing system. The integrated manufacturing system is the most economical solution. I am sure there is a place for a machining centre in an integrated manufacturing system.

H. M. LEBRECHT (*Kearney & Trecker*): The machining centre is the simplest form of manufacturing system. It fits in extraordinarily well with certain aspects of manufacturing systems.

There are two quite separate areas. One is the extremely flexible transfer machine, the other is the computer control of n.c. machines (which the Americans call d.n.c. – direct numerical control) which links numerically controlled machines to other management communication systems, including production control. Existing machining centres can be a very large proportion of the hardware of a d.n.c. system, but even on the transfer line type of machine, the machining centre may win economically over the special-purpose machine. Using machining centres you only need one fixture whereas with any kind of platen system you require a number of platens. It is really a question of quantities: which is the most economic for the application?

A. TACK (*Rolls-Royce*): I contend that the machining centre still has a very large place in manufacturing industry as a stand-alone machine, but my concept of the manufacturing complex is that it is ideal for the one-off. The manufacturing complex will treat a large range of components which require many operations which cannot necessarily be handled by a machining centre. With the classical machining centre we have considerable difficulty in turning. The manufacturing complex will include this type of operation. My view of the machining complex is that we can put one-offs down a line of compatible unit machines which can produce the whole of the component, and therefore have a throughput in the shortest possible time.

H. M. LEBRECHT (*Kearney & Trecker*): Would Mr Tack agree that machining centres could be part of that line?

A. TACK (*Rolls-Royce*): Most definitely.

C. B. PERRY (*Cincinnati Milling & Grinding Machines*): The concept of a machining centre has been that of a single work station with the ability to produce a completed part. Now, if we are looking at a production requirement involving more than one such station we have an option – either build three identical machining centres or build three specialised stations. But by specialising the function of the three stations we move up to a new level of manufacturing efficiency. Our concept in variable mission is that most stations will normally see the feeding in their queue of different parts – we call this *continuous random order of manufacture* – though we take the view that the machining centre is probably in jeopardy wherever you need the capacity of more than one. The kind of machining centre you will see in station systems will be a different breed with shallower specialisation.

A. TACK (*Rolls-Royce*): I agree with Mr Perry. The full multi-axis requirement does not apply to every machine. There will be a version simpler than the present machining centre. Where there is, say, a four-full-axis requirement, you get a machine that looks very much like a machining centre as we know it today.

C. B. PERRY (*Cincinnati Milling & Grinding Machines*): Yes, perhaps a highly versatile single station that might reduce the complexity of other stations would be a current investment. In this form it no longer functions alone as a total manufacturing capability.

C. W. DEE (*Aerostatic*): In the U.K. most manufacturing effort is in smaller firms. They cannot afford the complexes that you are talking about. Mr Perry explained experimental and prototype manufacture. He said that if one takes a machining centre and incorporates the additional machining facility it becomes literally a machining complex. Could we expand more on the feasibility of literally a single machining centre which would enable the smaller organisations to get their lead-times down?

C. B. PERRY (*Cincinnati Milling & Grinding Machines*): The low end of the job-lot spectrum probably does not lend itself to the multiple-station system. I admit one other point, the cost of a versatile tool-changing machining centre right now is rather high. We propose basic building blocks to build a machine with standard elements compatible with multi-station system design. We feel that the way to sell multiple-station systems is to offer an economic solution to 'one of a kind' machine acquisitions. Each machine we may so sell is like planting seeds that may grow into a small system and hence a big system.

B. J. DAVIES (*Staveley Engineering*): If one can take the manufacturing system concept down to very elementary level, one can take almost conventional numerically controlled tools organised along the lines of an integrated manufacturing system and gain substantial advantages.

C. W. DEE (*Aerostatic*): I am more interested in a single machine.

Professor D. S. ROSS (*Strathclyde University*): Can anyone comment on the machine known as the Sundstrand Partsmaker which takes bar stock and produces completed parts from it?

J. J. PATERSON (*Rolls-Royce*): I don't think it would suit Mr Dee's purposes at all, but it may be in principle what you are interested in. The machine accepts bar extruded stock and by orientating it towards the cutters produces some unique shapes. It is the type of thing you are after.

J. P. DRISCOLL (*Molins Machine Co.*): I am a little doubtful whether it would be economic to use numerically controlled machines to produce one-offs. If they are prototypes, larger batches will follow and then the programming effort is not wasted.

C. W. DEE (*Aerostatic*): I should have said 'manually programmed machine' was what I had in view.

J. W. ROBB (*Rolls-Royce*): Why has the machine tool industry shown remarkable reluctance to design a turning machine to produce small parts, that is, parts which are turned, milled and drilled?

R. H. McCALL (*Herbert B.S.A.*): We have had two attempts at this problem. One is the Batchmatic, which is essentially an n.c. turning machine. It does not complete the unfinished component in terms of a second operation such as drilling and milling. The Herbert turning centre does this very thing – provides turning, milling, drilling, tapping, right-angle attachments. This is a machine of capacity roughly 20 in diameter and 36 in length, with fairly substantial power. If we can get the cost of control down, then undoubtedly I see that application in smaller machines.

J. R. McINTOSH (*Ferranti*): In answer to one delegate's query on cutting down development times I would say that we have equipped our development shop with two or three fairly simple numerically controlled machines. We make the tapes in the drawing office from the draughtsman's layout without using any detailed drawing at all and we use a very simple input language. We think this significantly cuts down lead times.

C. M. McCOY (*Joseph Lucas*): We have been talking here about the use of highly sophisticated techniques of machining. Surely we are now paying a tremendous price for producing scrap? Shouldn't we be concentrating on the use of more sophisticated techniques for the 100% utilisation of materials in such forms as extrusions?

Professor D. S. ROSS (*Strathclyde University*): That is a good question. Which of the chipmakers would like to answer?

J. P. DRISCOLL (*Molins Machine Co.*): These processes obviously lend themselves to particular types of production in the larger producing businesses. These particular processes are not as economical as machining for one-off or small batches.

C. M. McCOY (*Joseph Lucas*): We try, I would hope, to persuade our designers to get away from machining as much as possible, to go into chipless techniqes. Surely, this is the future for us, not machining. You get nothing for scrap materials unless you find some unique way of using your scrap.

A. TACK (*Rolls-Royce*): My own company is on both sides of the field. We chip-machine where it is most economical to do so. We forge or precision-cast or use plastics where it is economic to do so. There is a place for both. The delegate is quite right that there is not enough development work going on in this field, and there should be considerably more. Over the next few years we are going to see a considerable reduction in the amount of chip machining as processes become more economic. There will always be an economic break-even point.

T. LINDEM (*Herbert-Ingersoll*): In speaking of numerically controlled machines, we must not think completely of manufacturing systems as necessarily involving this type of sophisticated control. A hand-operated drill process is a manufacturing system. If we broaden our approach to the system concept, I think then it can permit us to look at our own individual problems in the light of existing technology and make the right decision.

A. S. CARRIE (*Strathclyde University*): Surely there is not necessarily any correlation between numerical control and the manufacture of chips? Could we not just as well have numerically controlled non-chip manufacturing machines, e.g. die casting machines or completely different processes such as electrochemical machining perhaps?

C. B. PERRY (*Cincinnati Milling & Grinding Machines*): I agree that we can. Generally machine-tool builders are interested in increasing the number of options available to product designers, to manufacturing engineers. Chipless conversion of material into finished form is one of the preferred ones. We make a shear-forming machine which takes discs and forms chiplessly. We form splines and gears by chipless methods. The shear-forming machine lends itself beautifully to numerical control. What we are talking about is more numerous options and lower costs for converting raw material into finished products.

R. FLEMING (*Hunting Engineering*): I would like to get some feel for manufacturing systems, not as a technical concept, but as an actual, innovatory process. I would like to get some feel for the time scale and the cost of introducing such systems. These are the main parameters. How long will it be before a system with, say, six machines is available to manufacture any sort of component – available as a package deal, that is, to someone who just simply wants to buy it as such, and is neither concerned nor has the capacity or ability to develop it? Secondly, in broad terms again, what would you forecast the cost of that particular system to be?

Professor D. S. ROSS (*Strathclyde University*): That is rather like the question, 'How much does die casting cost?'. The specification might not be enough for an answer, but we will put it to the panel anyway.

R. FLEMING (*Hunting Engineering*): That is quite true, but so often the last thing suppliers want to speak of is cost. So far as manufacturing is concerned it is of prime importance.

A. TACK (*Rolls-Royce*): The introduction of a complete six-machine system requires a minimum of a year's preparation to get the company's own organisation sorted out. Introduction followed by subsequent management of the system would take the order of at least two years.

For a computer-controlled manufacturing system I would think that we start at maybe £0·5m and go up to maybe something in the order of £2m, depending on what we are after.

R. C. PARKER (*Ferodo*): I would like to speak on behalf of the manufacturer mentioned in Mr Rushton's paper. We have about 30 000 part numbers of which in any one week we manufacture about 20 000. We have very short runs, ranging from dozens to rarely about more than 2000. Manchester University people coded our products. Following this coding, which cost very little, they started putting up machine cells which were then connected by conveyors. In about two years, in the area in which they were looking, they decreased the manufacturing time by a factor of 8·4 at virtually no cost at all. The system is very efficient. It showed that we had more machine capacity than was necessary.

We started planning in 24 hours on a Gant system manually, then we planned on a week system manually, and then on a computer for the week's loading. Over the next five years, we should extend the system over the whole of the factory.

The point I am making is: can we have a little more attention to firms such as ours, which, with application of thought and system, can contribute greatly to the economy of the country without great capital expenditure?

Professor D. S. ROSS (*Strathclyde University*): Group technology does bring out something that has not really been very evident: that we look at the overall manufacturing system as applying to the whole system, including the planning. Would any of the forum like to comment?

T. LINDEM (*Herbert-Ingersoll*): Our own system for the manufacture of small parts on a one-off basis, i.e. a completely random pattern, incorporated generally-available standard machines – some with numerical control, some without. With a unique, closely controlled and closely monitored handling and scheduling system we found that it was not the cutting time at the spindle that was the problem, but the lead time between the moment at which the part arrived and left and moment at which the next part came to the machine. This was a problem requiring special handling, special production control and special methods for moving parts around – reducing inventory and lead time confusion.

E. ROSMARIN (*Dexion*): Our production is in the field of sheet and strip manipulation, testing, perforating – the general shaping in use of strip material. Can anybody tell me whether any work has been done in that particular sector as far as the machining centre concept is concerned?

C. B. PERRY (*Cincinnati Milling & Grinding Machines*): I have heard of the numerically controlled shear, but I am not aware of any other work in the sheet and metal field.

A. L. WILLETT (*Ministry of Technology*): I am sure most delegates in this country will know that we have set up a centre to assist industry to adopt group technology and to minimise the amount of repetition of analysis that each organisation might have to do – the centre is operating and uses this technique quite extensively.